WORLD®
AIR POWER
J O U R N A L

Aerospace Publishing Ltd
AIRtime Publishing Inc.

Published quarterly by
Aerospace Publishing Ltd
179 Dalling Road
London W6 0ES
UK

Copyright © Aerospace Publishing Ltd

Cutaway drawings copyright
© Mike Badrocke/Aviagraphica

ISSN 0959-7050

Aerospace ISBN 1 874023 47 6
                (softback)
                1 874023 48 4
                (hardback)
AIRtime ISBN   1-880588-07-2
                (hardback)

Published under licence in USA and
Canada by AIRtime Publishing Inc.,
10 Bay Street, Westport,
CT 06880, USA

Editorial Offices:
WORLD AIR POWER JOURNAL
Aerospace Publishing Ltd
3A Brackenbury Road
London   W6 0BE   UK

Publisher: Stan Morse
Managing Editor: David Donald
Editor: Jon Lake
Editorial Assistants:
        Robert Hewson
        Soph Moeng
        Tim Senior
Sub Editor: Karen Leverington
Origination and printing by
    Imago Publishing Ltd
Printed in Singapore

Europe Correspondent:
    Paul Jackson
Washington Correspondent:
    Robert F. Dorr
USA West Coast Correspondent:
    René J. Francillon
Asia Correspondent:
    Pushpindar Singh

The publishers gratefully acknowledge
the assistance given by the following
people:

James Ragsdale, Director of
Communications, and Denny
Lombard, Public Information
Photographer, of the Lockheed
Advanced Developments Company,
Major Earl Shellner and Robert
W. Pepper of the 49th Fighter
Wing/Public Affairs Office, Jay Miller,
author of Lockheed's Skunk Works: The
First Fifty Years published by Aerofax
Inc., and Marty J. Isham for their
invaluable help with the Lockheed
F-117 article.

The author would like to thank Mr
Sergei V. Mikheyev, Designer General
of the Kamov OKB, Evgeny Sudarev,
head of the Conceptual Design
Department, Kamov OKB, and Boris
Rybak of AviaData for their invaluable
help in the preparation of the Kamov
Ka-50 article.

We would like to thank Tom
Kaminski, Paul Hart, Michael Anselmo
and Robert L. Lawson for their help
with the F-14 article, and at Grumman-
Henry Janiesch, VP of F-14 Programs,
Kurt Hofman, John Aris, Bob Bidonde,
Lois Lovisolo and Bill McDonald.

World Air Power Journal is a
registered trademark in the
United States of America of
AIRtime Publishing Inc.

World Air Power Journal is
published quarterly and is
available by subscription and
from many fine book and hobby
stores.

SUBSCRIPTION AND BACK
NUMBERS:

UK and World (except USA and
Canada) write to:
Aerospace Publishing Ltd
FREEPOST
PO Box 2822
London
W6 0BR
UK

(No stamp required if posted in
the UK)

USA and Canada, write to:
AIRtime Publishing Inc.
Subscription Dept
10 Bay Street
Westport
CT 06880
USA
Toll-free order number in USA:
1 800 359-3003

Prevailing subscription rates are
as follows:
Softbound edition for 1 year:
        $58.00
Softbound edition for 2 years:
        $108.00
Softbound back numbers
(subject to availability) are:
$17.95 each. All rates are for
delivery within mainland USA,
Alaska and Hawaii. Canadian
and overseas prices available
upon request. American Express,
Discover Card, MasterCard and
Visa accepted. When ordering
please include your card
number, expiration date and
signature.

Publisher, North America:
    Melvyn Williams
Subscription Director:
    Linda DeAngelis
Retail Sales Director:
    Jill Brooks
Charter Member Services
Manager:
    Janie Munroe

CONTENTS

Military Aviation Review

International

Eurofighter airborne

The roar of two Turbo Union RB199 turbofans was figuratively drowned out by the collective sigh of relief from Eurofighter GmbH personnel when the prototype Eurofighter 2000 lifted off from Manching on 27 March. As first of seven development aircraft to be built by partners Alenia, BAe, CASA and DASA, DA1/9829 was airborne for an initial 45 minutes, piloted by Peter Weger of DASA. Just 11 days later, on 6 April, DA2/ZH588 was taken aloft at Warton for 50 minutes by Chris Yeo of BAe, achieving 250 kt (287 mph; 462km/h) and 10,000 ft (3048 m) during handling checks. Delayed by software problems for the best part of two years, Eurofighter 2000 was at last starting its 4,500-hour test programme.

More challenges await Europe's foremost warplane in the months ahead. A few minor snags are known to remain in non-critical elements of the aircraft's computer systems, but more destabilising to the programme are the continuing arguments over responsibility for the delayed first flight and an approaching international row on the thorny question of workshares. Illustrative of the breakdown in communications on the software side, it emerged in April that design authority DASA had prepared an alternative digital flight control programme without informing its own principal sub-contractor, GEC-Marconi of the UK.

With the aircraft now flying, thoughts have turned to production. Since the workshare was first determined, Germany's prospective order for Eurofighters has reduced from 250 (33 per cent of the planned international total) to 120-140 (about 20 per cent). Britain's has remained unchanged at 250, but this now is equivalent to 43 per cent. The Italian requirement for 130 and Spain's 87 are approximately the same, at 22 and 15 per cent, respectively. However, posturing for an approaching general election, the German government had refused to accept any reduction in

workshare.

One immediate result of this stance was postponement of plans to transfer the first German prototype to Warton after 10 hours of flight-testing, thereby combining the trials effort. In order to keep staff occupied at Manching, a revised plan called for 9829 to remain on site for an unlimited time.

Peace Partnership expands

NATO's Partnership For Peace initiative received a significant boost on 2 March when – despite its earlier criticism of the arrangement – Russia agreed to join. The Partnership, which is a means for consultation in military matters and a framework for joint exercises and peacekeeping deployments, is viewed as a first stage towards possible full NATO membership. As detailed negotiations progressed into May, NATO was continuing to resist Russian demands for a special status to reflect its significant military position. Albania, Bulgaria, the Czech Republic, Estonia, Hungary, Latvia, Lithuania, Poland, Romania, Slovakia, Slovenia and Ukraine had already joined by the time of the Russian decision, and Moldavia is expected to follow. Taking seriously its membership of Partnership for Peace, the Czech air force announced plans to take part in a joint exercise with Western compatriots before the end of 1994.

decided to withdraw the type, it emerged in March that SABCA is modifying the original quantity in the hope of being able to sell the aircraft abroad. All 10 were to have been completed by late 1993, but only four had been finished by the end of March 1994 and the 20th is not due until late 1995. The first and second MIRSIPs, BA60 and BA11, were delivered to the FAeB/BLu reserve base at Weelde for storage on 16 March, while the third conversion, the two-seat BD01, was undertaking flight trials from Brustem in March.

Chile has been mentioned as one possible buyer for Belgian Mirages, in view of the impending retirement of its Hunters. A further 35 Mirages remain in storage at Weelde and Koksijde, including 16 reconnaissance 5BRs. Following retirement of the Mirage and part of the Fighting Falcon strength, Belgium's front line comprises 72 F-16As and 18 F-16Bs. Deliveries of F-16s to storage at Weelde began on 16 March with the first five aircraft. Eventually, some 45 will be held at Weelde for possible resale.

FRANCE:

Second Rafale order

The slow pace of Rafale funding was criticised by Dassault during the spring as the Defence Ministry confirmed its 1994 budget plans with a contract for a further three aircraft: a two-seat Rafale B for the air force and two Rafale Ms to be supplied to the navy. This follows the first production order, placed on 26 March 1993, for one of each variant. Budget restrictions are responsible for the leisurely pace of orders and are in stark contract to the early

years of the Mirage 2000 when, apart from a launch order for four, contracts varied between 24 and 35 per annum. According to Dassault, small orders can not be executed efficiently and only increase the aircraft's price.

Rafale Ms will initially operate from the carrier PA *Foch* pending completion of the nuclear-powered PA *Charles de Gaulle*. The latter was launched on 30 April and is to complete fitting-out in mid-1999. A sistership, PA *Richelieu*, is required to complete the new carrier force, but there are concerns that it can not be afforded. A go-ahead for construction is due in 1997. Delivery of Rafale Ms is to begin in 1998, followed by the first aircraft for the air force in 2000, with IOC two years later.

Hawkeye plans

A decision by the US navy to retain the Grumman E-2C Hawkeye in production beyond the end of the century has removed the urgency from a French order for this AEW aircraft. The planned purchase of Hawkeyes accordingly has been reduced from four to two, plus two options which can safely be left until later. In a draft of the 1995-2000 military plan, funds are reserved for two aircraft to operate from *Foch* beginning in 1999, passing then to *Charles de Gaulle*. The *Foch* is

An unusual type in French service is the Pilatus Turbo-Porter, used by the ALAT at Montauban for liaison and parachute training.

Western Europe

BELGIUM:

A 109 force complete

Re-equipment of Belgian Army Light Aviation was completed on 4 February when the last of 46 Agusta A 109s was delivered. Currently under a cloud of corruption charges associated with their purchase, the helicopters are all based in Germany with 17 Battalion at Werl and 18 Battalion at Merzbrück. Each has nine 109HO scouts and 14 TOW missile-armed 109HAs, some of which are loaned from time to time by

the Light Aviation School at Brasschaat. Both squadrons were due to relocate to Bierset later in the year. Meanwhile, at Bierset, 3 Wing of the FAeB/BLu disbanded on 31 March, its sole Mirage squadron (No. 42) having previously stood down.

Mirages upgraded for resale

Although Belgium reduced its Mirage 5 MIRSIP upgrade programme from 20 (15 BAs and five BDs) to 10 (five and five) aircraft at the time it was

C-135FRs have recently been fitted with wing refuelling pods. Here two Mirage IVPs and a Mirage 2000N-K1 join up, two of the aircraft carrying ASMP nuclear missiles.

to be fitted with a variable 'ski-jump' which will be angled at 11° for Rafale take-offs, but lowered flush with the deck when Hawkeyes are launched.

Third Atlantique 2 squadron

The Aéronavale's third squadron of second-generation Dassault Atlantique 2s achieved IOC on 1 February when 21 Flottille at Nîmes-Garons was recommissioned with its first three aircraft. The squadron previously operated the Dassault-Breguet Atlantic, like its compatriots at Lann-Bihoué which have also re-equipped: 23F, which reformed on 1 February 1991, and 24F, likewise on 1 September 1992. Last to convert will be the Nîmes-based 22F.

GERMANY:

New Huey squadron

A new unit of UH-1D utility helicopters formed by the Luftwaffe at Nörvenich on 1 April was designated 2 Staffel of the Cologne-based Flugbereitschaftstaffel, the VIP squadron. The Huey unit has a strength of 20 helicopters obtained from the disbanded HTG 64 which continue their role of routine light transport and SAR.

Nörvenich – a Tornado IDS base – was chosen in order to maintain an even spread of UH-1 units over Germany.

New structure for Luftwaffe

The organisational plan for Germany's Luftwaffe came into effect on 1 April, raising Berlin to the status of a major centre for the administration of combat aircraft units. Immediately following unification, 5 Air Division was established at Berlin/Eggersdorf to control the air defence MiG-29s of 3 Wing. Now forces have been spread more evenly, with the result that the old 3 Division at Kalkar has disbanded and transferred its designation to Berlin. The air force remains divided into threee major commands, but the previous Tactical Command has been expanded with the addition of the transport force (previously attached to Central Office) and renamed to reflect its changed status.

Luftwaffen Führungskommando (LwFüKdo) at Köln/Wahn is the new Leader Command, its components being:

LwKdo Süd (Southern Command) at Messstetten, comprising 1 Division at Karlsruhe (JBG 32, JBG 34 both with Tornados; the German NATO E-3A element; and FLGp at Fürstenfeldbruck with Alpha Jets), and 2 Division at Birkenfeld (JBG 33 with Tornados, JG 74 with Phantoms);

LsKdo Nord (Northern Command) at Kalkar, comprising 3 Division at Berlin/Gatow (JG 72 with Phantoms; JG 73 with Phantoms and MiG-29s), and 4 Division at Aurich (JBG 31 and JBG 38, both with Tornados; and JG 71 with Phantoms);

Lufttransportkommando (Air Transport Command) at Müster with LTBs 61, 62 and 63 operating C.160s and UH-1Ds; FlBschftStf (VIP squadron) at Köln; and SAR detachments;

Lw Führungsdienstkommando (Service Command) at Köln/Wahn for ground radar and communications.

The two remaining major commands are essentially unchanged, apart from the loss of any flying units. Luftwaffenamt (Central Office) at Köln/Wahn is concerned with ground training and miscellaneous tasks, although it does administer the flying training organisation in the USA, and Luftwaffenunterstutzungskommando (Support Command) at Köln is responsible for supplies and infrastructure.

NETHERLANDS:

Run-down begins

Disbandments of front-line RNethAF squadrons (all equipped with Lockheed F-16A Fighting Falcons) began on 1 April when No. 316 was consigned to oblivion. Its operational conversion task has passed to 313 Squadron at Twenthe, while No. 314 will also disband on 1 January 1996. Established at Eindhoven on 1 April 1953, No. 316 was initially an auxiliary unit equipped with Republic F-84G Thunderjets. After disbanding in July 1955, it was reborn on 1 August 1956 with F-84F Thunderstreaks, but disbanded again on 15 January 1958. In its third incarnation, the squadron formed with Canadair/Northrop NF-5A/Bs at Eindhoven on 1 July 1971, transferring to Gilze-Rijen on 26 April 1972, once training had been completed. After flying its last F-5 sortie on 1 May 1991, No. 316 returned to Eindhoven and began F-16A/B conversion. It was formally re-established on 1 October the same year, but as a non-operational unit responsible for the Theatre Operational Conversion Course of pilots trained in the USA.

Three additional Fighting Falcons are to be converted to F-16A(R) reconnaissance configuration. Donated by 312 Squadron, the trio will receive minor modifications to enable them to carry the Oude Delft Orpheus pod with 306 Squadron. The latter operates survivors of the original batch of 22 new-built F-16A(R)s, J-627 to J-648. Steps are being taken by the KLu to obtain a laser designator pod for some of its F-16s, allowing 311 Squadron to return to full operational status with LGBs. The unit previously relied on RAF Buccaneers with Westinghouse AN/AVQ-23E pods, but the last of these aircraft was withdrawn in March.

PORTUGAL:

First Fighting Falcon

An eighth NATO air force became an F-16 Fighting Falcon operator when Portugal's first aircraft was handed over in the USA on 18 February. Destined for delivery to Esquadra 201 at Monte Real after initial crew conversion in the USA, the aircraft is one of 17 single-seat F-16As and three F-16B trainers on order.

SPAIN:

Mirage F1 stretch-out

Having put back two years to 2002 the delivery of its first Eurofighter 2000s, Spain spent the early part of 1994 looking for a stop-gap fighter to see the EdA through until at least the service-entry of Eurofighter in 2005. Among solicitations received was one from the USAF for 40 secondhand F-16A/B Fighting Falcons from the stock of some 400 early F-16s which it wants to sell in order to raise funds for 100 F-16C/Ds. The American bid was unsuccessful when Spain took the more logical step of expanding and upgrading its fleet of Dassault Mirage F1s. The 30 F1CE interceptors, 17 multi-role F1EEs and three F1BE trainers remaining from 73 aircraft originally received are to be augmented by 11 F1EDAs and two F1DDs from the Qatar Emiri Air Force, plus three F1Cs and two F1Bs provided by France. Earlier negotiations for Kuwait's F1s appears to have been inconclusive. The reinvigorated Spanish F1 fleet will undergo a limited mid-life update in 1995-97 for continued service with Escuadrons 111 at Manises, 141 and OCU 142 at Los Llanos, and 462 at Gando (Canaries).

SWEDEN:

NATO associate membership

In addition to forming a bridge between former adversaries on each side of the dismantled Iron Curtain, the NATO Partnership for Peace was further expanded in the spring when Sweden announced its intention of applying for membership. This is in spite of the traditional neutrality of the Nordic state, which has never been a member of a military alliance. Unlike most other central and southern European nations, Sweden has increased defence spending recently, responding to the resurgence of nationalism in Russia and the fact that much of the Russian military equipment withdrawn from the Central Front is now in the Kola Peninsula.

French E-3Fs have been busy flying missions around Bosnia. A recent addition to the aircraft is the unit badge for EDA 36.

Military Aviation Review

Illustrating Dutch UN peacekeeping efforts are these two helicopters. Above is an Alouette III festooned with elephants to commemorate the aircraft's use in Cambodia, while below is a BO 105 of 299 Sqn prior to departure to Bosnia, where four are based at Srebrenica.

Interestingly, papers made public in February revealed that Sweden was less than neutral during the Cold War, in spite of its protestations of impartiality. During the early 1950s, it was disclosed, defence plans were handed to the UK for information, runways in eastern Sweden were lengthened to accommodate NATO aircraft, and much effort was invested in preparing sites for NATO reinforcements in the event of a Soviet invasion. In reciprocation, Stockholm was advised of Western plans to assist in Sweden's defence.

BAe markets Gripen

A memorandum of understanding signed in Stockholm on 11 February between the governments of Sweden and the UK paves the way for closer collaboration between Saab and BAe. In the first instance, BAe will direct its efforts towards promoting the Gripen, in return for manufacturing and development work and probable involvement in providing the weapons system. In the last-mentioned connection, it is possible that Sweden will order the BAe Active Sky Flash as the Gripen's medium-range, active radar AAM.

TURKEY:

Thunderbolts declined

In April, Turkey reluctantly abandoned plans to acquire 50 secondhand A-10A Thunderbolt IIs and seven KC-135Rs, all of which were to have been provided free by the USAF. Related support costs are understood to have been too much for the THK, although it hopes to be able to obtain some unrefurbished KC-135As from storage at Davis-Monthan AFB.

Starfighter twilight

Turkey's penultimate Starfighter squadron, 181 Filo at Diyarbakir, flew its final F-104G sortie in April, prior to re-equipping with F-16Cs. It will receive the last 20 of the original order for 160 Fighting Falcons, having been preceded by 141, 142 and the Oncel Filo at Mürted; 161 and 162 Filos at Bandirma; and 191 and 192 Filos (ex F-104S and F-104G, respectively) at Balikeshir. In February, Turkey confirmed the option on the second half of its March 1992 follow-up F-16 order, which will now comprise a further 80 aircraft, the first of which will go to 182 Squadron from July 1996 as replacements for CF-104 Starfighters, the last flight of which will be made late in 1995. The remainder are earmarked for 151 and 152 Filos at Merzifon, replacing F-5As. With the 160 forming the initial contract, THK commitments are currently for 240 F-16s (204 Cs and 36 Ds), of which 136 had been delivered by February. TUSAS is also building 46 Fighting Falcons for Egypt.

UNITED KINGDOM:

White Paper is blank sheet

Virtually nothing of genuine news value was revealed by the UK's 'Statement on the Defence Estimates' when it was presented on 26 April. Publication found the armed forces implementing the already-announced 'Options for Change' package of cuts and steeling themselves for the 'Front Line First' defence cost studies report to be published in July. The latter is the result of 33 separate cost-cutting reviews, one of which would allegedly involve the sacking of 10,000 RAF personnel, leaving the service with 60,000, compared with 89,000 in 1991.

The White Paper reaffirmed that five more Sea Harriers will be upgraded to FRS.Mk 2 standard, following two prototypes and 29 aircraft in the first conversion lot. However, that announcement was overtaken by the shooting-down over Bosnia of one of the candidates for conversion. For the RAF, the most important news was that the Tornado GR.Mk 4 upgrade is to go ahead, despite opposition from the Treasury. No quantities or dates were revealed, despite reports that cost-cutting has eliminated several important items of avionics from the programme.

Details which became available later reported only 80 aircraft earmarked for the first Mk 4 conversion contract, to be undertaken between 1996 and 2000. An option is held on a further 62 for the period 2000-2002, a decision on these to be made in 1996. The MLU incorporates a digital map generator, pilot's multi-function display and HUD, computer loading system, FLIR, enhanced armament control system, GPS and an interface for the GEC TIALD laser designator. Items deleted include terrain-referenced navigation, more 'stealthy' air intakes and canopy, and a fuselage plug to provide additional internal space.

The White Paper promises the Army Air Corps a contract for a new attack helicopter next year, although the 1998 in-service date will probably slip by two years. No decision on the type to be ordered has yet been made. The AAC favours AH-64 Apaches, but the Eurocopter Tiger, Bell AH-1W Venom and Agusta A 129 have been long-term contenders, joined in May by the Atlas Rooivalk. This became politically acceptable with the South African all-race elections, resulting in a teaming arrangement with Marshall Aerospace of Cambridge for possible UK assembly. Atlas lost no time in shipping a Rooivalk to the helicopter trade show at Middle Wallop on 12-15 May and giving evaluation flights to UK officers.

In a statement related to economy drives, Defence Secretary Malcolm Rifkind confirmed that although the 'Red Arrows' had been considered for disbandment, this threat has now been lifted. The unique Hercules W.Mk 2 weather research aircraft is less lucky, having also been subject to financial scrutiny. Funding is assured only until 31 March 1995, when the position will be reviewed.

Among other proposals under consideration as a means of saving funds is an increase in the number of combat aircraft in squadrons from the current 13 to 18, with a corresponding reduction in numbers of squadrons. Further running down of No. 2 Group in Germany is another option, probably to involve closure of Laarbruch. In this event, the two Harrier squadrons (Nos 3 and IV), plus the Chinooks and Pumas of No. 18 Squadron, would be moved to Brüggen, from where two of the present four Tornado GR.Mk 1 squadrons would also transfer to the UK to make room. With the Warsaw Pact threat gone and low flying consequently prohibited by the German government since reunification in 1990, No. 2 Group aircraft have to go elsewhere for realistic training and so spend much of their time flying to and from the UK. This, and the abundance of empty bases at home, make further withdrawals from Germany inevitable.

New Command under threat

Among other possibilities for savings raised by the White Paper was dissolution of RAF Logistics Command and transfer of aircraft second-line maintenance and storage to the private sector. The proposal was not without its irony, as RAFLC was formed only on 1 April, with 13,000 staff and HQ at Brampton, out of part of the disbanding Support Command. Training (including flying) assets of Support Command were formed into Personnel & Training Command at Innsworth.

Harrier II for two

The first BAe Harrier built at Warton made its initial flight on 7 April when Jim Ludford and Graham Tomlinson were airborne in the first of 13 Harrier T.Mk 10s for the RAF. Due to enter service in 1995, the Mk 10 is an operational trainer version of GR.Mk 7, equipped with night vision systems and eight wing pylons, but no Angle Rate Bombing Set in the nose. Currently, pilots convert to STO/VL in first-generation Harrier T.Mk 4s. These are

The Italian Capitanerie is a quasimilitary organisation concerned with maritime policing. The radar-equipped Piaggio P.166-DL3 is operated on patrol duties.

The improved Chinook HC.Mk 2 is now entering RAF service. One was lost in June when it struck a hill while carrying key members of the Northern Ireland security forces.

earmarked for conversion to T.Mk 6s (having the Mk 7's night vision systems) until it was appreciated that the differences in handling compared with the Harrier II would make this a questionable exercise.

Harrier GR.Mk 3s officially departed RAF service on 31 March when late production aircraft ZD668 and ZD670 were disestablished at No. 20 (Reserve) Squadron at Wittering, having been used as instructors' chase aircraft. However, with the 25th anniversary of the Harrier's entry into RAF service fast approaching, the pair was given a life extension to take part in a flypast over Wittering for a reunion on 20 May. Because of bad weather, the event was reduced to a demonstration by ZD670, the last Mk 3 built.

Scouts reach end of trail

A flypast of 17 Westland Scout AH.Mk 1s at Middle Wallop on 30 March marked the withdrawal from service of the UK's first operational turbine helicopter. The Scout and its navalised sister, the Wasp, derived from the Saunders-Roe P.531, were first flown in July 1958. Used for anti-tank operations with Aérospatiale (Nord) SS.11 missiles as well as for unarmed observation and liaison, the helicopter suffered a hasty departure from service when a planned rotor replacement programme was judged to be uneconomical. The final two home-based units with Scouts were 666 Squadron (TA) at Netheravon, which converted to Gazelles, and co-located 658 Squadron, which operated a mixture of Scouts and Gazelles and continues to fly the latter. In the Far East, 660 Squadron at Sek Kong, Hong Kong, stood down on 31 December 1993, leaving its 'C' Flight at Seria, Brunei, to stand alone as the final Scout unit. Redesignation as 7 Flight (the former Berlin garrison unit) was due in October 1994, at about which time the three Scouts will be replaced by a new helicopter – possibly the Bell 212/412, for commonality with Royal Brunei Armed Forces equipment.

Maritime Tornado force

Transfer of the maritime Tornado force to Lossiemouth as Buccaneer replacements was completed on 27 April when No. 617 Squadron left Marham to join No. 12. The Lossiemouth wing was at that time less than fully operational, having received only a handful of Tornado GR.Mk 1Bs capable of launching the BAe Sea Eagle anti-ship missile. The 'prototype' Mk 1B, ZA407, was delivered to No. 617 on 18 February after trials with the A&AEE at Boscombe Down, although 'production' conver-

sions have come out of the Engineering Wing at RAF St Athan, from where ZA456 arrived on 14 February. Simultaneous deliveries are being made to No. 12 Squadron. Painting of GR.Mk 1Bs in an overall grey camouflage began in May.

Buccaneer bows out

Conversion of Tornados to maritime roles was made necessary by withdrawal of the venerable BAe (Blackburn) Buccaneer S.2B on 31 March. The final two squadrons were both Lossiemouth-based, comprising No. 12 (disbanded on 30 September 1993) and No. 208 (31 March 1994). No. 12 was immediately reborn by redesignation of No. 27 Squadron, while No. 208 became a Hawk T.Mk 1/1A squadron at No. 4 FTS, Valley, on 1 April (replacing the disbanded No. 234 Squadron there). Designed as a naval interdictor, the Buccaneer first flew in April 1958 and served the Fleet Air Arm until 1978. Adopted by the RAF to replace the cancelled BAC TSR2 and General Dynamics F-111K, it flew in the land-based nuclear strike role from 1969. South Africa bought 16 Buccaneer S.Mk 50s, which were operated until No. 24 Squadron disbanded on 31 March 1991.

Overshadowed by the Buccaneer's departure, the RAF's last Hawker Hunters slipped out of the inventory at the end of March. In latter years, the type's *raison d'être* had been as a two-seat trainer for the Buccaneer force, there being no dual-control version of the latter. Naturally, parallels between the two aircraft were few, but Hunters equipped with the Buccaneer's angle-of-approach indicator and its unusual strip-type (as opposed to dial) cockpit indicators were useful for introductory training and proficiency checking. The Hunter is best remembered as the RAF's prime single-seat day fighter in the second half of the 1950s and as a ground attack and tactical reconnaissance machine thereafter. The type continues in naval service for target facilities, although the first replacement BAe Hawk T.Mk 1 was delivered to the Fleet Requirements and Air Direction Unit at Yeovilton in May. Several

overseas countries continue to fly Hunters, most of them produced during the 1960s and 1970s by remanufacture of UK-, Belgian- and Netherlands-built airframes.

VIPs go by car

Deep cuts in the VIP transport force were effected on 31 March when Northolt-based No. 32 Squadron suffered the enforced retirement of its four BAe 125 CC.Mk 1s and completed withdrawal (begun six months earlier) of four Andover C.Mk 2s and three Andover E.Mk 3As. Subsequently offered for civilian sale, the BAe 125s had been delivered in March-May 1971 and upgraded by BAe at Hawarden to partial CC.Mk 3 standard (with quieter Garrett TFE731 engines and an APU) in 1982-83, although the original designation was retained. The squadron continues to operate with two 125 CC.Mk 2s, six 125 CC.Mk 3s and four Gazelle HT.Mk 3s. The Queen's Flight, which has three BAe 146s and two Westland Wessex HCC.Mk 4s at Benson, survived a costings review in early 1994, but will merge with No. 32 Squadron at Northolt in 1995.

Return of the blimp

The non-rigid airship returned to UK military service for the first time since World War I when a Skyship 600 (prototype G-SKYC) began military trials wearing the serial number ZH672. Conducting its maiden flight at Cardington on 6 March, the airship initiated a programme of evaluation sorties believed intended to assess its suitability for surveillance operations over Northern Ireland.

Naval flying training changes

The quest for cost-savings through privatisation was advanced in naval aviation on 1 April when the Gazelle HT.Mk 2-equipped basic helicopter school, 705 Squadron at Culdrose, was placed in the hands of civilian staff, and

the Flying Grading Flight at Plymouth/Roborough underwent a change of both personnel and equipment. The FGF's ageing DH Chipmunks were retired in March and replaced by five civil-registered Grob 115D2 lightplanes which officially became operational on 1 April, operated by Airwork Ltd. On 12 April, the aircraft were given the type name 'Heron', recalling the DH Sea Heron which was a stalwart of naval communications flying for nearly three decades.

At the time these changes were taking place, the whole subject of helicopter training for the UK armed forces was under scrutiny for the 'Front-Line First' defence costs study. This area is seen as a prime target for tri-service standardisation, as Gazelles are used by three schools: 705 Squadron, No. 2 FTS at Shawbury (RAF) and 670 Squadron (AAC) at Middle Wallop.

'Single-engined' Hercules

Curiously described as the 'single-engined demonstrator', leased RAF Lockheed Hercules C.Mk 1 XV181 took to the air at Cambridge on 19 March to begin a programme of test flying with an Allison AE2100 turbine engine and Dowty six-bladed propeller in the No. 2 (port inner) position. Complete with many UK-produced accessories – such as cowling produced by Westland, Lucas digital engine controls and IMI Marston oil cooler – the powerplant installation was engineered by Marshall Aerospace for trials in connection with the forthcoming C-130J version of Hercules, in which the RAF is interested. Both engine and propeller have flown before, so XV181's 50-hour test programme was specifically directed towards examining the physical aspects of a Hercules installation, including stresses, vibration and noise characteristics.

Fresh impetus was given to the RAF's Hercules replacement programme by a report of the Commons Defence Committee, published on 30 March. This recommended that the RAF should replace half its current 60 Hercules with up to 30 C-130Js

Having lost its Buccaneers, the Lossiemouth maritime strike wing now has Tornado GR.Mk 1Bs. Shown above is a No. 617 Sqn aircraft with dummy Sea Eagle anti-ship missiles, while the aircraft below demonstrates the newly-acquired mid-grey camouflage.

immediately, but leave open the possibility of buying the EuroFLA transporter to complete the process after 2005. Such a move is opposed by BAe, which is a private-venture member of the EuroFLA consortium and has warned that a C-130J order will sink the UK's chances of receiving any EuroFLA work. Having pointed to EuroFLA's turbofan engines as evidence of its modernity, the aircraft's proponents were forced to revise their sales pitch in April when it became clear that the concept was undergoing radical redesign to include four turboprops. It is understood that turbofan engines were unable to offer the ruggedness and short-field performance demanded by the aircraft's specification.

Keen to gain a sizeable launch order for the C-130J, Lockheed was offering the RAF generous terms during the early months of 1994, its bid assisted by the engagement of 20 UK firms to produce parts for all C-130Js sold anywhere in the world. In order to leave open as many options as possible, RAF opinion was reported to have swung in favour of leasing C-130Js. The proposed Hercules C.Mk 4 would be a long-fuselage (-30) version with a refuelling probe on the port side of the forward fuselage at eye-level, instead of above the co-pilot, as on the current RAF Hercules. Deliveries could begin as early as 1996, as Lockheed proposes to convert the production line to the new model (at the rate of 36-42 per year) soon after building an initial five during 1995. The USAF is planning to buy 165 to replace C-130Es, but only in small batches, beginning with two to be funded in FY 1994.

The 30 Hercules which the RAF plans to retain into the next century were receiving upgrades to their self-defence equipment early in 1994. Long-delayed addition of General Instrument AN/ALR-66 radar warning receivers to the wingtips was initiated in January by Hunting Aviation at East Midlands, while Shorts was proceeding with installation of Loral AN/ALQ-157 infra-red jammers at the rear of the undercarriage panniers. The company is modifying 23 aircraft as a follow-on to two similarly upgraded by Marshall Aerospace in 1988.

Chinook Mk 2 into service

Allocation of upgraded Chinook HC.Mk 2s to bases other than Odiham began on 1 February when ZA714 was issued from there to No. 18 Squadron at Laarbruch. A few days before, ZA710 began the long sea journey to No. 78 Squadron on the Falkland Islands. By mid-May, 11 Mk 2s had been returned to the RAF and, of the Mk 1s, 17 were undergoing rework with Boeing, two were being prepared for shipping to the US and two remained in service with the No. 7 Squadron detachment at Aldergrove, Northern Ireland. Odiham's Chinook HC.Mk 2s were being operated in a pool by Nos 7 and 27 (Reserve) Squadrons during the first half of 1994, but the latter was due to resume Chinook conversion courses thereafter.

DRA concentrates at Boscombe

Two historic centres of research flying closed at the end of March when the Defence Research Agency (DRA) bases at Farnborough and Bedford transferred their activities to Boscombe Down, home of the Aircraft and Armament Evaluation Establishment (A&AEE). DRA flying has been privatised, the initial 10-year contract won by the A&AEE and an in-house management team from DRA. Aircraft modification remains in the hands of the DRA's fleet department, with flying by A&AEE staff. Laboratories and wind tunnels at Farnborough and Bedford are unaffected and, of course, Farnborough continues to be a business aviation centre and location of the SBAC show.

Movement of the DRA fleet to Boscombe involved a reduction in size from 29 aircraft to 19, of which two are soon to be withdrawn. The situation at 1 April was three BAe One-Elevens, two BAC Canberras, one HS Hunter T.Mk 7, three HS748/Andovers, one BAe Harrier T.Mk 4, one Panavia Tornado GR.Mk 1, one Tornado F.Mk 2 (TIARA), one SEPECAT Jaguar T.Mk 2A, two Westland Lynxes, three Westland Sea Kings, and one Westland Wessex. Additionally, a One-Eleven and two Tornado GR.Mk 1/1As are on loan from other establishments.

On 1 April, the RAF Institute of Aviation Medicine at Farnborough began a two-year programme of integration within the DRA, which is forming a new Human Factors establishment, incorporating similar branches of the army and navy. The IAM currently operates a Hawk and a Jaguar. Another Farnborough resident, the unique Hercules W.Mk 2 of the Meteorological Research Flight, transferred to Boscombe on 1 April. Under threat from defence cuts, the aircraft has funding to operate only until 31 March 1995, when its future will be reviewed.

Eastern Europe

CZECH REPUBLIC:

Air force looks west

An interview given by the Commander-in-Chief early in 1994 revealed that the CRAF is looking in the long term at ways of obtaining aircraft in the class of F-16 and Mirage 2000 to re-equip its front line, as well as missiles like MICA and Sidewinder, to enhance its Russian equipment. The Czech Republic is keen is dispose of its MiG-29s as soon as possible because of serviceability problems resulting from irregular supplies of spares. It also plans to cannibalise some other Russian types to keep the remainder operational. MiG-21s will be reduced from about 80 to 40, Su-22s from 30 to 20, and some of the 75 or so MiG-23s stripped down for spare parts. Su-25s will remain at about 20-22. The CRAF also wants more funds to increase the extremely low flying rate from 60 hours per pilot per year to about 90 – in other words, still only half of the NATO current minimum.

HUNGARY:

New training aircraft

Financial restrictions have intervened in plans to re-establish HAF pilot training schools – possibly with Western equipment – as illustrated by the delivery in March and April of 12 Yak-52 piston-engined primary trainers, built in Romania. Also in process of receipt during the spring were 20 ex-German Aero L-39ZO Albatros advanced jet trainers. The central section of the training syllabus is expected to be provided by a dozen PZL-130TB Orlik basic trainers ordered early in 1993. In Warsaw Pact days, Hungarian pilots received most of their training in Czechoslovakia. After considering the options following the Russian withdrawal, it was decided to establish a training course in Hungary. Yak-52s are now based at Szolnok and L-39s at Kecskemét.

POLAND:

Iryda gathers momentum slowly

Delivery to the Air Academy in February of three PZL I-22 Iryda jet trainers increased to five the number serving with 58 Lotnicza Pulk Szkolny at Deblin. A further four were anticipated in service before the end of 1994, but disparity between batches will complicate any attempt to conduct advanced training of students on the new aircraft. The original two I-22s were delivered in October 1992, powered by a pair of PZL K-5 turbojets, each of 2,425 lb st (10.78 kN). The three received early in 1994 are similar, but the next four (completing the first firm order for nine, from 50 eventually required) have 3,305-lb st (14.69-kN) K-15s and a new avionics suite provided by SAGEM of France.

RUSSIA:

Last fighters leave Germany

Russia's last fixed-wing combat aircraft departed Germany during April, virtually bringing to an end the withdrawal of 691 aeroplanes, 600 helicopters, 4,000 tanks, 8,000 armoured vehicles, 3,500 artillery pieces, 677,000 tons of ammunition, 337,800 troops and 208,000 supporting civilians once based in the former East Germany. On 7 April, Sukhoi Su-17M-4 'Fitter-Ks' of the 20th Guards Fighter-Bomber Regiment left Templin for Russia. In a two-stage operation beginning on 7 April, MiG-29 'Fulcrums' of the 33rd Interceptor Regiment transferred from Wittstock to Damgarten, leaving there for Russia on 11 April in company with the latter's 733rd Interceptor

This Hercules C.Mk 1P is the engine testbed for the Allison AE2100 turboprop intended for the C-130J. The new engine is the port inner, with a six-bladed propeller.

Regiment MiG-29s. Thereafter only a few helicopters remained to be repatriated, together with a handful of transports. All were due to have departed by 31 August, when a ceremony marking the withdrawal of the last Russian soldier was due to take place in Berlin.

In a related departure from elsewhere in the CIS, the final four of 40 Tupolev Tu-95MS 'Bear-Hs' were withdrawn from 79 Heavy Bomber Division at Semiplatinsk, in Kazakhstan, to an undisclosed base in Russia on 19 February. A few early production, non-nuclear 'Bears' are reported to remain at Semiplatinsk. The only strategic nuclear aircraft remaining outside Russia after the withdrawal from Kazakhstan were in Ukraine, where 16 Tu-95MS bombers are based at Uzin Cheplevka and 16 Tu-160 'Blackjacks' with 194 Heavy Bomber Regiment at Priluki. These suffer low serviceability, as their Russian personnel have departed following the Soviet Union's break-up.

Su-34 flight tests begin

Flight trials were begun at the LII flight-test centre at Zhukhovskii in March of the first pre-production Sukhoi Su-34 interdictor following its delivery from the Novosibirsk assembly plant. The aircraft, coded '43', follows two similar side-by-side two-seat Su-27IBs ('41' and '42'), the first flown on 13 April 1990. There is, as yet, no formal production contract for the Su-34, nor a firm indication of the number of aircraft required. However, it is intended that the aircraft will replace all Su-24 'Fencers' in Russian service by 2002.

Novosibirsk was the manufacturing plant for some Su-24s and it is of interest that the Su-34 is also being built there instead of at the regular 'Flanker' factories at Komsomolsk (single-seat) and Irkutsk (tandem-seat). No. 43 made its first flight at Novosibirsk in December 1993, piloted by Igor Votintsev and Evgeny Revunov, and it was Revunov and Igor Soloviev who conducted the non-stop ferry flight to

Zhukhovskii in March. Additional distinguishing features of the Su-34 include tandem mainwheels and an inordinately long tailboom containing rear-looking radar. Internally, there is 1,000 kg (2,204 lb) of armour protecting the crew from shell fragments or rounds up to 17 mm (0.7 in). The crew enters the aircraft from below.

A formidable armoury can be carried on up to 11 external hardpoints, including X-25M (AS-10 'Karen'), X-29 (AS-14 'Kedge'), X-31, X-35, X-58 (AS-11 'Kilter') and X-59 (AS-13 'Kingpost') ASMs, plus laser-guided bombs. Defensive missiles include R-73 (AA-11 'Archer') and R-77 (AA-12). A variant of the latter could be installed for rearward firing to attack a following interceptor.

Sukhoi is making slow progress with the Su-35 air superiority fighter, also developed from the basic 'Flanker'. A production order was anticipated during 1994, clearing the version for manufacture at Komsomolsk. At least 10 Su-35s, numbered 701 to 710, are flying on trials at Zhukhovskii, Ahktubinsk and possibly elsewhere.

Carriers 'mothballed'

It was learned during the spring that three of Russia's first-generation aircraft-carriers – *Kiev*, *Minsk* and *Novorossiysk* – have been paid off and their Yak-38 'Forger' VTOL fighter-bombers retired. The fourth vessel of the class, *Gorshkov*, remains operational at Murmansk, although its Yak-38s will also be withdrawn, reducing it to a helicopter-carrier. Of the larger ships due to follow, equipped with Su-27K 'Flankers' and the prospective Yak-144 AEW aircraft, only the *Admiral Kuznetsov* has been completed. Development of the VTOL Yak-141 successor to the Yak-38 is no longer contemplated.

UKRAINE:

Israel aids Antonov

Revealed in February was a teaming arrangement between Antonov and Israeli Aircraft Industries under which

The Sea Harrier FRS.Mk 2 is under intensive trials with an Operational Evaluation Unit within No. 899 Sqn.

IAI is adding Israeli avionics to the An-72P maritime patrol version of 'Coaler' transport. The An-72P was displayed for the first time at Farnborough in 1992 as a minimum-change adaptation. In January, an An-72 was delivered to Israel to receive Elta EL/M-2022A maritime surveillance radar, an Elop long-range, day/night observation system, Elisra electronic warfare suite and provision for laser-guided bombs.

Nuclear weapons dismantled

An agreement with Russia and the US was put into effect on 5 March when the first 60 former Soviet strategic nuclear warheads were transferred in a special train from Ukraine to Russia for destruction. Dissolution of the USSR conveyed upon Ukraine the dubious honour of being the world's third-largest nuclear power but, after hard bargaining for economic concessions from the West, the government

in Kiev agreed to the weapons' destruction. The armoury comprised 224 RK-55 (AS-15 'Kent') cruise missiles for 14 Tu-95MS16 'Bear-Hs' at Uzin Cheplevka; 195 RK-55s for 16 Tu-160 'Blackjacks' at Priluki; 780 warheads in 130 RS-18 (SS-19 'Stiletto') ICBMs of the Pervomaysk missile field; and 460 warheads of the 46 RS-22 (SS-24 'Scalpel') ICBMs in the Khmelnitskiy missile field.

As strategic systems, both aircraft and missiles are nominally the national assets of the CIS. However, fearful of Russian nationalism, Ukraine had threatened to retain the aircraft and their weapons and break the ICBM's launch codes until the withdrawal agreement was reached. There were renewed calls for nuclear disarmament to cease after the pro-Russian Crimea region of Ukraine declared its independence on 20 May and friction increased between Kiev and Moscow over the disputed Black Sea Fleet, divided equally between the two states in 1993.

Middle East

EGYPT:

Falcons from Turkey

Egypt's fourth batch of F-16 Fighting Falcons began arriving at Saqqara in April, the aircraft having special significance in coming from the TAI assembly line at Mürted, Turkey. All but one of the earlier F-16s received to re-equip the EAF originated with GD/Lockheed at Fort Worth. Four wings now operate the aircraft, the first at Genaclis to where 34 F-16As and eight F-16Bs (including one of the latter from Fokker) were supplied in the Peace Vector I programme. Later batches comprised F-16C/Ds, the quantities of which were slightly altered between order and delivery. The actual position is 34 F-16Cs and six F-16Ds from Block 32 to Beni Sueif Wing (PV II); 35 F-16Cs and 12 F-16Ds from Block 40 to Abu Sueir Wing (PV III); and the TAI batch of 34 and 12, also to Block 40 standard (PV IV). In all, therefore, Egypt will receive 175 Fighting Falcons, of which the first 82 are equipped with Pratt & Whitney F100 powerplants, the remainder having GE F110s.

ISRAEL:

Panthers for naval aviation

A long-standing requirement for up to 20 naval helicopters appeared to have been satisfied in April when the Israel Defence Force placed an order with Eurocopter for an undisclosed number of AS 565 Panthers. This followed experience gained from naval operation of a pair of similar AS 365G Dauphins bought from the US Coast Guard in 1985 after their duties as trials aircraft for the HH-65A Dolphin had been completed. The Dolphins have operated from the decks of two Saar 4½- class missile boats, but the navy has now gained a third example of the type, plus two Saar 5 vessels. The Panthers will be fitted with an advanced search radar and navigation suite being developed by the US subsidiary of Israeli avionics company, Elbit.

Some of the roles allocated to the Panther are those originally reserved for the recently-revealed – and cancelled – IAI Hellstar. The latter was an unmanned helicopter based on the airframe of the Gyrodyne QH-50 DASH drone which was abandoned in 1993

After nearly 50 years, Russian fighters departed from German soil on 11 April 1994, when the final MiG-29s left Damgarten. This aircraft was the very last machine to leave.

as the result of guidance problems and lack of funding in the IDF/Navy budget. The Hellstar would have had a day/night observation system and laser rangefinder/designator.

Phantom upgrade complete

By April, IAI had delivered the last of an undisclosed number of upgraded McDonnell Douglas F-4E Phantoms to the IDF/AF, completing the Phantom 2000 programme. Key items in the programme are a Norden AN/APG-76 multi-mode radar, Kaiser wide-angle HUD, multi-function display screens and complete rewiring and associated refurbishment. The prototype flew in August 1987, but a proposal to add PW1120 turbofans in place of GE J79s was not taken up and the so-called Super Phantom prototype remained a one-off. About 100 Phantoms remain in service under the local name of Kurnass (Sledgehammer), their operating units believed to be Nos 69 and 109 Squadrons, plus No. 142 (Reserve) Squadron all at Hatzerim, and Nos 119 and 201 at Tel Nov.

US draw-down benefits IDF

The US announced that Israel is to be the recipient of 50 Lockheed F-16A/B Fighting Falcons made surplus by recent reductions in USAF strength. Delivery was due in October, following the July arrival of 10 Sikorsky UH-60 Black Hawks promised in 1992. Other recent deliveries have included 25 McDonnell Douglas F-15A/B Eagles and 24 McDonnell Douglas AH-64A Apaches.

Israeli F-15I

The Israeli Air Force/Defence Force agreed in May 1994 to purchase 21 McDonnell Douglas F-15I Eagles, with options for four more. Deliveries are to begin in 1997. To assure a night-fighting capability, the F-15E derivatives will be fitted with some of the 30 Sharpshooter targeting pods purchased for Israel's F-16 fleet; Israel will then buy new, standard LANTIRN (Low-Altitude, Navigation and Targeting, Infra-Red, for Night) navigation pods to complete the F-15I's night vision suite.

KUWAIT:

War damage repaired

KAF operations returned to normal on 7 February when the air base at Ahmed al Jaber was recommissioned, following repair of war damage. The KAF resumed flying from Kuwait City IAP immediately after the 1990-91 conflict and later was able to return to Ali al Salem on completion of essential rebuilding.

PAKISTAN:

F-16 compromise offered

At loggerheads with Washington over its suspected nuclear weapons capability and therefore denied US arms exports, Pakistan was offered a compromise in March, allowing delivery to proceed of some of its embargoed Lockheed F-16A/Bs. By that time, 22 aircraft had been collected at Davis-Monthan AFB, with a further six to follow by the end of 1994. A 'stop work' order affects the remaining 43 of the batch of 71 on order. As a one-off gesture, the US government indicated its willingness to release the 28 Fighting Falcons built, plus a further 10, to equal the $658 million value of payments made by Pakistan before instalments were halted.

'New' Mirages

Pakistan obtained for refurbishment at Kamra what are probably the world's lowest-houred Mirage IIIs when the PAF bought 10 aircraft from Lebanon early in 1994. The nine Mirage IIIELs and single IIIBL trainer remain from 10 and two, respectively, delivered between 1967 and 1969. Some were immediately placed in storage at Qoliaat and the remainder soon followed, remaining undisturbed for 19 years.

SRI LANKA:

Mi-17s boost helicopter fleet

In spite of some serviceability problems with the three Mil Mi-17 'Hips' bought in 1993, the SLAF placed a follow-on order early in 1994 for a similar number. At one-third the price of Western equivalents, the Mils were an irresistible buy. They will enter service with 4 Wing at Katunayake, which also has approximately 14 Bell 212/412s in its fleet.

Far East

CHINA:

Private-venture trainer

With the backing of Baoshan Iron and Steel of Shanghai, the Canadian company Venga hopes to put its TG-10 advanced jet trainer into production in China within the next few years. Resembling a V-tailed Northrop F-5 built in composites materials and powered by a single General Electric J85-GE-5 of 2,925 lb st (13.01 kN), the TG-10 was designed in the mid-1980s, but failed to attract sufficient funding for a prototype to be built. That problem has now been overcome, and the first aircraft was taking shape at Montreal early in 1994. A second will be shipped to Shanghai early in 1995 as a pattern for series production. Venga has one civilian and four military customers interested in a combined total of 86 TG-10s.

INDONESIA:

Joint training with Singapore

Having conducted combined military exercises since the mid-1970s, Indonesia and Singapore increased their level of collaboration early in 1994 with the opening of the Pekan Baru air combat manoeuvring range in central Sumatra. The range, incorporating the previous-ly established Saibu air weapons range, is the first in the world to use satellite datalinks to convey information to ground monitoring stations for later play-back and analysis.

JAPAN:

Japan UC-X requirement

The Japan Air Self-Defence Force (JASDF) has formalised its UC-X requirement for a replacement for its current fleet of Beech B65 liaison/training support aircraft. The Canadair Challenger, Falcon 900 and Gulfstream 4 were to be evaluated, with one of the types to be chosen by August 1994. Two airframes, initially, are to be funded in 1995.

Fighter scrambles decline

As elsewhere, the reduction in Russian military activity has been felt in the JASDF, which scrambled 311 fighters to investigate unidentified aircraft in the 12 months to 31 March, compared with 331 in 1992 and 488 in 1991. Most active was 2 Air Wing at Chitose, whose two F-15J Eagle squadrons are responsible for northern Japan. It was also notable that the most common targets were no longer bomber and reconnaissance aircraft but helicopters scouting for fishing fleets.

Southern Asia

INDIA:

MiG-29M promoted

Unsuccessful in persuading Russia's air forces to order the upgraded MiG-29M 'Fulcrum-E', Mikoyan turned to India early in 1994 with an offer of 20 aircraft, plus an option on 10 more. With fly-by-wire controls, 'glass' cockpit and provision for a wide range of air-to-surface missiles, as well as the new AA-12 AAM, the MiG-29M first flew in 1989. The version passed examination by the Air Force Scientific Research Institute before being abandoned by its manufacturer in mid-1993 when funding failed to appear.

1994 budget approved

Major item in the 1994 (Japanese FY 6) budget approved shortly before the start of the fiscal year on 1 April was a second pair of Boeing 767 AWACS, completing the Air Self-Defence Force requirement for early warning aircraft. The unusually small total of 20 aircraft for the ASDF also includes four Mitsubishi F-15J Eagles (making 192 F-15Js and F-15DJs), nine Kawasaki T-4s (now 153), two Beech 400T transport conversion trainers (now eight), a Raytheon (ex-BAe) U125 for SAR (five) and two Mitsubishi UH-60J Seahawks (16) in the same role.

Naval aviation was assigned funds for only eight aircraft, comprising one Kawasaki P-3C Orion (the 103rd), a UP-3D (now six), five SH-60J Seahawk anti-submarine helicopters (58) and one SAR UH-60J (11). Ground forces are to obtain two Fuji AH-1S Cobras (now 87) for anti-tank missions and 16 Kawasaki OH-6D (182) observation helicopters. Small numbers of orders reflect both the end of the Cold War and the slowing of production as previously determined totals of Eagles, Orions and Cobras are approached.

The 767 AWACS are taking a substantial share of the current funding over the coming two years. With that peak passed, however, attention will turn to obtaining a replacement for the Kawasaki C-1A jet transport, 28 of which are in service. Against local industry preference to design a replacement, the ASDF is considering the McDonnell Douglas C-17 Globemaster III, among other options.

MALAYSIA:

Hawk deliveries begin

Overshadowed by political allegations that they were ordered as part of a secret 'arms purchase in return for aid' agreement between London and Kuala Lumpur, delivery of the RMAF's BAe Hawks began in April when the second of 10 Mk 108 trainers (M40-02) departed the UK. They will be followed by 18 single-seat Hawk

Mk 208s, of which the first (M40- 21) made its initial flight at Warton on 4 April.

SINGAPORE:

Chinook order

Six Boeing CH-47D Chinooks were ordered during April in satisfaction of a long-held RSiAF requirement for medium-lift helicopters. Delivery is due in 1996-97 and duties will include SAR for the civilian authorities.

Enforcer clarified

Secrecy over Singapore's order for Fokker 50s was penetrated only after deliveries of the first of nine aircraft were initiated in November 1993. The first aircraft (two 50UTA-A and two UTA-B variants of the F 50 Utility) have entered service with 121 Squadron at Changi, replacing Shorts Skyvans in the general transport role. Later in 1994, the RSiAF planned to receive five Maritime Enforcer Mk 2s from an unannounced order.

TAIWAN:

Ching-Kuo in service

Taiwan's most advanced combat aircraft, the AIDC Ching-Kuo, entered service in mid-February when first deliveries were made to the 3rd TFW at Ching Chuan Kang. The first squadron will be equipped with 27 aircraft during 1994. Three squadrons of Lockheed F-104G Starfighters (the 7th, 8th and 28th) previously comprised the 3rd Wing, which otherwise goes by the code number of 427th TFW.

Taiwan's haste to replace Starfighters before the arrival of its 150 F-16s and 60 Dassault Mirage 2000-5s resulted in a requirement for a further 50 ex-USAF Northrop T-38A Talon supersonic jet trainers additional to the 40 already proposed. By early 1994, funds for the first batch had yet to be approved, however.

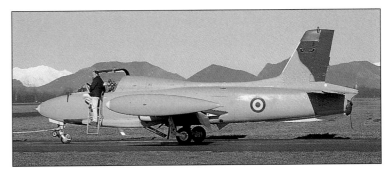

Above: Seen at Aermacchi's works at Varese-Venegono is an MB-326K of the Ghana air force.

Below: The Atlas Rooivalk ADM demonstrated its capabilities to the British army in 1994.

offshore aboard the USS *Peleliu* until May. The USAF also discontinued its patrols by 16th SOS AC-130H Spectre gunships out of Mombasa, Kenya, at the end of March. Four had been installed in June 1993, but one was lost on 15 March when it crashed off the Kenyan coast, killing eight of the 14 personnel aboard.

The UN took over the US security patrol responsibility, for which eight Bell AS-1S Cobras were leased for 10 months from the US Army National Guard's 1/193 Avn at Wheeler AFB, Hawaii. Continue Hope, the UN operation, began in May 1993, but had already proved to be ineffective before the last American troops left.

SOUTH AFRICA:

Air arms disbanded

South Africa's first universal election resulted in the disappearance in April of 10 'tribal homelands' established by the former white regime as reservations for ethnic groups. Of these, Bophuthatswana, Ciskei, Transkei and Venda possessed small air arms equipped with helicopters and light-planes which are expected to be passed on for civilian police use or sold. Another 'air force' within the republic is the Lugvleul, a collection of about 10 unarmed light aircraft flown by the right-wing AWB political party on paramilitary duties. AWB resistance to black rule suggests this unofficial air arm will be maintained as a shadowy force ready for possible action.

Rooivalk order

The election has also obviated the UN

arms embargo imposed on South Africa, making imports and exports possible. There is now no objection to the sale of Pilatus PC-7 TurboTrainers to the SAAF, nor the promotion of the Atlas Rooivalk combat helicopter in competitions currently under way in the UK and Netherlands. Having secured an order for four pre-series examples as recently as October 1993, the Rooivalk was launched into full-scale production with the announcement in March of a follow-on batch of 16 for one squadron of the SAAF and the promise of another contract to follow. The second prototype, ZU-AHC, was air-freighted to the UK in May for demonstrations, having previously appeared at the Dubai trade show in search of Middle East orders. Atlas plans to fly a third prototype, the Engineering Development Model, in mid-1996. In this, crew positions will be reversed, with the pilot sitting at the rear.

UK officials discussing the possibility of a Rooivalk purchase for the Army Air Corps were reported to have looked into the possibility of obtaining up to a dozen redundant SAAF Aérospatiale Pumas to alleviate the RAF's shortage of tactical transport helicopters.

Even faster Cheetah

Information released shortly before the South African election revealed that a dozen of the SAAF's Atlas Cheetah Es (modified Mirage IIIEZs and Kfir 1s) were being further upgraded with features including replacement of their SNECMA Atar 09C reheated turbojets by 09K-50s taken from Mirage F1CZs retired in September 1992. In addition,

Africa

SOMALIA:

US forces withdraw

In spite of a promising beginning to the massive US operation to end the civil war and ensure safe delivery of relief supplies, Somalia was left entirely in the hands of a UN contingent when the final American forces withdrew (in Operation Quickdraw) on 25 March. The December 1992 'invasion', Provide Hope, achieved most of its objectives, but the failure to disarm warring factions proved to be a critical error as they used the stability of peace to regroup and rearm. Accordingly, US and UN peacekeepers increasingly

became the targets of warlords seeking to re-establish their influence while renewed extortion from aid agencies ($100,000 per week from the Red Cross alone) filled depleted arms chests. Although alleged to be still haunted by memories of Vietnam, the US contrived to commit exactly the same mistakes in Somalia by isolating themselves in fortified compounds and allowing politicians to meddle in military decisions.

The 25 March pull-out involved 15 US Army AH-1 Cobra gunships withdrawing to vessels off shore and a C-5 Galaxy taking personnel and supplies out of Mogadishu. A US Marine Corps force with helicopter support remained

Two Peruvian aircraft seen at FIDAE 94 were a Mirage 2000P of Escuadrón 412 from La Joya, and an Antonov An-32 of Escuadrón 842 from Lima-Jorge Chavez. The FAP has 12 Mirages, including two 2000DP two-seaters.

the Cheetah Es are having their Elta EL/M-2001 ranging radars replaced by EL/M-2035 fire-control radars based on technology developed for the cancelled IAI Lavi fighter. The programme, which will run until 1995, is known as Project 855, which happens to be the serial number of the former Mirage IIIR2Z acting as the testbed for a modified 'combat wing' with drooped leading edge and provision for wingtip missiles.

Two Mirage F1CZs which remain in flying condition at the Arniston test centre are believed to have been fitted with Kilmov RD-33 reheated turbojets, as installed in the MiG-29 'Fulcrum'. The prototype installation was undertaken in Moscow in 1991 and the second machine fitted with one of the two RD-33s delivered to South Africa for evaluation (see *World Air Power Journal*, Volume 10).

South America

ARGENTINA:

Skyhawk contractor

In February, the UK firm Smiths Industries was spared the embarrassment of working for the Argentine air force when its proposal for refurbishment of 36 McDonnell Douglas A-4M Skyhawk fighter-bombers was passed over in favour of Lockheed Aircraft Services. The first 18 ex-USN aircraft will be overhauled at Ontario, California, but the second batch is to be upgraded locally with Lockheed kits by the air force's maintenance unit (Aérea de Material) at Cordoba.

BRAZIL:

Armed Super Tucano

Developed to meet the USA's JPATS trainer programme, the stretched, uprated EMB-312H Super Tucano has been further enhanced as an armed border patrol aircraft. EMBRAER was

hoping to secure an order from the FAB for the combat Tucano – designated ALX – in March, shortly before the company was due to be privatised. The contract failed to materialise, even after the sale was postponed for two months to 20 May.

CHILE:

New combat aircraft sought

Plans for early retirement of the last eight HS Hunters of Grupo 8 at Antofagasta became known in April when a Chilean delegation visited Belgium to examine 20 surplus Mirage 5BAs being upgraded by SABCA for possible sale. In the event of an agreement being reached, the FACh was planning to take delivery of 10-12 Mirages in 1994 and the remainder in the following year, as soon as they come off the modification line. As such, the Mirage 5s would complement Mirage 50s of Grupo 4 at Punta Arenas, these also having undergone

recent upgrading to Pantera standard. After protracted trials with a prototype, the first Panteras returned to service in mid-1993.

With its Northrop F-5Es also being retrofitted to Tiger III standard (two of the 13 completed by early-1994), the FACh is next looking for a follow-on to its Cessna A-37 Dragonflies flown by Grupo 3 at Temuco and Grupo 12 at Iquique. Aircraft as diverse as F-16 Fighting Falcons and ex-Kuwaiti A-4KU Skyhawks have been considered, but the favoured option is currently Saab Gripens to be obtained in 2005. Of a more immediate nature, Chile took delivery of the first pair of four CASA C.212 Aviocar light transports in February and one of two IAI (Boeing 707) Phalcon AEW aircraft in May.

COLOMBIA:

Cobra request

Responding to the threat posed to security forces by heavily-armed drugs-growing organisations, Colombia made a request to the US early in 1994 for 12 Bell AH-1W Cobra helicopter gunships. The Cobras are required to escort Sikorsky UH-60 Black Hawks (also supplied by the US) carrying raiding parties to the drug-growing areas. Backing the UH-60s is the FAC's fleet of Bell UH-1H Iroquois, an initial 30 of which are due to be upgraded by Bell to 'Huey II' standard with a more powerful T53-L-700 turboshaft.

Enstrom helicopter delivery

A dozen Enstrom F28F light helicopters were delivered to Colombia's air force between March and May, having been obtained via the United States' Foreign Military Sales programme. Purchased at a cost of $4.1 million, the F28s are used for training.

North America

CANADA:

Defence cuts and base closures

Having cancelled the EHI EH.101 helicopter contract within days of taking power, Canada's new Liberal government continued cuts in the armed forces when the 1994 budget was published on 22 February. Over the next four years, Canadian Forces' (CF) manpower (including civilians) will be reduced from 108,400 to 91,900, comprising 66,700 in uniform and 25,200 for support. The CF will lose 21 bases and have activities reduced at a further nine, the air bases to be closed comprising Chatham, Ottawa (Uplands) and Toronto (Downsview).

Largest of these is Uplands, Ottawa, where 7 Wing is resident with 412 Squadron (CC-109 Cosmopolitan and CC-144 Challenger) for VIP transport and 450 Squadron (Bell CH-135 Twin Huey). No. 450 will move to St Hubert and No. 412 will sell its seven CC-109s from October 1994, but remain as a lodger at Ottawa's airport, flying its CC-144s. Toronto (Downsview) is a helicopter base, where 2 Wing has 400 (OCU) and 411 Squadrons flying Bell CH-136 Kiowas. These squadrons will remain as lodgers at the airport. Bases ear-

marked for a reduction in activities are Edmonton/Namao (18 Wing), Gander and North Bay. Edmonton's helicopters – 408 Squadron with CH-135s and CH-136s – will remain in an enclave of the former air base and become a detachment of 11 Wing at St Hubert. No. 435 Squadron will move with KCC-130 Hercules tankers to 17 Wing at Winnipeg, its transports to be shared by the units already at Trenton (8 Wing). The same fate will befall No. 440's SAR-tasked Hercules following disbandment of the unit. CC-138 Twin Otters of No. 418 will move to Yellowknife, joining the squadron's long-term detachment.

Plans have also been revealed for a reduction of activities at Shearwater, from where 434 Squadron and its electronic warfare training CT-133s and CC/CE-144s will be relocated to Greenwood, presumably in company with 420 Squadron, a supporting unit of reservist personnel.

A future administrative change will be the fusion in mid-1996 of Air Transport Group, 10 Tactical Air Group and Fighter Group into a new Air Combat & Mobility Group which will control most air assets apart from maritime and training.

The CF is giving consideration to appointing a civilian contractor to operate the CT-114 Tutors of 2 FTS at Moose Jaw, continuing the trend begun in 1991 when primary, multi-engined and basic helicopter training was privatised.

UNITED STATES:

F-15C Eagles shoot down Black Hawks

On 14 April 1994, two US Army Sikorsky UH-60 Black Hawk helicopters were shot down by US Air Force McDonnell Douglas F-15C Eagles of the Spangdahlem-based 52nd Fighter Wing in northern Iraq's 'No-Fly Zone'. Twenty-six American and United Nations personnel were killed while on a humanitarian mission to Kurdish areas of Iraq.

The Pentagon's investigation of this fratricidal incident attempted to determine how several things went wrong at once, including a failure of visual identification. A preliminary report places much of the blame on the AWACS crew guiding the F-15Cs, some of whom knew about the helicopters.

Although they wore the American flag, the UH-60s lacked high-visibility markings such as the vertical yellow stripes worn by Black Hawks operating in the Korean armistice zone at Panmunjom. Worse, the Black Hawks were carrying external fuel tanks on sponsons which resemble the stubby wings of the Russian-built Mil Mi-24 'Hind' helicopter, used by Iraqi forces. Superficial appearances probably contributed to the fatal mishap.

The F-15s were cleared to fire by the AWACS (Airborne Warning and Control System) E-3B Sentry overseeing their patrol in the area. The Pentagon now says that some members of the AWACS crew did not know what other members knew. The helicopter pilots may have turned off their IFF (Identification Friend or Foe) transmitter, a device which misbehaves on the ground and may have been left off because the helicopters were making short, village-to-village hops of 10 minutes or less.

USAF Brigadier General Scott Pilkington had flown in a Black Hawk on 11 April and an F-16 on 13 April to "reassure himself" that communications procedures worked north of the 36th Parallel, where the coalition has barred Iraqi aircraft. US Army European Command chief Lieutenant General Richard F. Keller said that the Black Hawk mission was "routine" and had been "rehearsed" to assure its safety.

The two-ship F-15C flight was led by a captain; flying wing was a lieutenant colonel and squadron commander who had shot down an Iraqi helicopter during Operation Desert Storm, in February 1991. One F-15C fired an AIM-120A AMRAAM radar-guided missile, the other an AIM-9 Sidewinder.

No fewer than 1,400 US helicopter flights and 27,000 fixed-wing sorties had been flown over northern Iraq without mishap, Defense Secretary William Perry said after the shoot-down. Nine British troops were killed by US 'friendly fire' during the Gulf War when an A-10 destroyed UK armoured personnel carriers.

F-15C 'Wild Weasel' study

The US Air Force has awarded a contract to McDonnell Douglas to explore the use of current avionics technology in a single-seat F-15C Eagle for the Suppression of Enemy Air Defense (SEAD) mission now carried out by the two-place F-4G Phantom II. Plans (not currently funded) call for eight aircraft, equipped to fire AGM-88 HARM anti-radar missiles, to attain IOC (Initial Operating Capability) by August 2000. The Air Staff is sceptical of a modified F-15C as an F-4G replacement, but is pressing ahead to evaluate two sets of avionics, in two configurations, both of which create distinctive 'cheek' fairings on the F-15C.

F-15E engine woes

Engine failures in Alaska-based McDonnell F-15E Strike Eagles – which would support forces in Korea in time of war – led in mid-1994 to a prolonged grounding of many F-15Es powered by Pratt & Whitney F100-PW-229 engines. The problem, tentatively blamed on stress-related cracking of the powerplant's fourth stage turbine blades, will ground 75 Strike Eagles at Elmendorf AFB, AK, RAF Lakenheath, England, and Nellis AFB, NV, for much of the summer of 1994, or restrict them to speeds below 550 kt (631 mph; 1016 km/h) while corrections are made. Although 54 Lockheed F-16C/D Fighting Falcons at three bases are powered by the same engines, interim blade fixes introduced in 1993 have kept them on full status.

NDAA solicited as alternative to C-17

The US Air Force, which once wanted nothing to stand in the way of its McDonnell Douglas C-17 Globemaster 3 transport, is now soliciting commercial or non-developmental airlift aircraft (NDAA) to substitute for part of its projected C-17 force.

In autumn 1993, then-Pentagon acquisition chief and now Deputy Defense Secretary John M. Deutch put the planned purchase of 120 C-17s on 'probation'. Deutch guaranteed the manufacturer that the first 40 would be bought, but stipulated that the USAF would look at other ways to fill remaining air transport needs, including cargo models of the Boeing 747, McDonnell Douglas MD-11, or newly produced Lockheed C-5 Galaxies. The C-17 has overcome technical hurdles and is performing well, but critics argue that the aircraft is too costly, and has capabilities – such as being able to make an assault landing on an unpaved airstrips near the battlefield – not

Also at FIDAE was this Argentine navy Super Etendard, still wearing kill markings for the Exocet sinking of HMS Sheffield during the Falklands campaign. The marking for Invincible relates to an attack which Argentina erroneously thought had damaged the carrier. The IA-63 Pampa (below) is now in Fuerza Aérea Argentina service in the advanced training role.

worth their price tag. Impetus for a solution comes from the relentless deterioration of the Air Force's Lockheed C-141 StarLifter fleet. In recent years, C-141s have repeatedly been grounded for a series of alterations as most of the 260 StarLifters approach the end of their projected 45,000-hour airframe life.

NDAA has become big business at Boeing, Lockheed and McDonnell Douglas (which is competing with itself by offering the civil MD-11 as a C-17 alternative). A decision on the number and type of alternative airlifters needed by the Air Force is to be made in a November 1995 Defense Acquisition Board proceeding.

Though they offer the economic benefit of coming straight 'off the shelf', freighter versions of the 747 or MD-11 lack the roll-on/roll-off and rapid turnaround capabilities of military transports. A new batch of C-5s would offer these advantages, plus the C-17's ability to handle outsized cargo, but at higher start-up costs. Lockheed still has the production tooling which was used to manufacture two batches of C-5s in the late 1960s and mid-1980s.

As part of its NDAA effort, the US Air Force conducted loading exercises at McChord AFB, WA, with a Boeing 747-400F freighter borrowed from Cathay Pacific Airways (before the type was put into service by the carrier in June 1994). The Air Force also evaluated the McDonnell Douglas MD-11

transport and carried out tests on a KC-10 Extender to establish baseline data. US Army vehicles, including M35A2 2.5-ton trucks, were among the cargo items loaded aboard the transports being evaluated.

Boeing claims that the longer-range 747-400F (as compared with the C-141B StarLifter) could have saved 350 million US gal (1325 million litres) of fuel during Operations Desert Shield and Desert Storm, and is pushing the US military to buy a fleet of slightly modified 747-400Fs as low-cost, supplemental military freighters. Lockheed is proposing what it calls the C-5D (formerly C-5B Plus), a 'new build' aircraft based on the C-5B with upgraded engines (of a type yet to be determined) and a 'glass' cockpit.

A major problem with the C-17 programme emerged on 1 October 1991 when the 'static test article' had a wing structural failure under much less demanding conditions than had been foreseen. The test was a simulation of load conditions with vertical gusts of 55 ft (16.76 m) per second at an altitude of approximately 32,000 ft (9754 m) at a speed of 275 kt (315 mph; 508 km/h) with a heavy weight of 585,000 lb (265356 kg). These were conditions not likely to be encountered in the real world, but theoretically possible for a heavily laden C-17 just after refueling in flight. At Charleston AFB, SC, 437th Airlift Wing commander Brigadier General Thomas Mikolajcik acknowledged that "we're going to

Canada's No. 412 Sqn finally retired the CC-109 Cosmopolitans in 1994. Here four of the veterans (one with an RCAF 70th anniversary badge) line up at Ottawa.

have to see a resolution of the structural problem before we can bring [the C-17] on line." The US Air Force claims that further engineering work and a vigorous, almost fault-free test programme have resolved the structural issue.

The first production C-17 was delivered to Mikolajcik's wing on 14 June 1992. The wing's 17th Airlift Squadron is now operational.

US operations in Rwanda

To support humanitarian relief efforts for the civil war in Rwanda, the US Air Force's Air Mobility Command (AMC) set up operations at Mwanza, Tanzania, on 10 May 1994. The group, a tanker airlift control element, consisted of personnel from the C-141B StarLifter-equipped 438th Airlift Wing, deployed from McGuire AFB, NJ.

Four C-141Bs and seven crews from McGuire flew 478,000 lb (216820 kg) of relief supplies for Rwandan refugees through 21 May, when the bulk of operations were taken over by the 62nd Airlift Wing from McChord AFB, WA.

C-12F order

In May 1994, the US Army placed an order with Beech Aircraft for three C-12F aircraft, with follow-on options for as many as 26. Two of the aircraft will be assigned to the US Army Reserve at Willow Grove, PA, the third at Glenview, IL. Previously, the C-12F designation has been used for US Air Force versions.

APG-73-equipped Hornets

On 25-26 May 1994, the first two F/A-18C Hornet strike fighters fitted with Hughes AN/APG-73 radar were delivered to the US Navy. The radar has greater speed and memory than the AN/APG-65 now in use on Hornets. The first two operational Hornets with the new radar went to squadrons VFA-146 'Blue Diamonds' and VFA-147 'Argonauts' at NAS Lemoore, CA.

E-2T Hawkeye delivered

The first of four Grumman E-2T Hawkeye early warning aircraft was delivered to Taiwan on 1 June 1994. Northrop Grumman, which clinched the sale with an offset deal, is also helping Taiwan to improve its F-5E fighters and UH-1H helicopters. Northrop Grumman has begun moving its Calverton, NY, E-2C Hawkeye production line to its St Augustine, FL, facility in anticipation of a US Navy order for four more of the airborne early warning aircraft in FY 1995. When the move is completed, Long Island, once home to Republic and Grumman, will have no factory which produces aircraft. The last aircraft to come off the Calverton line will be an E-2T for Taiwan in November 1994.

Apart from the US Navy, the manufacturer expects France to order four E-2Cs. Sales are also being considered to Korea, Thailand and Turkey.

Making a rare deployment to England, the F-16 Block 15 ADFs of the 182nd FG were based at RAF Fairford. This unit is outside the US defence network, so its ADFs wear standard ACC tailcodes.

Chrysler-modified E-6A delivered

Chrysler Technologies Airborne Systems delivered the first Boeing E-6A Mercury strategic communications aircraft with a new avionics suite to the US Navy on 16 June 1994. The aircraft incorporates Avionics Block Upgrade capabilities into the TACAMO communications system. The ABU is designed to enhance message handling and processing capabilities, improve navigation, improve frequency and timing standard, and extend satellite communications abilities of the aircraft to the EHF frequency range.

KC-135s to Turkey

In June 1994, the US Department of Defense told Congress it wanted to give Turkey 10 KC-135 tankers from storage and sell $560 million worth of upgrades for the aircraft. The tankers will provide a refuelling capability to Turkey's F-16 force. Boeing Wichita and CFM International will upgrade the KC-135As to KC-135R standard with CFM-56 engines.

AH-1W Night Targeting System

Bell delivered its first AH-1W Night Targeting System-equipped AH-1W

The 53rd FS made the short trip from Bitburg to join the 52nd FW at Spangdahlem. The unit was involved in the tragic fratricide of two UH-60 Black Hawks over northern Iraq.

Super Cobra gunship to the US Marine Corps on 15 June 1994. The system also has two prospective foreign customers. The NTS, built in the US by Kollsman, will be provided for AH-1s in service with Taiwan and Turkey. Taiwan is to receive 52 of the systems, Turkey 13. Turkey, which has 10 AH-1Ws, is also considering buying excess US Army AH-1Ps and fitting them with some of the NTS capability, enabling them to designate targets for the AH-1W.

Yet another potential buyer is the Netherlands, which plans a competition for up to 40 AH-1W Super Cobra or 33 AH-64 attack helicopters to replace its Alouette fleet. The Netherlands is expected to spend a year or more reviewing its two candidates before making a choice.

USAF to acquire C-130Js

The US Air Force will acquire two Lockheed C-130J Hercules 2 transports for evaluation. The Pentagon approved a proposal to use FY1994 Air National Guard and Reserve funds to purchase two C-130Js for the active-duty force. The arrangement is a exchange which will not increase the number of Hercules purchased overall. Lockheed now plans to built five C-130Js by 1996, including two for the USAF and two for the Royal Air Force, which is considering the C-130J as a replacement for its current Hercules force.

By December 1994, the company will have completed a full-scale manufacturing mock-up of the C-130J aimed at assisting in the design and development phase of the programme.

General Ronald Fogleman, head of Air Mobility Command, recently told Congress that the Air Force is interested in adding the C-130J to its inventory. No requirement has been formalised, however, and tentative plans to procure further C-130Js in FY1996 will need greater support to move ahead.

NASA acquires D-21 drones

On 1-2 June 1994, NASA's Dryden Flight Research Facility at Edwards

AFB, CA, took delivery of four Lockheed D-21 reconnaissance drones for possible future research. Twenty-two D-21 drones were manufactured by Lockheed's 'Skunk Works' in the 1960s under the secret Tagboard (later Senior Bowl) programme.

The D-21 is a tri-sonic, air-launched, unmanned reconnaissance vehicle to be launched by an A-12, SR-71 or B-52H. Power is provided by a 3,000-lb (13.35-kN) thrust Marquardt RJ43-MA-11 ramjet engine and the aircraft is capable of flying as high as 95,000 ft (28956 m). The drone was not successful in reconnaissance operations largely because of mating problems with 'mother' aircraft.

NASA has no immediate plans to use the D-21s. When it learned that 17 surviving D-21s stored at the Davis-Monthan AFB, AZ, 'boneyard' were to be offered to museums, NASA decided to request four in the event they might be needed later.

Boeing 767 for VIP missions

Boeing is proposing that the US Air Force's 89th Airlift Wing, Andrews AFB, MD, replaces its seven ageing VC-137C executive transports (Boeing 707-320B derivatives) with new, more fuel-efficient 767s. The VC-137C special air missions aircraft, or VIP transports, have relatively low airframe hours, and no requirement for a replacement has been put forward. The manufacturer argues that they do not meet noise requirements at current civil airfields, need a high level of on-site ground support and, with range of 3,400 nm (3,910 miles; 6292 km), lack the reach for today's fast-paced global diplomacy.

USAF studies reactivating SR-71

The Pentagon tasked Lockheed with studying the cost of reactivating three SR-71 Blackbird reconnaissance aircraft and operating them for a year. The study was prompted by tensions in Korea, where the SR-71 had a critical role for many years until its retirement in 1992. An SR-71 could take off from the manufacturer's 'Skunk Works' at Palmdale, gather photographic and radar imagery of all North Korean nuclear sites, and land at Kadena AB, Okinawa, five hours later. Arguments for and against reactivating an SR-71 force continue in the Pentagon.

B-1B problems

In July 1994, the 28th Bomb Wing, Ellsworth AFB, SC, began a six-month operational assessment of maintenance, spares and support for the Rockwell B-1B Lancer bomber. Support problems have plagued the B-1B force, which has a 55 per cent mission-capable rate and requires a separate logistics 'tail' for each airframe by serial.

For the evaluation, the US Air Force will equip Ellsworth with a full complement of spare parts and crews, drawing on assets from two other bomb wings. As part of the test, one of the 28th Bomb Wing's two squadrons will be deployed to Roswell, NM, in November 1994 to assess mission-capable rates for B-1Bs operating from a remote location.

USAF plans (most of them not yet funded) call for equipping the B-1B fleet with a full range of conventional ordnance, including the JDAM (Joint Direct Attack Munition) and JSOW (Joint Stand-Off Weapon). The B-1B will use rotary launchers for weapons of 2,000 lb (907 kg) or more, and traditional-style bomb racks for munitions of less weight and greater numbers. JDAM is to be fielded on B-1Bs in FY2001 and the full fleet of B-1Bs is to be modified by 2003. B-1Bs are also to be upgraded with GPS navigation and anti-jam radios.

Congress is balking at plans to upgrade the 95 operational B-1Bs. At the same time, legislators question whether the USAF can meet American security needs with its planned total of 210 manned bombers, including 184 which are fully operational, the number deemed necessary to achieve a goal of 100 deployable bombers.

In April 1994, members of the 184th Fighter Group, Kansas Air National Guard, became the first all-Guard aircrew to fly a B-1B on a low-level training sortie. In July, the unit was redesignated the 184th Bomber Group.

Apache redesignated

The US Army has decided to designate all 750 remanufactured McDonnell Douglas AH-64 Apaches as AH-64Ds, instead of only the 227 that were to be equipped with the Longbow fire control radar system. The remaining 'rebuilt' Apaches, formerly designated AH-64C, will be equipped to receive the Longbow system if operational requirements dictate.

27th FW at Proud Shield

The 27th Fighter Wing, Cannon AFB, NM, won the Fairchild Trophy in April 1994 as winners of Proud Shield '94, Air Combat Command's bombing competition. Held at Barksdale AFB, Louisiana, Proud Shield involved F-111F, F-15E, B-52 and B-1B crews.

1995 defence budget may see massive cutbacks

The 1995 budget request has been set at $43.5 billion for defence procurement, which will enable only 127 new aircraft to be ordered for all four services. Among the programmes approved for the US Air Force are $2.5 billion devoted entirely to research and development of the F-22 Lightning, and $2.9 billion for the purchase of six C-17As, together with

Two ANG units currently operate the C-141B, this aircraft being from the 164th Airlift Group. More are expected to be transferred.

ongoing development. The sum of $793 million has been allocated to Northrop for B-2 equipment prior to the production line closing. Two Grumman E-8C J-STARS will be acquired at the cost of $754 million.

The Navy and Marine Corps will receive 24 F/A-18C/D Hornets, four E-2C Hawkeyes, 12 AH-1W Sea Cobras, and 12 T-45A Goshawks. The budget lacks any further orders for CH-53Es and SH-60B/HH-60Hs, the funding of which was terminated in the 1994 budget. Additional F/A-18C/Ds will be procured annually to fiscal year 1997, when production will switch to the F/A-18E/F (planned to involve 12 in FY97, 24 in FY98 and 36 in FY99). E-2 procurement, which was terminated in FY93, has been reinstated for FY95, as it has been established that the purchase of new aircraft was actually cheaper than upgrading older models. Hawkeye procurement is planned at four per year until FY99.

The Army has $393 million for the final batch of 60 UH-60Ls, thereby ending Black Hawk production, with the last example due for delivery by mid-1997. In addition, some $525 million will be made available to continue research and development of the RA-66 Comanche attack helicopter.

The defence procurement budget includes funding for day-to-day operations, although drastic pruning will necessitate severe cutbacks in the number of manned bomber units within Air Combat Command. The budget will enable the Command to fund only 38 B-1Bs and 24 B-52Hs, with an additional 10 B-1Bs and eight B-52Hs financed for service with the reserves. A further dozen B-1Bs and eight B-52Hs will be assigned to training, with the remainder stored, retired or used for parts reclamation. The above funding ensures a total of only 60 B-1Bs and 40 B-52Hs.

The Air Force has an approximate total of 95 B-1Bs in operational service, along with a similar number of B-52Hs. The B-52Gs do not figure in

the equation, as they will have been virtually all retired from service by the end of 1994. The eight B-52Gs operated by the 34th BS, 366th Wing at Castle AFB, California, as part of the air intervention composite wing, were retired from service during the spring of 1994. The squadron is in the process of moving to Ellsworth AFB, South Dakota, gaining 10 B-1Bs. By the middle of 1993, some 113 B-52Gs had been retired from service, entering storage with the Aerospace Maintenance and Regeneration Center (AMARC) at Davis-Monthan AFB, Arizona. The remaining 40 or so were retired during the winter and spring of 1994, with the 93rd BW at Castle AFB, California, likely to be first to lose its complement. The 93rd BW has conducted training for B-52 aircrew for four decades, although this duty is due to be relocated to Barksdale AFB, Louisiana, prior to Castle AFB closing to flying duties at the end of 1994.

The Air Force is likely to store, retire or cannibalise 35 B-1Bs together with 63 B-52Hs. The first examples of the latter have already begun to enter storage with AMARC, with the 12 examples assigned to the 325th BS, 92nd BW at Fairchild AFB, Washington, being withdrawn by the summer of 1994. Other units which will lose their complements will be the 644th BS, 410th BW at K. I. Sawyer AFB, Michigan, whose 19 B-52Hs will be retired by late 1994, along with the 10 aircraft of the 668th BS, 416th BW at Griffiss AFB, New York. The retirements announced cover 41 B-52Hs, although the target of 63 aircraft will be achieved by further units reducing their complements, with the possibility of additional bases closing. The reduced funding could well see the US

The weapons-capable AT-38B fleet is now distributed to three training wings, the 12th FTW (illustrated), 14th FTW and 80th FTW.

Air Force pruned to the level where it would be difficult to perform its remit of conducting two medium-sized conflicts simultaneously.

The 1995 budget will affect the level of manpower and equipment operated by the reserves for the first time in many years. Funding for the Air Force Reserve and Air National Guard has almost been sacred, as these two services have been seen as a cheaper alternative to the active-duty Air Force in certain aspects. The Guard will retire its last 18 RF-4Cs, which are at present operated by the 193rd RS at Reno-Cannon IAP, Nevada. The ANG will reduce strength by 21 F-15s and 41 F-16s, which will be drawn from numerous units which will reduce complement from 18 to 15 aircraft (see later for details).

The Air Force Reserve will be cut by 18 A-10s (probably from the 45th FS at Grissom AFB, Indiana, which is scheduled to inactivate), together with 24 F-16s. The authorised strength of the ANG will be reduced from 1,571 to 1,505 aircraft, while the AFRes will shrink from 542 to 496. However, some of the reductions will be compensated by the planned conversion of units from the fighter to the air refuelling role with the assignment of the KC-135E/R.

F-4G continues operations in Europe

Despite being withdrawn from USAFE service during February 1994, the F-4G has continued to be employed in the 'Wild Weasel' role in Europe and the Middle East. The F-4G has been stationed at Incirlik AB, Turkey, as part of the Provide Comfort force package to patrol the United Nations 'No-Fly Zone' above northern Iraq. The 52nd FW was tasked with the duty until early in 1994, when the 561st FS, 57th FW at Nellis AFB, Nevada, assumed the commitment with four aircraft.

The 561st FS performed operations with the 4404th Composite Wing at Dhahran International Airport, Saudi Arabia, as part of Southern Watch for a short time. The squadron commenced operations during September 1993, but was replaced in January 1994 by the 124th FS from Boise Air Terminal,

The T-1 Jayhawk now serves with three flying training wings within AETC. The 47th FTW is at Laughlin, this aircraft carrying a 'Del Rio' legend and a Texas flag.

Idaho. The six-month ANG detachment was conducted with personnel exchanged at more regular intervals than their active-duty opposite numbers, who spend three months at a time in-theatre.

Keflavik reduces Eagle presence

The 57th FS at NAS Keflavik, Iceland, reduced its complement from 12 F-15C/Ds to just four on 1 April 1994. The requirement to police the Faroes/Iceland gap has been much reduced since the long-range Russian bombers, which regularly probed Western defences during the Cold War period, have become virtually non-existent.

The squadron is assigned to the 35th Wing, which also has responsibility for the MH-60Gs of the 56th RQS, together with the Iceland Air Defense System. Iceland-based USAF operations were previously part of the 1st Air Force with headquarters at Tyndall AFB, Florida, under Tactical Air Command. The transfer of most TAC assets to Air Combat Command in June 1992, and the subsequent relocation of Tyndall AFB to Air Education and Training Command in July 1993, resulted in the 35th Wing joining the 8th Air Force with HQ at Barksdale AFB, Louisiana.

USAF unit news

The US Air Force is continuing its programme of retaining units with a lengthy historical background. The 20th FW, inactivated at Upper Heyford at the end of 1993, but was reformed during January 1994 at Shaw AFB, South Carolina, replacing the 363rd FW. The three former F-111E squadrons were also reactivated at the same time, with the OA/A-10A-equipped 21st FS becoming the 55th FS, while the F-16C/D-equipped 17th and 309th FS were replaced by the 77th and 79th FS. The final Shaw-based squadron was the 19th FS, also with the F-16C/D, which became the 78th FS, another former USAFE squadron having previously been assigned to the 81st TFW.

The 438th AW at McGuire AFB, New Jersey, is to be redesignated 305th Air Mobility Wing during October 1994. McGuire AFB will receive 10 KC-10A Extenders from the 458th Operations Group at Barksdale AFB,

Louisiana, in mid-1994, followed by 12 more in late 1994 and the final two by mid-1995. The resident C-141B fleet will be cut by 18 aircraft from late 1994, with some joining the reserves while others will be scrapped. The 305th was previously an air refuelling wing at Grissom AFB, Indiana, until inactivated during 1993. The 305th AMW will become the major East Coast hub, while Travis AFB, California, will house the West Coast equivalent in July 1994 when the 60th Airlift Wing becomes an air mobility wing. The 60th AMW will receive 24 KC-10As with 10 transferring from March AFB, California, in mid-1994, followed by the remainder in mid-1995. In return, the wing will lose three C-5A/Bs in late 1994, together with 16 C-141Bs.

The 58th FW at Luke AFB, Arizona, became the 56th FW in April 1994. The 56th was previously at MacDill AFB, Florida, until inactivated following the reassignment of its F-16s. The F-15E-equipped 555th FS was stationed at Luke AFB until transferred to USAFE on 1 April. In its place, the 550th FS has been reactivated as the second F-15E unit at Luke AFB, alongside the 461st FS. The presence of the two F-15E units will only be short term, as Strike Eagle training is to be consolidated under the 4th Wing at Seymour Johnson AFB, North Carolina, from late 1994.

The 58th numerical identity was transferred to Kirtland AFB, New Mexico, as a special operations wing in April 1994, replacing the 542nd CTW. The wing performs training of aircrew destined for assignment to special operations and rescue units. Among the types employed are the HC-130N, HC-130P, MC-130H, UH-lN, NCH-53A, MH-53J and MH-60G.

Following the withdrawal of the B-52H from Fairchild AFB (see earlier), the 92nd BW will change designation to become an air refuelling wing, absorbing the KC-135Rs of the 43rd and 92nd ARS which are currently assigned to the 453rd Operations Group on a tenancy basis. The group has 30 tankers assigned, but will increase its responsibility to a total of 60 tankers. This will involve the 92nd ARW becoming the parent unit for squadrons located elsewhere and which are currently under parental control of the 43rd ARW at Malmstrom AFB, Montana, as the latter is to be reduced to group status.

The 93rd BS at Barksdale AFB received its first B-52H, 60-0045, on 7

December 1993. After a period of training and familiarisation, the unit flew its first operational mission on 1 February and expects to be combat ready with eight aircraft by mid-l995.

Big Hit – the revised force structure

US Air Force personnel have described the recently announced revised force structure as the Big Hit. Primarily a reduction in the size and composition of the forces remaining, the revision is not confined to the active-duty Air Force, as the Air National Guard and Air Force Reserve are included. The details are not seen as revelations, as it was only a matter of time before the reserves would be the subject of cuts to the number of aircraft and personnel assigned to many of its units. The primary cause of the massive reduction in front-line and reservist forces during the first half of the present decade has been simply a much smaller operating budget and a new mission in the light of the post-Cold War period. The perceived threat has switched from an all-out confrontation between the US forces and their NATO allies against the Soviet Union and its Warsaw Pact partners to that of global policeman required to rapidly deploy forces to support friendly nations when required. The Gulf War was a perfect example of this new role, to prevent an ally being overrun by a neighbour with hostile intent. To this end, the active-duty Air Force has amalgamated some of its front-line assets into composite units, while aircraft types playing a supporting role are being grouped to enable a swifter response to the need.

The Air National Guard will see many of its fighter units reduced in size alongside a loss of more than 1,400 personnel. Many of the units involved operate the F-16 and will reduce their complements from 18 to 15 aircraft each. However, a conversion programme is continuing, with several squadrons due to complete or commence acquisition of the F-16C/D in place of the F-16A/B. Squadrons involved are 121st FS 'DC' at Andrews AFB, Maryland; 107th FS 'MI' at Selfridge ANGB, Michigan; 119th FS at Atlantic City IAP, New Jersey; 134th FS at Burlington IAP, Vermont; 157th FS at McEntire ANGB, South Carolina; 159th FS 'FL' at Jacksonville IAP,

Although no longer on military charge, this T-34B serves with El Toro's flying club.

Florida and 170th FS 'SI' at Capital MAP, Illinois.

Of these, the 119th, 134th and 159th FS have operated the F-16A/B Air Defense Fighter version dedicated to the interceptor role, although the transition to the F-16C/D will result in these squadrons switching to conventional fighter duties. The 169th FS 'IL' at Greater Peoria Airport, Illinois, will exchange its F-16A/Bs for the C-130E during mid-1995.

The first F-16A/Bs to be retired from service began entering storage with AMARC at Davis-Monthan AFB, Arizona, during 1993, with three aircraft from the 138th FS at Syracuse-Hancock Field, New York, followed by 17 examples from the 160th FS at Montgomery-Dannelly Field, Alabama. Seventeen embargoed Pakistani aircraft were also in storage, although this was only temporary pending agreement between the two governments on the issue of Pakistan's nuclear capabilities. By the spring of 1994, the number of F-16s in store had doubled and was expected to exceed 150 by the autumn.

The ANG has six F-15 squadrons, two of which will see an even more drastic cutback involving the loss of nine aircraft each. The 122nd FS at NAS New Orleans, Louisiana, and 199th FS at Hickam AFB, Hawaii, are the two units involved, each of which will halve their complements, while the 101st FS at Otis ANGB, Massachusetts, 110th FS at Lambert-St Louis IAP, Missouri, 128th FS at Dobbins ARB, Georgia, and 142nd FS at Portland IAP, Oregon will lose three aircraft each. ANG air defence units are responsible for 24-hour alert commitments within 14 squadrons, although four of these will cease this duty. F-15s in AMARC storage had exceeded 60 by October 1993, with more than 100 expected by late 1994.

Seventeen of the 19 ANG air refuelling squadrons will reduce their complements slightly. The standard size of Stratotanker squadrons will fall from 10 to nine aircraft for those equipped with the KC-135E, and one fewer for units operating the KC-135R. In each case, funding will be available for eight operational aircraft, the ninth being officially classified as a 'spare'. The only unit which will increase its capability is the 203rd ARS at Hickam AFB, which will add four KC-135Rs to the five already assigned. Three squadrons which are in the process of converting to the KC-135 are the 106th RS at Birmingham MAP, Alabama, 136th FS at Niagara Falls IAP, New York, and 173rd RS at Lincoln MAP, Nebraska. These units are converting from the RF-4C and F-16C/D, and should have completed re-equipping with the tanker by late 1994.

The Air Force Reserve will not escape the cuts, as their seven F-16 units are also reducing their complements from 18 to 15 aircraft. The eighth unit, the 89th FS, 906th FG at Wright-Patterson AFB, Ohio, will retire its F-16A/Bs in exchange for the C-141B, joining the 356th ALS, 907th

The F-16N is a vital part of the US Navy's adversary programme. The NFWS aircraft above wears a new 'Flanker'-style scheme, while the VF-45 aircraft (right) displays a new 'Blackbirds' tail marking.

AG at the same base. AFRes and ANG C-5, C-130 and C-141 squadrons may standardise at eight aircraft, although this has yet to be finalised.

The active-duty Air Force is being reduced towards the eventual goal of having the equivalent of 13 fighter wings. To this end, the OA/A-10A-equipped 354th FS at McChord AFB, Washington, will inactivate later this year. The squadron was part of the 355th Wing with headquarters at Davis-Monthan AFB, Arizona, and was established to support US Army forces based at nearby Fort Lewis. The 354th FS was not assigned to the resident 62nd AW, as the Air Force wished to avoid creating another composite unit. The assignment of the A-10 to McChord does not seem to have been successful, resulting in the inactivation.

At Langley AFB, Virginia, the three squadrons of F-15C/Ds assigned to the 1st FW are to reduce their complements from 24 to 18 aircraft each, effecting an overall wing reduction of 25 per cent. Other Air Combat Command units will make similar reductions in due course, with the 1st FW seen as a test case.

The recent announcements concerning the reorganisation of Air Mobility Command tanker assets have been reported piecemeal within this section. With the majority now implemented, it is worth a cursory review. The Air Force will have two airlift and tanker 'hubs', designated the 60th and 305th AMW, stationed at Travis AFB, California, and McGuire AFB, New Jersey. The two units will operate the majority fleet of KC-10As, plus a number of C-141Bs, while the 60th AMW will have the addition of C-5A/B/C model. These hubs will be the primary gateways into the United States, although existing AMC bases at Charleston AFB, South Carolina, McChord AFB, Washington, and Dover AFB, Delaware, will continue to function in the intercontinental airlift role for passengers and freight. Air refuelling 'core' wings are being established within the 22nd ARW at McConnell AFB, Kansas, 92nd ARW

at Fairchild AFB, Washington, and 319th ARW at Grand Forks AFB, North Dakota. Two additional units will be equipped with tankers, composed of the 19th ARW at Robins AFB, Georgia, and the 43rd ARG at Malmstrom AFB, Montana. The air refuelling wings will be equipped exclusively with KC-135R and T models.

AMC decided in May 1993 to standardise the complement of aircraft to 16 C-5s and C-141s within its airlift squadrons, and 12 KC-10 and KC-135s in its air refuelling squadrons. The C-17 squadrons will also have 12 aircraft assigned. Active-duty C-130 squadrons have a complement of 16 aircraft, although the 23rd Wing at Pope AFB, North Carolina, had only nine C-130Es within the 2nd ALS during October 1993, while the 41st ALS was assigned 32 aircraft. The latter squadron is believed to be holding the 16 C-130Es scheduled to join the 347th Wing at Moody AFB, Georgia, by mid-1994, to become the next composite unit. The 2nd ALS transferred nine non-AWADS equipped examples to the 314th AW at Little Rock AFB, Arkansas, during 1993, and was awaiting replacements due towards the end of the year. The 50th ALS at Little Rock AFB began receiving the first of 16 brand new C-130Hs at the end of 1993, with delivery due for completion by August 1994.

The Air Force attempted to accelerate the closure of Plattsburgh AFB, New York, with the transfer of KC-135s beginning in April 1994. However, legal action was taken to prevent the Pentagon from removing aircraft from the base as local interests

lobby to maintain the facility for tanker operations. In the meantime, the resident 380th ARW accepted delivery of the first KC-135T versions of the tanker earlier this year. The first example was 58-0061 and was followed by a further few examples by the spring. The KC-135T appellation has been assigned to former KC-135Q models following modification and re-engining by Boeing with General Electric/SNECMA F108-CF-100 turbofan powerplants.

The Kansas Air National Guard's 184th FG at McConnell AFB performed its first B-1B sortie on 20 April with an aircraft borrowed from the resident 384th BG. The unit will start conversion to the Lancer during the summer, with aircraft transferred from the 384th BG as the latter unit relinquishes its complement. In the meantime, the unit has already gained some former Air Combat Command B-1B aircrew to enable the switch from the F-16 to go as smoothly as possible.

The missile wings of US Space Command are gradually reducing their complements of ICBMs. The 44th MW at Ellsworth AFB retired the last of its LGM-30F Minuteman IIs with their removal from the launch facility for storage and subsequent scrapping. The destruction of the missiles is taking place in accordance with the Strategic Arms Limitation Treaty (SALT). The 44th MW is due to be inactivated on 4 July 1994. The 91st MW at Minot AFB and the 321st MW at Grand Forks AFB, both located in North Dakota, will change to group status on 1 July 1994. The two units have the LGM-30G Minuteman III assigned.

Blue Sword over Bosnia

As the Bosnian conflict entered its second year, NATO air power was increasingly being called upon to protect United Nations ground troops from attack. Here we review the situation up to June 1994, and detail the air assets assigned to the UN efforts.

The spring of 1994 saw the United Nations at last use air power in the war-torn former Yugoslav republic of Bosnia-Herzegovina, under the codename Blue Sword. In the first weeks of the year the UN mission to the country was in crisis, with Britain and France talking publicly about withdrawing their troops. The arrival of Lieutenant General Sir Michael Rose as no-nonsense commander of the UN's Bosnia-Herzegovina Command (BHC) on 24 January 1994, and the massacre of 68 civilians in Sarajevo's market place two weeks later, transformed the situation. On 9 February NATO governments finally lost

patience with the Bosnian Serbs and ordered them to withdraw all their heavy weapons out of a 20-km (12-mile) exclusion zone around Sarajevo or face NATO air strikes. The success of the NATO ultimatum and other UN operations incensed the Bosnian Serb military leadership, who decided to put the UN back in its place. Over the next two months they took the UN to the brink.

Balkan air power

Over the previous eight months, the NATO's 5th Allied Tactical Air Force (5 ATAF) had been building up the forces and

command structure necessary to bring air power rapidly to the assistance of General Rose's troops. More than 350 aircraft from 12 nations had deployed to the Bosnian theatre of operations to take part in the UN and NATO efforts, making this the largest Western air campaign since the Gulf War.

Central to the effort was 5 ATAF's Combined Air Operations Centre at Vicenza, in northern Italy, under the direction of Lieutenant General James Chambers, USAF. His multi-national staff choreographed every aircraft movement over Bosnia to ensure that the UN 'No-Fly Zone' was enforced, close-air support (CAS) aircraft were always airborne over the country ready to help UN troops, the humanitarian air bridge and airdrop aircraft safely reached their destinations, airborne intelligence gathering regularly took place and UN liaison aircraft carrying commanders and international peace negotiators could fly safely around the former Yugoslavia. 5 ATAF was linked to the UN through the BHC's Air Operations Control Centre, which was based until early March in Kiseljak and then moved to General Rose's Headquarters inside Sarajevo. Secure satellite and radio links, via orbiting USAF EC-130E Airborne Battlefield Command and Control Centre (ABCCC) aircraft, between the AOCC, the CAOC and UN ground troops to allow NATO aircraft to be directed to crisis points within minutes of a

The most potent strike aircraft assigned directly to the Blue Sword force are the F-15Es of the 492nd FS, 48th FW, deployed to Aviano from RAF Lakenheath. F-15Es routinely carry GBU-12 500-lb LGBs on missions over Bosnia.

Above: A pair of Jaguar GR.Mk 1As launches from Gioia del Colle on an armed reconnaissance mission. The Jaguars have been very active over 'BH', monitoring the positions of the warring factions.

Right: Throughout the fighting the airlift has continued under the auspices of UNPROFOR. Key aircraft on the runs to Sarajevo and other towns are the Il-76s and An-32s from the Ukraine.

request coming from General Rose. Almost daily, aircraft were directed to overfly UN troops under fire. In most cases, the presence of aircraft overhead defused the situation. During the Gorazde crisis, NATO aircraft had to drop bombs in anger for the first time in the alliance's history. Unlike the Gulf War, NATO and the UN were not combatants fighting a high-intensity campaign to defeat a military opponent. This was a crisis management operation designed to contain the war, deliver humanitarian aid and allow peace talks to come to a successful conclusion. Officially NATO and the UN were neutral in the war. According to a notice in General Rose's headquarters, "Air should be used to move the blocks on the road to peace – not destroy the goddam road." Or, as one NATO pilot said, "the whole of this war is political."

Sarajevo ultimatum

In the wake of the Sarajevo ultimatum, the Bosnia capital became the focus of attention for NATO's airmen. Before attention turned to offensive operations, the more immediate aftermath of the market massacre had to be dealt with. Two USAF C-130s and a Ukrainian Il-76 hired by the International Red Cross made a daring flight into Sarajevo's UN-controlled airport to begin the evacuation of the wounded. This was unlike any other medical evacuation from Sarajevo because prior permission had not been sought by the Bosnian Serbs, who showed

their displeasure by mortaring the UN armoured column carrying the wounded to the airport. Two more USAF C-130s made the flight to Sarajevo the following day to evacuate more wounded, bringing the total evacuated to 61 injured civilians and 116 accompanying family members. More wounded were brought out of the city three days by a Royal Swedish air force C-130.

In the 10 days before the NATO ultimatum came into effect, NATO photo-reconnaissance aircraft mounted a major effort to find every tank and heavy weapon inside the exclusion zone. The daily workload of RAF Jaguars, for example, went up from launching one pair of photo-reconnaissance aircraft over 'BH', as Bosnia is know to NATO airmen, to two pairs daily. The taskings of each aircraft went up from photographing 10 targets in a mission to 20 targets. French Mirage F1CRs and Dutch F-16A(R) reconnaissance pilots were also heavily tasked, along with aircraft from carriers in the

French Jaguars from EC 11 fly from Istrana, providing CAS/BAI cover for UN forces. This aircraft carries four-round rocket pods.

Adriatic. These included TARPS-pod equipped US Navy F-14Bs from the USS *Saratoga*, Royal Navy Sea Harrier FRS.Mk 1s from the *Ark Royal* and French Etendard IVPs from the *Foch* (later replaced by the *Clemenceau*). The situation on the ground was changing by the minute as

Blue Sword over Bosnia

Bosnia Serb army (BSA) units began to slowly move their heavy equipment out of the exclusion zone, so much so that tactical controllers on ABCCC aircraft often had to retask the reconnaissance aircraft in mid-mission to investigate tension zones. The weather occasionally interrupted the reconnaissance effort but the thick snow made tank tracks and soldier's footprints stand out on aerial photographs.

As detailed information from the reconnaissance squadrons came into the CAOC's photographic interpretation cell, General Chambers' staff began to put together detailed plans for destroying any offending heavy weapons remaining in the exclusion zone. The EC-130Es started to fly 24-hour orbits over the Bosnian capital to ensure close control of the regular waves of close air support aircraft that were maintained over the city. Some 25 pairs of aircraft patrolled over the city in a 10-hour period, in a rotating shift pattern, with aircraft spending one hour each over Bosnia. The threat from Serbian radar-guided anti-aircraft systems was real, and US Navy EP-3E Aries II Elint aircraft were spotted over the city on 18 and 21 February. While A-10As, Jaguars, F-16 Fighting Falcons, F/A-18 Hornets, Mirages F1CTs, Sea Harriers and Super Etendards patrolled during the daylight hours, at night F-15E Strike Eagles, A-6E Intruders, F/A-18s and AC-130H Spectre gunships prowled the skies over Sarajevo.

Up until the ultimatum NATO aircraft were tasked for CAS, and the joint UN/NATO rules of engagement (ROEs) only allowed them to attack targets that had been identified by UN Tactical Air Control Parties (TACPs) on the ground. Although ROE details are still highly secret, it is believed NATO and the UN commanders agreed plans and associated ROEs that allowed strike aircraft to attack targets selected by air commanders. In military jargon, the *modus operandi* of 5 ATAF shifted from CAS to battlefield air interdiction (BAI) against tanks, artillery, supply dumps and headquarters behind the Serb front line. French Jaguars, for example, started to sport ASL30 and 1000-kg (2,205-lb) laser-guided bombs, while US Marine Corps Hornets were decked out with GBU-15 500-lb (225-kg) Paveway laser-guided bombs. In the run-up to the ultimatum, three American aircraft were lost in accidents but all aircrews escaped safely. An F-16C from the 526th Fighter Squadron crashed over Slovenia on 16 February and an F-14B from the Saratoga was lost after a mid-air collision with a Hornet on 12 February. The F/A-18, however, safely made it back to a diversion field at Brindisi.

Russian intervention

Tension at this time was very high in Sarajevo, but things started to ease after Russian envoy Vitali Churkin flew to the Bosnian Serb capital Pale in a BSA Mi-8 to negotiate a face-saving formula with the rebel Serb leadership. The Serbs then agreed to pull back their tanks and artillery. Senior NATO leaders met at Aviano AB, Italy, on 20 February to study the latest reports from Sarajevo before deciding on whether to carry out any air strikes.

A number of VIP aircraft, including Admiral Mike Boorda's VP-3A and a USAF C-9, were seen at the base. As a precaution, the UN suspended aid flights to Sarajevo on 20 February. They resumed on the next day when the NATO deadline passed peacefully.

NATO air operations reverted to their primary CAS role. The reconnaissance effort continued to be a high priority because the UN was now allowed to authorise air strikes against any heavy weapons illegally inside the exclusion zone. UN troops in Sarajevo made great efforts to keep tabs on Serb heavy weapons in a number of collection points. Two French Det ALAT Pumas were in the thick of the drama of the Sarajevo ultimatum when they flew to the city's airport on 21 February carrying UN observers to take control of Serbian gun positions in NATO's artillery exclusion zone. They were the first UN helicopters ever to operate over the Bosnian capital, and to be on the safe side flew with 7.62-mm door guns. UN helicopter activity became intense over the next couple of weeks. British Sea Kings, French Pumas, Norwegian Hueys and Dutch BO 105s were heavily involved flying casevac missions for wounded civilians, transporting visiting politicians and generals around Bosnia. Tension eased considerably, with the UN air bridge to Sarajevo reopening and even the EC-130Es going back to flying only daylight orbits.

Tension mounts

While the peace deal between the Croats and Muslims seemed to be holding, the Bosnian Serbs continued to test the will of the UN and NATO in other parts of Bosnia. In the Nordic Battalion's area, a convoy of Swedish troops came under mortar fire on 22 February. General Rose asked for NATO close air support and one pair each of Royal Navy Sea Harriers and A-10As were vectored to the crisis zone.

Before they were able to engage any targets the UN commander in all of the former Yugoslavia, General Jean Cot, called them off because a 'clear target' was not available. UN commanders in Croatia also pressed for NATO air support after a confrontation with Serb forces earlier in the day at Bosanska Gradiska. NATO, however, did not send any aircraft as the crisis quickly passed.

On 28 February NATO fighters shot down four BSA Jastreb fighters after they attacked the Bosnian government-held town of Novi Travnik in a blatant breach of the 'No-Fly Zone'. UNHCR relief flights into Sarajevo were cancelled, along with that night's airdrops, to await the response from the Bosnian Serbs to the incident. Immediately after the Novi Travnik incident the Belgrade government and its Bosnian Serb allies denied involvement, so the air bridge reopened and airdrops resumed the following day.

On 8 March the Serbs got their revenge when a Spanish air force CASA C.212 light transport aircraft was targeted by Krajina Serb anti-aircraft defences. The plane was flying NATO search and rescue staff officers from

Vicenza via Zagreb to a meeting with UN personnel at Split when an SA-7 anti-aircraft missile exploded near it. Polish UN troops stationed near Karlovac saw the missile being fired from Serbian positions. In spite of being peppered with shrapnel, the plane managed to make an emergency landing at Rijeka in Croatia. Four passengers suffered light injuries. The NATO aircraft was not flying in the designated 'safe' air corridor along the Croatian coast but chose to take a route that took it almost over the Serbian-held positions. A C.160 had previously come under fire in the same region.

Serbian pressure

More pressure from the Serbs came on 10 March when French UN forces in Bihac were fired upon. NATO bombers buzzed the Serbs and the threat disappeared. Two days later, the French in Bihac came under tank fire and their commander asked for air support. Two AC-

While daytime cover has been provided by Jaguars, Mirages, F-16s and the like, more sophisticated US aircraft operate at night. F-15Es (illustrated), A-6Es and F/A-18Ds have partnered AC-130Hs in providing nocturnal cover.

RAF Jaguars have been used in both attack (above) and reconnaissance roles. Shown at right is the LOROP camera pod which has a rotating nose section.

130Hs, A-10As and Mirages located targets and prepared to attack; however, it took some three hours for the UN command in Zagreb to approve the request for close air support and, by that time, the offending Serb forces had withdrawn.

On 15 March Royal Navy Sea Kings flew British Special Air Service (SAS) commandoes into the besieged Muslim enclave at Maglai to mark drop zones for US C-130s, which were the only source of food for the town's 19, 000 residents. In yet another test of wills with the UN, the Serbs had been pounding the town and refusing access to UN relief convoys for six months. During February and March, the besieged Bosnian town became the main focus of attention for Operation Provide Promise airdrops. Night after night the C-130s and C.160s made repeated runs over the town. On two occasions their missions were aborted when NATO air reconnaissance spotted what appeared to be Serb SA-9 anti-aircraft missile

vehicles near the town. The operation to relieve the town come to a conclusion on 20 March when a British aid convoy punched a corridor through to the town. Heavy air cover from Sea Harriers and F-16s was provided, with the aircraft popping flares to provide a psychological impact on the besieging Serbs.

On the same day the UN staged a football match in Sarajevo, with close air support from RAF Jaguars and Royal Navy Sea Harriers. French Pumas and Norwegian Hueys flew security missions around the stadium and dropped a freefall SAS parachute display team. The RAF even flew in the band of the Coldstream Guards

Blue Sword over Bosnia

Despite the attention turning to air-to-ground missions, the Deny Flight air exclusion mission continues, the RAF making a major contribution with Tornado F.Mk 3s from Gioia del Colle.

by Hercules from Britain for the event. Two days later, a UNPROFOR Il-76 flew into Tuzla to symbolically open the airport for aid flights, but continued haggling over the details of checking aid prevented the UNHCR aid flights getting to the new airhead. The need for airdrops receded considerably with the opening of the land route to Maglai and, on 25 February, the Provide Promise aircraft stood down for six days. They were seen as a standby delivery force when other methods failed.

The decreased need for airdrops allowed the USAF to reduce the number of committed air-

Covering all options, F-16Cs taxi out for a mission armed with AIM-9M and AIM-120 air-to-air missiles and a pair of iron bombs. The 'AV' tailcode is for the recently re-established 31st Fighter Wing now at Aviano. The constituent squadrons are the 512th and 555th FS.

craft from 12 to six a night, and the Germans dropped from three to two from 1 April. In the 13 months since the start of the airdrops, some 17,500 tons (15875 tonnes) of aid had been dropped to besieged communities in Bosnia. A French C-130 flying from Split on 28 March was the 10,000th aircraft to fly into the Sarajevo air bridge, bringing to more than 100,000 the total tons of aid flown into the city since 28 June 1992.

Gorazde

On 29 March the Bosnian Serbs shelled Gorazde, so the airdrops were called into action again to cover for the lack of road convoys to the 60,000 people in the enclave. This was the first indication that the eastern Bosnian town was to be the venue of a major showdown between General Rose and the Bosnian Serb army. The UN commander planned to visit the town on 6 April but he was turned back at a BSA check-point. A seven-strong SAS team, designated as UN Military Observers (UNMOs)

or Joint Commission Observers, was allowed into the town. The Serbs made great play of trying to start ceasefire negotiations, then began an offensive to attack the UN 'safe area'. By late in the afternoon on Sunday 10 April, the Serbs were on the hills overlooking the town and began to fire at the SAS troops. Lacking heavy weapons to take on the Serb T-55 tanks, the British troops radioed to an EC-130E asking for CAS to protect them. The ABCCC relayed the request to the AOCC and CAOC, both of whom approved it. Some 25 minutes later the EC-130 handed over a pair of F-16Cs of the 526th FS to the SAS forward air controller (FAC), who directed them to their targets. The F-16s were swung from a fighter CAP mission after French Mirage F1CTs and US Marine Corps F/A-18s had failed to find the offending tanks, but the USAF fighters lacked equipment, such as the LANTIRN pod, to accept ground laser target marking. The FAC therefore had to talk the pilots onto their targets using visual reference points and data from handheld GPS

Helicopters continue to fly some of the most dangerous missions in Bosnia, tasked with combat rescue, movement of troops, resupply, insertion of FAC teams and casualty evacuation. The French army has four Gazelles (top) and six Pumas (below right) operating from Split and Sarajevo, the Pumas especially having made some extremely hazardous flights into Gorazde. Royal Navy helicopters (far right) are also heavily involved in-country, including Sea King HC.Mk 4s (flying) and HAS.Mk 6s operating from Ark Royal.

satellite navigation devices. Although the air strike calmed the situation, this respite was only temporary. French Mirage F1CRs were directed over the town to provide post-strike reconnaissance photographs.

Late the following morning, the SAS soldiers came under further attack. The SAS requested air support to stop the fire, with a EC-130E relaying the calls for help to Sarajevo and Vicenza. Tactical directors in the ABCCC then started a constant stream of aircraft over the town in a show of strength. Two fighters made low passes over the BSA positions at 11:45 , but there was no reduction in the level of shelling.

General Rose then directly telephoned the BSA high command to warn of air strikes if the shelling did not stop. More fighters were sent over the town, firing flares from their defensive pods. By 13:14 the Serbs were still firing. Within the hour, General Rose gave the EC-130E clearance to direct an air strike against the town. A pair of VMFA-251 F/A-18As was on station when the CAS request was authorised and made a pass against a group of Serb armoured vehicles. Three 500-lb Mk 82 bombs were dropped and 20-mm cannons were used to strafe the targets. It later emerged that two of the bombs' fuse-arming wires were defective, so the bombs did not explode. NATO bomb damage assessment did confirm that the impact caused considerable damage, destroying their targets.

Weather problems

The weather plagued NATO air operations over the Bosnian town, with low cloud and thunderstorms making it difficult to find targets. NATO reconnaissance aircraft were prohibited from flying below 5,000 ft (1525 m) to protect them from Serb AAA and heat-seeking shoulder-launched SAMs, so spent a week frustratingly trying to bring back good photographs of the crisis zone. The danger was highlighted on 15 April when a French Etendard IVP from the *Clemenceau* was hit by an SA-7 over Gorazde. In spite of being seriously damaged, the aircraft made it back to the carrier. On the ground two SAS were wounded, one fatally. Two French Pumas from Sarajevo dodged heavy fire to bring the soldier's body out of Gorazde, but heavy fire on the landing zone meant they could not lift out the other SAS man.

It was the turn of British Sea Harriers to go into action the following day. Terrible weather and the terrain prevented them finding their targets. After six passes over the town a Serb SAM team found its mark on a Sea Harrier. The pilot successfully ejected to the west of the town with a minor flesh wound. US Navy fighters circled over him until he could make his way to Muslim lines and the protection of the SAS team, and an EC-130E co-ordinated the search and rescue operation. French Pumas at Sarajevo prepared to launch to pick him up but the situa-

tion was considered so 'hot' they were kept on the ground. Later in the day USAF A-10As were called in to provide more CAS for the SAS, although bad weather prevented them finding their targets. Two days later the SAS and the Royal Navy pilot made their escape from the town, walking through Serb lines to a pick-up point where French Pumas lifted them to safety in Sarajevo.

New ultimatum

The deepening crisis in Gorazde at last stung NATO into action and they issued a new ultimatum, ordering the Serbs to pull back their infantry 3 km (1.8 miles) from the centre of Gorazde and heavy weapons back 20 km (12.4 miles). UN troops were also to be allowed free access to the town. Threats were made that other exclusion zones would be declared around four other UN safe areas if the troops came under attack.

5 ATAF again switched to BAI mode, to be ready to hunt down Serb tanks and artilleries. Unlike in Sarajevo, there were no UN troops to provide targeting information. The reconnaissance units intensified their operations, the EC-130Es started to fly 24-hour orbits again and BAI ordnance was loaded on US and French aircraft.

By the time the ultimatum expired on 24 April, the Serbs had largely complied with the terms. UN helicopters in Sarajevo responded immediately to the reduction in fighting and flew to Gorazde to evacuate wounded civilians.

Three British Sea Kings and two British Pumas evacuated wounded to a makeshift landing zone in Sarajevo's Kosovo stadium. The airlift continued for three days, bringing out some 400 people, with a number of the wounded being flown to UK hospitals by an RAF Hercules on 26 April. A US Navy F/A-18C Hornet was lost and its pilot killed in a catapult accident on the USS Saratoga on 28 April.

As the crisis in Gorazde developed, the Serbs responded by blockading Sarajevo. The only way into the city was by air. UNHCR aid flights were suspended on 11 April but UNPROFOR Il-76s and An-32s continued their dangerous shuttle service into the city. UN helicopters also continued to operate around the city to monitor Serb compliance with the artillery exclusion zone and to resupply UN troops guarding weapons collection points.

Tension was sustained elsewhere in Bosnia between the UN and the BSA. British troops came under mortar fire at Dobaj on 17 April and US Navy A-6 Intruders buzzed the offending Serb positions. NATO jets spent three hours overflying Serb positions after they fired on UN troops near Tuzla on 15 April. On 2 May NATO jets were called to frighten off Serb troops who were trying to retrieve heavy weapons from a French-held collection point near Sarajevo.

Blue Sword over Bosnia

Above: Vital to the strike missions over Bosnia is the EC-130E ABCCC platform, identified by the large air scoop on the fuselage side (right). On board is a palletised command centre (above) from which operators can relay commands from the ground to attack aircraft in-theatre. Three EC-130Es are based at Aviano.

Below: At night AC-130H gunships from the 16th Special Operations Wing roam the Bosnian skies, flying from Brindisi. Such an aircraft, with its sophisticated night sensors and heavy armament, is ideal for this form of containment warfare. Note the new two-tone grey camouflage and ALQ-131 ECM pod.

At the beginning of May, the focus of the crisis shifted north to Tuzla and the Brcko corridor area. Serb commanders began to systematically harass UN Nordic troops. Tuzla airport came under regular fire, and it was only with heavy NATO fighter cover that a UNPRO-FOR Il-76 was able to land there carrying a Jordanian mortar fire locating radar on 19 May. The day previous, the Nordic battalion commander had asked for CAS when his troops came under fire but his request was turned down by the UN high command. Aid flights into Sarajevo were temporarily halted for two days after two aircraft were hit on the ground by small arms fire on 4 May.

Maritime challenge

Tension shifted to a new theatre of operations on 1 May when three Yugoslav navy warships ventured into the Adriatic to challenge NATO ships in the process of arresting a tanker trying to breach the UN trade embargo against Serbia and Montenegro. NATO maritime patrol aircraft detected the Yugoslav ships and, as they came within feet of colliding with HMS Chatham, Italian air force Tornado strike aircraft armed with Kormoran anti-ship missiles were scrambled from Gioia del Colle to provide air support. This show of strength forced the Yugoslav ships to return to port empty-handed.

The USAF made major changes to its Bosnian airlift and airdrop operation at Rhein Main AB, Germany, in early May 1994. C-130 operations were drastically cut back after five

C-141Bs of the 437th Airlift Wing deployed to the base on 1 May from Charleston AFB, SC. The StarLifters can carry twice the load of the Hercules, at twice the speed. After flying missions to Ancona on 5 May and Zagreb on 6 May, the C-141Bs flew their first mission to Sarajevo on 7 May. The 38th Airlift Squadron (Provisional), 'Bravo Squadron', which had been activated on 3 January 1994 to allow the Bosnian aid mission to be doubled in size, started to wind down. In the first four months of 1994 a total of 44 C-130s was deployed to Rhein Main for Provide Promise, on average launching nine aircraft each night to fly airdrop missions over besieged enclaves and four aircraft to fly daily into Sarajevo.

By early June, five C-141Bs and 10 C-130s were assigned to Bravo Squadron, including six C-130s from the Air Force Reserve/Air National Guard and four active-duty Hercules from Rhein Main's resident 39th ALS. The reserve component aircraft and personnel were due to return to CONUS by 7 June. Because road convoys were at that time regularly getting through to Bosnian cities, the C-130 airdrops were scaled down. In May, only one airdrop mission was flown, on 25 May, and another was planned for 10 June.

As summer approached no end seemed in sight. The warring parties showed little interest in the latest UN peace plan, making it likely that NATO's air power will continue to be called upon to help protect UN troops at the sharp end of Europe's hottest war zone.

UN/NATO BOSNIA ORDER OF BATTLE, FEB-MAY 1994

BASE	UNIT	NUMBER	AIRCRAFT
Canada			
Sigonella	405 Sqn	2	CP-140 (until 13/5/94)
Ancona		1	CC-130
France			
Cervia	EC 12	10	Mirage 2000C
	EC 3	3	Mirage 2000N
	EC 3	3	Mirage 2000D
	EC 12	1	Mirage 2000B
Istrana	EC 11	8	Jaguar (reduced to 4 a/c in 5/94)
	EC 13	5	Mirage F1CT
	ER 33	4	Mirage F1CR
Clemenceau	17F	16	Super Etendard
	16F	3	Etendard IVP
	4F	6	Alizé
	32F	2	Super Frelon
		1	Dauphin
	ALAT	2	Puma
Foch	11F	18	Super Etendard
	16F	4	Etendard IVP
	6F	5	Alizé
	33F	2	Super Frelon
	23S	2	Dauphin
		1	Alouette III
Istres	ERV 93	1	KC-135FR
Avord	EDA 36	1	E-3F
Vicenza	EET 11/54	1	C.160G
Evreux	EE 51	1	DC-8
Sigonella/Elmas			Atlantic
Split/Sarajevo	Det ALAT	6	Puma
		4	Gazelle
Split	ET 2/61	1	C-130H/H-30
Rhein Main	ET 61/ET 64	1	C.160F/NG
Brindisi	EH 67?	2	Puma
Vicenza		1	Nord 262
Germany			
Sigonella/Elmas	MFG 3		Atlantic
Ancona		1	C.160D
Rhein-Main	LTG 61/63	2	C.160D
Italy			
Gioia del Colle	36° Stormo	8	Tornado IDS
Sigonella	41° Stormo		Atlantic
Elmas	30° Stormo		Atlantic
NATO Early Warning Force			
Geilenkirken/Trapani/Previza		8	E-3A
Netherlands			
Villafranca	322 Sqn	18	F-16A (four F-16A(R)) (from 1/4/94 311 and 312 Sqns)
Sigonella	320/321 Sqn	2	P-3
Srebrenica	229 Sqn	4	BO 105
Norway			
Tuzla	Skv 720	4	Bell 412
Portugal			
Sigonella	601 Sqn		P-3P
Spain			
Vicenza	Ala 37	1	CASA C.212
Sigonella/Elmas	221 Sqn		P-3B
Sweden			
Ancona	F7	1	C-130E/H
Turkey			
Ghedi	141 Filo	18	F-16C (from 5/94 replaced by 161 Filo)
United Kingdom			
Gioia del Colle	Comp Sqn	8	Tornado F.Mk 3
	Comp Sqn	12	Jaguar GR.Mk 1A
	39 Sqn	1	Canberra PR.Mk 9
Milan-Malpensa	216 Sqn	2	Tristar K.Mk 1
Aviano	8 Sqn	2	E-3D
Sigonella	Kinloss Wing		Nimrod MR.Mk 2P
	51 Sqn		Nimrod R.Mk 1P
Split/Sarajevo	845 Sqn	4	Sea King HC.Mk 4
Ark Royal	801 Sqn	8	Sea Harrier FRS.Mk.1
	820 Sqn	7	Sea King HAS.Mk 6
	849 Sqn	3	Sea King AEW.Mk 2
Ancona	LTW	1	Hercules C.Mk 1/3

United States

Aviano – 401st Fighter Wing (Provisional) *(until 4/94)*		
31st Fighter Wing *(from 4/94)*		
81st FS	12	A-10A *(formerly 510th FS)*
512th FS	12	F-16C *(526th FS until 4/94)*
VMFA(AW)-25	18	F/A-18A
7th ACCS	3	EC-130E
493nd FS	8	F-15E
Sigonella HC-4		CH-53E
VP-26	8	P-3C *(replaced by VP-23 during 2/94)*
Det 4 VRC-40	2	C-2A
CINCSOUTH	1	VP-3A
Pisa Det 100th ARW	5	KC-135R
Istres Det 100th ARW	5	KC-135R *(moved from Sigonella on 12/2/94)*
Bari Det HC-4	2	CH-53E
Brindisi 21st SOS	4	MH-53J
7th SOS	2	MC-130E
16th SOS	3	AC-130H
Rota VQ-2		EP-3E
Mildenhall Det 55th Wing		RC-135
Alconbury 9th Wing OL-UK		U-2R
Akrotiri 9th Wing Det 3		U-2R
USS *Saratoga* VF-103	14	F-14B
VFA-81	11	F/A-18C
VFA-83	11	F/A-18C
VA-35	14	A-6E (SWIP)
VAQ-132	4	EA-6B
VAW-125	4	E-2C
VS-30	5	S-3B
VQ-6	2	ES-3B
HS-9	4	SH-60F
HS-9	2	HH-60H
Rhein Main – Operation Provide Promise		
38th ALS(P)	19	C-130E/H
37th ALS	19	C-130E
317th AW Det 6		C-130
437th AW Det 5		C-141 *(from 5/5/94)*

Note: *Maritime patrol aircraft except for the Canadian and US assets are tasked for short (usually two-week) detachments in support of Operation Sharp Guard, the UN/NATO/WEU embargo of Serbia and Montenegro. US and Canadian MPA are on six-month deployments.*

Operating from Aviano are the A-10s and OA-10s of the 81st Fighter Squadron, 52nd FW, deployed from Spangdahlem. The OA-10s fly FAC missions for close support aircraft, carrying rockets in seven-round pods for marking targets.

Below: Five C-141Bs from the 437th AW joined the Sarajevo airlift on 7 May 1994, providing the international effort with a massive boost in capacity. C-130s from many nations (including France) maintained their effort.

Above: Supporting UN efforts in Bosnia is this Ala 37 CASA C.212. A similar aircraft was badly damaged in March by an SA-7, although it managed to land safely at Rijeka. The Spaniards also have Orions on blockade work.

BRIEFING

Slovenian Territorial Defence Force
New equipment for air force

The birth of the newly-independent Slovenian air force was described in *World Air Power Journal* Vol. 11. Since that time the small force has made some progress towards achieving its goals, but the country is seriously hampered by a United Nations arms embargo on all former Yugoslav republics. Slovenia is pushing the international community hard for this to be lifted, in the light of an unbroken peace since the end of the short period of fighting that marked its independence in 1991. The nation seeks only a small fighter and helicopter force sufficient to defend its small territory, and in mid-1994 the lifting of the ban seemed imminent. In March 1994, Slovenia was a signatory to NATO's 'Partnership for Peace' treaty, the only such former Yugoslav republic.

The three Zlin 242Ls will provide basic training and air experience pending the lifting of the arms embargo. More potent trainers and fighters are sought to follow.

In June 1992, when the Territorial Defence Force unveiled publicly its small air arm, Slovenia's military assets consisted of a single Agusta A 109, two Bell 412s and a single Soko-built Gazelle which had defected from the JRV. Soon after another Bell 412 was added. The air wing of the TDF is officially the 15th Brigade, whose badge is a witch riding a broomstick. This is now worn by the Bell 412s, which sport a tactical camouflage. The air force works closely with the 9th Brigade, which is responsible for air defence. The government VIP Learjet 24D is occasionally used for training air defences by posing as a low-level attacker.

Fixed-wing equipment arrived in early 1994 in the shape of four aircraft from the Czech Republic, comprising three Zlin 242Ls and a single LET 410. All wear civil registrations (Slovenia's prefix having changed from 'SL' to 'S5') but carry the Slovenian flag on the fin. The Zlin 242Ls (S5-DEJ/K/L) are

The existing Bell 412s have received a smart tactical scheme, and will shortly be joined by five more to equip an assault transport unit. The aircraft are used mainly in the mountains.

employed for primary training. This model of the popular eastern European trainer is equipped with Western instruments and a 200-hp (149-kW) Textron Lycoming AEIO-360-A1 engine. The LET 410 (S5-BAD) is used for paratroop training and for light transport work. In addition to these permanently-assigned aircraft, a privately-owned Pitts S-2B (S5-DDD) is used by TDF pilots for aerobatic training.

New equipment expected for the TDF includes a major order for Bell helicopters, comprising five 412EPs for assault transport, and two Bell 206Bs for rotary-wing training.

When the arms embargo is lifted, the air force hopes to receive a turboprop advanced trainer in the PC-9 class, and a squadron of about a dozen fighters. The IAI Kfir and ex-USAF F-16As have been reported as the candidates, the latter seeming the most likely.

This single LET 410 has been procured to provide parachute training for the army.

Lockheed P-3 AEW&C
Customs Service Orion

In the early 1980s Lockheed began development of an airborne early warning aircraft, using the P-3 Orion airframe as the basis. The aircraft had sufficient internal volume to accommodate the operator consoles and communications equipment, excellent long-endurance performance, a global support network already in place and low acquisition costs. Lockheed also proposed a similar system based on the C-130, which featured similar attributes.

To prove the aerodynamics, Lockheed reacquired an Australian P-3B for the P-3 AEW&C programme. The first aircraft

(155299/N91LC) flew with an empty 24-ft (7.32-m) diameter Randtron AN/APA-171 rotodome on 14 June 1984. The aircraft was later named Sentinel, and appeared at the 1987 Paris air show.

For military users, the P-3 AEW&C would have featured the APS-145 radar (as fitted to the latest fleet E-2 Hawkeyes), a command suite which could transmit on a wide range of frequencies

Prior to delivery to the Customs Service, the first P-3AEW&C wore the registration N91LC. Although it first flew with the rotodome in 1984, it was not until 1988 that radar was fitted.

(including AN/ARC-187 satcom) and a Collins EFIS-86B flight instrumentation system. Flyaway cost was quoted at $75 million for a new aircraft in the late 1980s, pitched midway between the shorter-range Hawkeye and more sophisticated Sentry. Potential customers included Australia, Canada, Japan (which subsequently purchased the Boeing 767 AWACS) and the RAF, which eventually

bought the E-3D Sentry after the failure of the Nimrod AEW.Mk 3 programme.

The first, and so far only, order came in May 1987 from the US Customs Service, for one aircraft with three options. By using existing airframes the price was considerably reduced, while the radar and rotodome were furnished by the government from US Navy stocks. Lockheed fitted the General Electric AN/APS-125 radar and testing began on 8 April 1988. The tests surpassed USCS requirements, the P-3 proving to be a better platform for the APS-125 than the E-2 Hawkeye which the service was operating on a loan basis. On 17 June the aircraft was delivered to the customer at CSS Corpus Christi, reregistered as N145CS and named Blue Sentinel.

Following the early success of this aircraft, the USCS took up its options, and in June 1989 a second P-3 AEW&C was delivered. This again was an ex-Australian P-3C (154605/N146CS), but it had the improved AN/APS-138 radar fitted. This unit was subsequently retrofitted to the first aircraft. The final two Customs Service aircraft (ex-US Navy P-3Bs 152722/N147CS and 154575/N148CS) were delivered on 26 June 1992 and in mid-1993.

In addition to the APS-138, the USCS aircraft are equipped with a

Hazeltine AN/TPX-54 IFF, a Control Data Corporation AN/AYK-14 central processor, Honeywell 1601M array processor and two large Sanders Miligraphics display screens. The latter are in full colour, and have touch-sensitive screens for rapid operation. All information regarding radar returns and IFF is displayed as a tactical display, overlaid on a map. A standard circular APA-125 display screen is retained as a back-up to the two main TV-style displays. The communications suite includes AN/ARC-182 VHF/UHF, AN/ARC-207 HF and Wulfsberg VHF/UHF-FM radios, all duplicated. The HF antennas are located in the tail sting, replacing the MAD of the standard ASW Orion.

Internally the P-3 AEW&C is configured with the operator consoles facing outwards along the port side of the cabin. In the rear of the cabin are rest stations. In terms of performance the P-3 AEW&C offers patrol endurances of 12-14 hours, with a radius of action greater than 2,000 nm (2,300 miles; 3700 km). At 800 nm (920 miles; 1480 km) from base, the time on station is about eight hours.

In addition to the four P-3 AEW&Cs, which are nicknamed 'domes', CSS Corpus Christi operates four P-3As on loan from the US Navy (150514/N18314, 151390/N15390, 151395/N16295 and 152170/N16370). These are variously designated UP-3A or P-3A(CS), but are universally known as 'slicks'. They are

equipped with an APG-63 fighter radar (from the F-15A) in place of the APS-80 search radar of the ASW Orion, and have a turret-mounted infra-red detection system. Sensor operator stations are provided in the cabin, and the aircraft have extra equipment to communicate with Customs Service ground units, Coast Guard vessels and other agencies.

The principal areas of operation are the Gulf of Mexico and Caribbean, Corpus Christi being an ideal location for reaching patrol

Seen on the USCS ramp at Corpus Christi are the first P-3 AEW&C, which retains its company demonstrator scheme, and one of the P-3A(CS) 'slick' Orions. These have F-15 radar in the nose and a retractable FLIR turret.

Three internal views show the Miligraphics tactical displays in the P-3 AEW&C (above), the APG-63 radar and communications panel in the P-3A(CS) (right), and the P-3A(CS) cockpit (below). The small square display above the pilot's thrust levers presents intercept vector data.

areas rapidly. The P-3 AEW&C is used in the C³I role, making the initial detection of suspect aircraft, which are then tracked. A typical flight profile is a racetrack pattern flown at about 25,000 ft (7620 m). The Orion's standard PB-20N autopilot has been modified so that, at the flick of a switch, it will command wings-level, rudder-only 'skid' turns so that the radar antenna is kept level.

The APS-138 radar scans 360° to a range of 288 miles (463 km), and from the sea/ground surface to an altitude of 100,000 ft (30480 m). In a single sweep it covers 12 million km³, and can detect up to 2,000 targets. Altitude of the target is calculated by measuring the delay of the secondary radar return which bounces back off the sea surface. This capability is dramatically degraded over land. Each operator can present different displays on his screen, but using the same central data base. Basic radar and IFF returns can be displayed in their raw state, or the AYK-14 can create sensor tracks, taking the average of radar/IFF readings to present a target track. The tactical track display is created by the operator, and is used in the final period of intercept when only one or two aircraft are under surveillance. Areas of heavy traffic can be designated by the operator so that returns are ignored, and the radar also has maritime search capability.

Once a suspect has been detected, information is handed over to another aircraft, often a P-3A(CS) 'slick', the two USCS Orion variants often operating as a 'hunter-killer' team. The 'slick' uses its fighter radar and IR system to intercept for a closer look. Alternatively, smaller interceptor aircraft, such as USCS Piper Cheyennes, the ANG UC-26C or Coast Guard HU-25Cs, can follow the suspect aircraft to its final destination, allowing ground forces to move in for the arrest. As part of its initial operations, the USCS P-3 AEW&Cs were used to evaluate the type's suitability against low-level targets on behalf of NORAD.

In service the aircraft have proved to be outstanding in the fight against drug-smuggling aircraft. During the first 10 months of operation, narcotics with a street value of $75 million were seized. In the first three years of operation, USCS Orions were responsible for the seizure of 13 tons of marijuana, 36 tons of cocaine and led to over 160 arrests. Since the US Coast Guard has transferred its EC-130V AEW Hercules to the USAF, the Customs P-3 'domes' are now the most sophisticated aircraft in use in the massive war against the drug scourge.

The fourth P-3 AEW&C was delivered in 1993. Although based at Corpus Christi, the aircraft also operate from other southern US bases. This aircraft was seen at March AFB, California.

IAI Kfir
Israeli Kfir Mods

Although the IDF/AF IAI Kfir force has now been reduced to no more than two front-line squadrons, the type continues to have a vital role to play. Many aircraft are reportedly in store, and would equip reserve squadrons in time of war. Surviving Kfirs continue to receive various upgrades and modifications, to enhance their capability. The accompanying photographs, taken at Ramon air base, show aircraft from a unit believed to be designated 111 Squadron, and normally based at Ovda.

Some surviving in-service Kfirs now carry an unidfentified under-nose pod under the forward fuselage, immediately ahead of the nosewheel bay. This could house an IRST, an illuminator for a semi-active missile or perhaps some kind of navigation or targeting pod for the air-to-ground role. One of three aircraft photographed at Ramon was equipped with the device.

The drawdown of the Kfir fleet has resulted in some airframes becoming surplus to requirements

Armed with Rafael Python 3 IR-homing air-to-air missiles, and with an unidentified undernose pod, a Kfir-C7 of 111 Squadron takes off from Ramon. Colourful squadron markings are de rigeur on Israeli fighters, although the IDF/AF maintains its policy of trying to keep squadron identities secret.

(even for reserve use) and this has been reflected by intensive recent efforts by IAI to find export customers for 'used' Kfirs. IAI is reported to have offered Kfirs to Chile, the Philippines, Slovenia, and Taiwan in recent months. Even more interestingly, *Flight International* have reported that South Africa has been taking delivery of upgraded ex-IDF/AF Kfirs with their J79 engines replaced by SNECMA Atar 09K-50s, bringing them to the same standard as the indigenous Cheetah modification. This would infer a very major modification, with significant structural changes, since the Kfir's usual J79 and the Atar 09K-50 are not installationally interchangeable or compatible. No photographs of the new Kfir-based Cheetahs have

been seen, and it is not known whether the aircraft retain a Kfir-style dorsal airscoop at the base of the fin. The conversions, apparently funded under a $1.7 Bn contract signed in 1988, might account for the 'extra' Cheetahs referred to on p. 117 of *World Air Power Journal,* Volume 15. Sources suggest that at least 19 single-seat Cheetah Es were produced from 14 Mirage IIIEZs available for conversion (in addition to the Cheetah Rs produced from the four Mirage IIIRZs and three IIIR2Zs), and that at least 12 two-seat Cheetah Ds were produced from eight available Mirage IIIDZs. South Africa, it has been alleged, thus received at least nine extra Mirage airframes from an undisclosed source. The apparent disparity in

The Python 3 acquisition rounds carried by this Kfir-C7 lack rear control fins, but retain forward fins. This brown, sand and green camouflage has replaced the air superiority grey scheme previously used on the Kfir, which in turn had replaced a sand, dark brown and dark green camouflage.

numbers could be explained if the extra aircraft were actually converted from redundant IDF/AF Kfirs, such a supposition being supported by the 1988 contract. *Flight* suggests that such Kfir deliveries are ongoing, and that deliveries of the 'undisclosed number' of aircraft will end in 1995. It is widely known that Israel continued to supply weapons and military equipment to South Africa after the imposition of a UN arms embargo in 1987.

Turkey

Türk Hava Kuvvetleri (Turkish Air Force)

1ci Taktik Hava Kuvveti Komutabligi (First Tactical Air Force)

The roles of some of the units assigned to the First Tactical Air Force are not as given in our original article. Konya is a training base, with only a secondary commitment to the front-line roles described. 131 Filo is assigned to combat and tactical training duties, while 133 Filo is the F-5 OCU. 132 Filo is now operational again, borrowing aircraft from 131 and 133 Filo as required to fulfil its role as the F-5/F-4 tactical training unit.

At Mürted, now known more properly as Akinci, the F-16 units are assigned to air defence duties only, while Bandirma's squadrons are also assuming a secondary close air support role. By May 1994 seven F-16s had received LANTIRN modifications locally, and 161 Filo will be fully LANTIRN-equipped by the end of 1996. At Balikesir, 192 Filo stood up as an F-16 close air support unit in June 1994, with 191 Filo following in September. 193 Filo was to have been the recipient of the ex-USAF A-10s, but is now unlikely to reform. RT-33As have been withdrawn from service from all base flights, which are officially designated Egitim-Irtibat Kita (Training and Liaison Flight).

2ci Taktik Hava Kuvveti Komutabligi (Second Tactical Air Force)

More detail has become available relating to forthcoming changes which will affect the Second Tactical Air Force. Merzifon has lost the 153rd Filo, and all F-5 OCU flying is now undertaken by 133 Filo at Konya.

At Erhaç there will be a number of changes from late July/early August 1994, with a complete reshuffle of aircraft and roles within 7 Ana Jet Üs. 171 Filo will assume a reconnaissance commitment in place of its ground attack role and will assume the designation 173 Filo, while the old 172 Filo will change designation to 171 Filo, retaining its ground attack tasking. 173 Filo will be redesignated 172 Filo and will remain primarily intercept-tasked.

At Diyarbakir, the F-5-equipped 184 Filo deactivated in July, passing its RF-5As to 151 and 152 Filos at Merzifon, where they are likely to be converted back to fighter configuration. 181 will reactivate as an F-16 air defence unit in December 1994 and 182 will follow in June 1995, also losing its close support task.

Hava Ulastirma Komutabligi (Air Transport Command)

Transport command has finally retired the Viscount, one going to a museum, the other to serve as the classroom of a civilian flying club. A retirement date of 1995 has now been set for the C-47, which has already been withdrawn from 222 Filo and 223 Filo, leaving about a dozen operational, divided between the two Tactical Air Force HQ flights, the Air Warfare School and 7 Elektronik Filo which operates three ECM-47s. 223 and 224 Filos now share 10 CN.235s (two in VIP configuration), 224 also operating two Cessna Citation IIs, two Citation VIIs, three Gulfstream IVs and five UH-1Hs.

Hava Okullari Komutabligi (Air Training Command)

Headquarters Training Command has a flight of three C-47s but their Gaziemir base has been renamed Adnan-Menderes. The C-47 detachment at Ezerum (from 123 Filo) has disbanded. With 121 Filo at Cigli the T-33 was withdrawn from use in the training role in September 1993, after delivery of a second batch of 40 T-38As, bringing the total to about 70. 123 Filo is actually based at Izmir-Kakliç and retired its T-43As in June 1993, and is no longer thought to operate the T-41 either. Instead, the unit uses some 39 SF.260Ds. The Air Force College at Yesilkoy has two separate flying units, with a handful of T-41Ds, four C-47s and two UH-1Hs for air experience flying, support and SAR at Yesilkoy itself, and a fully-fledged flying school at Yalova, where the bulk of the T-41s are based.

Türk Donanma Havaciligi (Turkish Naval Aviation)

Although Turkey's Grumman S-2Es are being maintained in airworthy condition and their pilots are keeping current on 123 Filo's Cessna T-41Ds, the aircraft are now grounded awaiting possible resale, following two fatal crashes during 1993. Engine reliability was already a problem, and airframe fatigue and corrosion mitigate against any upgrade for these veterans. Instead, the navy is actively looking for a replacement (with higher internal capacity for sensors, weapons and crew). Platforms examined so far include the CN.235MP and Fokker 50 Maritime Enforcer. Adding detail to our entry on 351 Filo, we can reveal that the unit currently flies three AB 204AS, 11 AB 212ASW and three AB 212EW.

Türk Sahil Güvanlik (Turkish Coast Guard)

Formed at Izmir-Topel (the primary operating location for the Türk Donanma Havaciligi) in November 1993, the aviation branch of the Türk Sahil Güvanlik (Turkish Coast Guard) operates three Agusta-Bell AB 206 Jet Rangers and a single Maule MX-7. These undertake patrols over the Black Sea, Aegean and Bosphorus. All four aircraft wear military-style serials with TCGS prefixes. Further expansion of this small force seems most likely.

Squadron markings are beginning to make a welcome appearance.

The badge illustrated (top left) was photographed on the nose of this 112 Filo F-4E at Eskisehir (which retains its 110th TFS sharkmouth).

Another aircraft wearing unit markings is this 184 Filo RF-5A, seen here with gun bay access doors open. 184 Filo deactivated in July 1994.

This is one of Turkey's last two Viscounts, now withdrawn from use. China may be the only possible military operator of this classic type.

These F-104Gs are lined up, withdrawn from use, at Diyarbakir. 182 Filo will deactivate in September 1994, bringing the European Starfighter era to a close.

This badge, featuring a tiger with binoculars, is common on RF-5s.

Wearing a bee and honeycomb badge on its intake, this T-38 bears clear traces of its previous owner, the dark blue undersides and white US Air Force being still just visible.

The CN.235 is rapidly supplanting the Douglas C-47 in Turkish service. This aircraft is one of two in VIP configuration, standard transports wearing green and brown camouflage. The type serves with 222 Filo, 223 Filo and 224 Filo, and will equip the various base flights.

Thirty-nine SIAI Marchetti SF.260Ds have replaced the T-43A in service with 123 Filo, which now operates from Izmir-Kakliç in the basic training role.

The badge of the Coast Guard air wing is a white pelican.

Turkish Coast Guard Agusta-Bell AB 206Bs wear a colour scheme similar to that applied to US Coast Guard helicopters. The aircraft have neither radar nor flotation gear.

A line-up of Grumman S-2E Trackers is caught at Topel. Airframe fatigue and corrosion make an upgrade unviable, but the aircraft are maintained in airworthy condition.

Türk Kara Havaciligi (Turkish Army Aviation)

Further to our entry on the Türk Kara Havaciligi, further details of re-equipment programmes and an order of battle have emerged. Influenced by current trends within US Army Aviation, the service is presently undergoing a major programme of rationalisation, with the primary aim of reducing the number of disparate aircraft types in service, in order to simplify, streamline and reduce the cost of training, maintenance and support.

The eventual aim is to standardise on the Cessna U-17 and T-41D in the fixed-wing training, liaison and observation roles, the Bell OH-58B and similar Agusta-Bell AB 206B in the observation/scout helicopter role, the Sikorsky S-70A in the utility role (eventually replacing the UH-1H and Agusta-Bell AB 205B) and the Bell AH-1P/W in the attack role. The army also hopes to gain funding for a CH-47D Chinook purchase.

Attack helicopters

The Turkish army has an eventual requirement for 140 attack helicopters, this requirement being regarded as an urgent priority. The preferred attack helicopter option is the Cobra, and Turkey's preferred variant is the Bell AH-1W, but the high cost of this aircraft (which is available only new-build) means that the single-engined US Army Cobra variants are more likely to be procured. Turkey reportedly bought up the entire US Army inventory of 32 surviving AH-1Ps (known as the Production AH-1S until 1988), but is not interested in the earlier AH-1S (Improved AH-1S until 1988) being offered by the US Army. The latter aircraft lack the new flat plate canopy and do not have the improved instrument panel of the AH-1P and subsequent models. The army is interested in the AH-1E (Up-Gun AH-1S until 1988) and the AH-1F (Modernised AH-1S or AH-1S(MC) until 1988) for which negotiations continue. Although the 28 AH-1Ps and 14 AH-1Ws received so far nominally serve with the army aviation school for 'attack training', they have reportedly proved remarkably effective against the PKK.

The handful of OH-58s already in service have proved equally popular and successful, and are to be augmented by a batch of 20 Agusta-Bell AB 206Bs, the first of which will be delivered late in 1994. The army's other 'new boy' is the Sikorsky S-70A-17 Black Hawk. Four are now in service with the Türk Kara Havacilik Okulu (Turkish Army Aviation School) at Güvercinlik, and others serve with the 3rd Aviation Regiment at Malatya. The type will eventually replace all the Hueys presently in use.

Organisational structure

Front-line army aviation units are known as Hava Taburu (Aviation Battalions), each of which operates about 30 aircraft and helicopters, and which can be further subdivided into Hava Bölük (Aviation Companies). Three such battalions form each Hava Alayi (Aviation Regiment). There are three numbered regiments, 1nci Hava Alayi at Istanbul-Samandra supporting army units in Western Turkey, 2nci Hava Alayi at Malatya supporting army units in central Turkey, and 3nci Hava Alayi supporting units in the east of the country. A further regiment is based at Izmir, and supports forces in the Aegean.

Army Aviation School

The Türk Kara Havacilik Okulu (Turkish Army Aviation School) at Güvercinlik comes under the direct control of the co-located Central Army Aviation Establishment. This fulfils a similar role to Britain's Army Air Corps Centre at Middle Wallop, being responsible for both training and a number of vital support functions, including tactical and equipment development and hosting a number of operational aircraft.

Primary and basic training is undertaken using 25 Cessna T-41D Mescaleros and 30 Bellanca 7GCBC Citabrias, plus nine surviving Robinson R-22 (of 10 delivered) and 25 Schweizer-Hughes H269C helicopters. The last OH-13s were finally retired in late 1992.

Observation role training is undertaken using 25 Cessna U-17B Skywagons and three Bell OH-58Bs, while four S-70A-17s, 12 Agusta-Bell AB 204Bs plus 26 Bell UH-1Hs and AB 205As are also in use for training support helicopter pilots.

Güvercinlik also houses a substantial fleet of aircraft used for liaison and light transport duties, including six Dornier Do 28Ds (two of these being equipped with huge radomes under the chin and belly, perhaps for Elint or electronic warfare duties), five Beech Super King Airs, four Beech T-42A Barons, three Cessna 421B Golden Eagles and a pair of Agusta Bell AB 212s.

Türk Kara Havaciligi

UNIT	TYPE
1nci Hava Alayi, Istanbul-Samandra	
1 - 3 Tabaru	OH-58B, U-17B, UH-1H/AB 205A
2nci Hava Alayi, Malatya	
1 - 3 Tabaru	OH-58B, U-17B, UH-1H/AB 205A
3nci Hava Alayi, Erzincan	
1 - 3 Tabaru	S-70A, OH-58B, U-17B, UH-1H/AB 205A
Aegean Hava Alayi, Izmir	
1 - 3 Tabaru	OH-58B, U-17B, UH-1H/AB 205A
Turk Kara Havacilik Okulu, Güvercinlik	
Basic training battalion	T-41D, Citabria, R-22B, Hughes 269C
Observation/liaison training battalion	U-17B, OH-58B, AB 204B UH-1H/AB 205A
Attack training battalion	
1 Filo	Bell AH-1W
2 Filo	Bell AH-1P
3 Filo	Bell AH-1P
Liaison and support squadron	Do28D, Baron, Super King Air Golden Eagle, AB 212

Our grateful thanks are due to our occasional Netherlands correspondent, Mr René van Woezik, who visited Turkey during April 1994, visiting all three Turkish services and interviewing many senior officers. Thanks also go to all those others who responded to our request for further information on the Turkish armed forces (p. 156 *World Air Power Journal*, Volume 17), but who have asked to remain anonymous.

The Bell AH-1P Cobra is the mainstay of Turkey's armed helicopter force, with 28 airworthy aircraft on charge equipping two squadrons, both of which are nominally based at Güvercinlik. The considerably more advanced AH-1W is available only in much smaller numbers, equipping a single co-located squadron, and further procurement of the more expensive Whiskey Cobra (which is not likely to be available as surplus) seems most unlikely. The AH-1Ps are identifiable by the early-type undernose gun turret and continue to wear basic US Army-style olive drab camouflage, while the up-gunned AH-1Ws wear a more attractive three-tone camouflage scheme. Turkey is likely to gain additional ex-US Army AH-1s as a result of post-Cold War defence drawdowns. The AH-1Ps have already proved extremely successful against Kurdish separatist guerrillas. All of Turkey's Cobras are compatible with the Hughes BGM-71 TOW (Tube-launched, Optically-sighted, Wire-guided) anti-tank guided missile, but these are seldom carried, and the anti-tank role is little practised. It is not known whether any air-to-air weapons (Sidewinder, Stinger or Sidearm) have been procured for use with the Turkish AH-1s.

The navy has three original *AB 204AS* anti-submarine helicopters, which are still in service with 351 Filo at Topel. The aircraft has skid-mounted flotation gear.

The first six *AB 212ASWs* were equipped with *SMA APS-705* search radar, the antenna for which is housed in a flat-topped thimble radome above the cabin.

The grounded *S-2E Trackers* are maintained in airworthy condition, and are regularly run up. In their final year of operation the aircraft were plagued by engine and systems faults, and two were lost in fatal crashes. Their end was inevitable.

The second batch of *AB 212ASWs* were equipped with *Ferranti Sea Spray Mk 3* radar, and have provision for *BAeD Sea Skua* missiles for ASV attacks.

A close-up view reveals the array of antennas mounted on the nose of an *AB 212EW*.

Three *AB 212EWs* (two of which are shown here) are operated by 351 Filo at Topel, alongside 11 *AB 212ASWs*. The EW aircraft have Sea Spray radar, like the later ASWs.

The early-style undernose gun turrets and late, flat-plate canopies identify these Turkish Cobras as *AH-1Ps*, which were AGH-1Gs brought up to AH-1S standard.

A pair of *Do 28Ds* is on charge with the army, the aircraft featuring large undernose and underfuselage radomes. The two aircraft may have an Elint or EW role.

Turkey's *AH-1Ws* wear a unique brown and green camouflage that is similar in some respects to the colours applied to Jordanian AH-1Fs. Ten of these aircraft have been delivered, together with 28 airworthy AH-1Ps and four airframes for spares recovery.

Kamov Ka-50 'Hokum'

The Kamov 'Hokum' represents the most radical approach to the design of a modern attack helicopter, with only a single crewman to fly the aircraft, acquire and attack targets in a high-threat environment. Kamov insists that this is made possible by the type's benign handling characteristics and highly automated systems, but others remain unconvinced. Kamov has claimed victory in the competition for a new Soviet army helicopter, although the truth seems to be that a competitive evaluation with the Mi-28, or perhaps the new all-weather Mi-28N, continues.

The success and obvious utility of the battlefield attack/anti-tank helicopter has led to a profusion of new designs intended to fulfil this vital role. Virtually all have followed the configuration of the Bell AH-1 Cobra (originally designed for the slightly different task of escorting troop-carrying helicopters in Vietnam), with an impossibly narrow fuselage giving negligible frontal area, an undernose cannon, stub wings for weapons carriage, a nose-mounted electro-optical sighting system and stepped tandem cockpits housing pilot (usually in the rear cockpit) and gunner/WSO (usually in the front). This logical formula has thus been adopted, with only minor variations, by Hughes (now McDonnell Douglas Helicopters) for its AH-64 Apache (first and most influential of the dedicated tank-killers), by Agusta for its A 129 Mangusta, by Aérospatiale and MBB (now Eurocopter) for the Tiger, by Atlas for the Rooivalk, and most recently by Boeing/Sikorsky for the RAH-66 Comanche. Even in the Soviet Union, the basic configuration seems to have won a degree of acceptance, with the second-generation Mi-24 'Hind-D' adopting similar tandem cockpits and the new Mi-28 following the Apache configuration slavishly enough to lead to the inevitable accusations of plagiarism.

The Mi-28 was designed to meet a Soviet requirement for a new attack helicopter for army aviation, chiefly as a replacement for the Mi-24, whose transport capability is little used. It remains uncertain as to whether the Kamov Ka-50 was originally designed to meet this same requirement, or a complementary one for a single-

Top: Prototype 018 (probably the fifth flying prototype) is seen here in high-speed low-altitude flight, carrying a pair of Vikhr ATGMs and an S-8 20-round 80-mm rocket pod under each wing.

Left: The Ka-50 was originally designed to meet the Soviet Army's need for a Mil Mi-24 'Hind' replacement. One of the prototypes is seen here flying past a typically Russian church. The end of the Cold War has left the church in a rather more secure position than the army in Russia.

Above: The second Ka-50 prototype had a very different nose configuration to later aircraft, with a circular port above it. It had no cannon. The aircraft is seen here with enormous square-section test pods under the outboard underwing pylons, and with upward pointing test cameras, looking at the coaxial rotors, inboard. The first prototype, 010, was painted black overall, and had a more streamlined nose. It lacked PZU intake filters.

Right: The second prototype flies in formation with one of the most recent aircraft (probably the sixth prototype) during the Moscow Aerospace show at the LII Gromov Flight Research Centre at Zhukhovskii. Differences between the two aircraft are largely confined to the nose area, although the silver-painted 012 lacks a gun and has smaller pilot's side windows.

seat 'fighter' or escort helicopter. It seems that the two requirements (if they ever existed as such) were eventually merged, leaving the Ka-50 and Mi-28 as *de facto* rivals. The massive differences between the two aircraft (perhaps reflecting their slightly different roles) have made it seemingly impossible to choose one or other, however, and pre-production batches of both now appear to have been ordered. Initial Western speculation that the Kamov aircraft was intended to be a dedicated naval attack helicopter, after a version of the Mi-24 proved unsatisfactory in the amphibious role in trials, was certainly erroneous (as were the 'Ka-41', 'Ka-34' and Ka-136' designations originally applied), the Ka-29TB 'Helix-B' fulfilling this function, as well as that of assault transport.

Kamov genesis

Kamov began serious work on an attack helicopter for army aviation in 1977, building on the experience gained with the successive helicopter designs (built, when successful, mainly for civil customers and the navy) produced during the previous decades. The Kamov Design Bureau (now officially known somewhat more clumsily as the Helicopter Scientific and Technical Complex named after N. I. Kamov)

was organised in 1947, though Nikolai Ilych Kamov himself had been designing rotorcraft since the 1920s, having been responsible for the underpowered (and flightless) KASKR-1 (a copy of the Cierva C.8, similarly using an Avro 504 fuselage) and KASKR-2 gyroplanes in 1929 and 1930, respectively, while employed by Grigorovich. Moving to TsAGI in 1931, Kamov designed the A-7 autogyro, which was built in small numbers for the VVS and used operationally for spotting. The atmosphere of fear at TsAGI (caused by Stalin's purges) stultified design work, leading to conservatism and an unwillingness to take risks, and Kamov moved again to the Smolensk factory set-up to build the A-7 and other autogyros. Here he drew up the AK autogyro, but design work was interrupted by the evacuation of the factory in 1941, in the face of the German invasion. Official disinterest in the autogyro led to abandonment in 1943. The first true helicopter produced by the Kamov Design Bureau (usually abbreviated to OKB) was the Ka-8 of 1948. This was a single-seat helicopter with coaxial main rotors, which were to become something of an OKB trademark. The Ka-10 of 1949 was similar, and led to the Ka-10M of 1954, about 10 of which saw service with the coast guard and

aboard whalers and icebreakers.

The first Kamov helicopter built in quantity was the two-seat Ka-15, which first flew in 1952, several hundred of which were built for the AV-MF, Aeroflot and a number of export customers. The Ka-18 was similar, but had a stretched fuselage accommodating two seats behind the side-by-side seats for the pilot and co-pilot (or third passenger). Alternatively, the aircraft could carry a stretcher in place of the co-pilot and one rear seat, with a doctor behind the pilot. This aircraft led directly to the naval Ka-20 and Ka-25, described in detail in *World Air Power Journal,* Volume 5. From 1969 it was the first helicopter in the world to be fitted with glass-fibre rotor blades.

The Ka-22 of 1960 was an unusual compound helicopter, essentially a large (70-100 seat) aeroplane of high-wing monoplane configuration with four-bladed rotors atop the wingtip engine nacelles, which also had conventional propellers for providing thrust in forward flight. Only one was built, but this set several records in the convertiplane class.

The Ka-26 of 1965 was a light utility helicopter (again with coaxial main rotors) used mainly for agricultural duties, and led directly to the turbine-engined Ka-126 and the mod-

Kamov Ka-50 'Hokum'

ernised and enlarged Ka-226. Finally, Kamov produced the Ka-27/-32 family for naval use and for civilian customers. Of similar configuration to the Ka-25, and with similar overall dimensions, this represented maturity for the coaxial rotor helicopter, and was perhaps most notable for its advanced autopilot/auto-hover/autoland and control system, which allowed it to be flown automatically from take-off to torpedo launch, entirely hands off, using a high degree of automation to reduce cockpit workload and to allow single-pilot operation.

Battles with Mil

Kamov enjoyed most success in selling its dependable and rugged helicopters to the navy and to Aeroflot, but often tried to gain acceptance for its aircraft as ground-based combat helicopters. As early as 1966, Kamov entered the Ka-25F in the competition that resulted in the selection of the Mi-24 for army aviation. Modification of the Ka-27 with a new forward fuselage and the weapons system of the Mi-24V resulted in the Ka-29TB to meet a naval requirement for an armed attack/assault helicopter.

The Ka-50 as it appears today began life as the V-80 (Vertolyet 80, or helicopter 80), one of a series of studies for a land-based attack helicopter. The requirement for such a helicopter

was issued as a direct result of American work on the YAH-63 and YAH-64, which first flew during 1975 and which were a major shock to the USSR, seemingly threatening overnight obsolescence for the Mi-24.

Soviet helicopter manufacturers clearly had to come up with a counter to the AH-63/-64, and were faced with a stark choice: to follow US design philosophy (accepting that the disadvantages of heavier Soviet equipment and technology would mean lower flight performance) or to take a radically different approach. While Mil started with the familiar AH-1/AH-63/AH-64 configuration, Kamov preferred to draw on its own experience, finding its own way in airframe design and suggesting new concepts of operation. Accordingly, the OKB drew up a number of studies which incorporated features flown on earlier Kamov designs, usually the coaxial rotor. This configuration offered compact overall dimensions, reduced vulnerability and greater efficiency. In a conventional helicopter, a proportion of engine power goes to the tail rotor, which serves only to offset the torque of the main rotor and does not contribute to either lift or thrust. The coaxial rotor provides for simple control, good manoeuvrability, a lack of rotor rpm limitations, and an ability to take-off and land regardless of windspeed and direction.

This view of 015 reveals the way in which the six Vikhr ATGMs are carried under each wing, while also showing the ribbed, upward-pointing engine exhausts fitted to some prototypes. The nose radome, EO window (with windscreen wiper) and air data probes are also well displayed.

Some of Kamov's internally competing designs have now been seen in model form in the OKB museum, offering a fascinating glimpse of what might have been. The V-50, for example, was a streamlined tandem rotor helicopter, with stepped cockpits and a stub wing with three underslung pylons set well forward (just below the pilot's cockpit) and with additional underfuselage pylons ahead of this. Twin engines were mounted on each side of the pylon for the rear three-bladed rotor. The forward main rotor shaft projected directly from the top of the fuselage, just aft of the stub wing and pilot's cockpit. The V-60 was more conventional in appearance, but very streamlined and with retractable undercarriage. The single engine was mounted above the cabin. Armament seems to have been restricted to side-by-side pairs of AT-6 'Spiral' launch tubes at the tip of each stub wing.

The most unusual of the designs was the V-100, whose compound configuration and streamlined, shark-like contours might have promised enormous speed. Three-bladed rotors were mounted at the tips of the broad-span, high-set wing, with a four-bladed pusher propeller at the tip of the tailboom (like the US AH-56 Cheyenne). Twin engines were mounted side-by-side above the wingroot, and the high-mounted tailplane carried enormous vertical fins, each with a large rudder. The V-100 had three pylons under each wing, close in to the fuselage, with further pylons on the lower 'shoulders' of the streamlined main undercarriage fairings. On the model shown, these carried a pair of Kh-25 air-to-surface missiles. An articulated cannon was mounted in the nose of each undercarriage fairing. The tandem cockpits were not stepped, and there appeared to be a periscopic sight mounted above the rear (WSO) cockpit.

A unique approach

Kamov claims not to have examined the conventional main rotor and anti-torque tail rotor configuration at all. The OKB's primary objection to the conventional helicopter configuration was their belief that it imposed an unnecessarily high degree of vulnerability to hostile ground fire, with the long transmission system (especially the tail rotor drive shaft and associated gearboxes) and highly-loaded tailboom coming in for particular criticism. The tail rotor itself was felt to be potentially hazardous to maintenance personnel and vulnerable to contact damage when hovering in confined spaces, as well as making production more complex and more expensive.

During this period, Kamov worked closely with Sukhoi, who had already solved many of the problems facing design of a single-seat close-support aircraft in the design of their Su-25 'Frogfoot'. Some standardisation between Ka-50 and Su-25 was contemplated, consideration even being given to use of the Su-25 cockpit.

The design selected for production was the V-80, although another model in the OKB museum (dated 1971) reveals that this design underwent major changes before metal was cut. The original V-80 design was more streamlined than the Ka-50 prototypes, and lacked a central vertical fin. The aircraft appears to have had tandem cockpits for two crew-members, and the

retractable undercarriage had a tailwheel in the boom, and mainwheels retracting into wingtip pods. A non-articulated cannon was housed in a strake running along the lower port fuselage, and the target illuminating/command guidance radar antenna was scabbed below the forward fuselage, like that fitted to the Mi-24D.

Increased weight

From the beginning, it was apparent that weight would be a vitally important factor in the equation, since Soviet avionics systems were heavier and bulkier than their Western equivalents, and this would tend to make a Soviet attack helicopter heavier than its Western equivalent (and thus have lower performance). In addition, the new machine was expected to offer better protection to its crew, have more powerful armament, and to be simple to repair in the field and cheap to produce. All of these factors seemed to point towards higher weight, and thus to threaten performance.

Kamov, led by Sergei V. Mikheyev since 1974, therefore began to search for a radical solution to the weight problem, eventually producing a controversial analysis which seemed to point to a reduction in the number of crew car-

ried, offering a 'strategic solution'. Kamov's long experience of designing naval helicopters seemed to show that increased automation would save structural weight (and cost), and provide systems which would be quicker and more accurate than a human operator. For the Ka-27, Kamov had designed equipment which allowed the ASW mission to be highly automated, with day/night all-weather navigation, automatic transfer of information to other aircraft and ships, automatic formation flight and highly-automated limited-space landing systems. In the Ka-27, Kamov claimed, the ASW mission could actually be flown by a single pilot. The OKB believed that a similar approach to systems design for the Ka-50 might ensure that the aircraft could be flown and operated by a single crewman. In December 1977, therefore, Kamov officially proposed a single-seat version of the V-80 to meet the Soviet army aviation requirement for an attack helicopter.

From the beginning, Sergei Mikheyev admitted that one pilot could not operate better than two. "There is no need to prove such a thing," he stated, "since no-one can prove the unprovable." Instead, his aim was to show that a single pilot in the Ka-50 could perform the same mis-

Above right: Development of the Ka-50 has been long and protracted, and 015 (probably the fourth prototype) was the first Ka-50 with a cannon fitted. The aircraft is seen here with its maximum warload of 12 Vikhr ATGMs and 40 unguided 80-mm rocket projectiles.

Right: Kamov claims that the Ka-50 is faster, more agile and better armed than its rival, the Mi-28, while also enjoying better battle damage resistance, but is still struggling to overcome scepticism about the single-seat configuration.

Kamov Ka-50 'Hokum'

Above: This Ka-50 (probably 015) carries box-like test pods outboard and external fuel tanks inboard during the initial phase of the evaluation against the rival Mil Mi-28. One of the four Mi-28 prototypes can just be seen in the background, behind the rotor mast.

sion as two crewmen in the competing Mil Mi-28 (or the AH-64, which the Kamov OKB soon began to regard as the 'real competitor'). Close examination of the Mi-24, say Kamov, revealed that in very low-level covert approaches to target, only the pilot flies and navigates the aircraft, acquiring the target and often aiming the weapons. The design of the Ka-50 was frozen in 1980, by the so-called mock-up review commission.

Many of the systems which would be required by the Ka-50 were already under development by the time the Ka-50 was launched, and some were even flying in testbed aircraft operated by the LII Gromov Flight Research Institute at Zhukhovskii. This included the single-seat cockpit itself, which was simulated inside a converted production Ka-29TB.

Systems integration was undertaken by NPO Elektro Avtomatika, the same company that had integrated the systems of the MiG-29 and Su-27. Four of this company's Orbita computers formed the heart of the Ka-50 avionics system, with one dedicated to navigation, one for mission control and planning, and two as back-ups. The Ka-50 uses the same HUD as the MiG-29, the same helmet-mounted sight, and many of the same instruments, although the Ka-50 panel is dominated by a rubber-shielded TV display. The Ka-50 weapons system is based around a modern inertial navigation and attack system, with a laser rangefinder/illuminator, a TV sighting system with automatic missile guidance, and a TV-type CRT display screen, linked to a secure, jam-resistant encrypted datalink.

Despite having confidence in their approach, the Kamov OKB quickly realised that the radical nature of their design would in some ways be a disadvantage. They would have to demonstrate its superiority and at the same time overcome the prejudices and preconceptions of a conserva-

tive General Staff conditioned to regard with suspicion a single-seat close support aircraft (let alone a helicopter), and with this suspicion apparently reinforced by international acceptance of the two-seat helicopter configuration. Furthermore, although the Deputy Minister of the Aviation Industry had made clear his feeling that selection of a winner could only follow the fullest evaluation of both aircraft types, the army continued to hope that the competition might be interrupted by a production decision if one aircraft seemed to be a clear winner. Thus, if Kamov's bid were to succeed they could not afford to let Mil get ahead at any stage of the competition, and prototype construction was accorded a high priority.

Airborne Ka-50

The first Ka-50 prototype, coded '010' and painted black overall, made its maiden flight on 27 June 1982, in the hands of N. P. Bezdetnov. Simulators were already operational, and were playing a vital part in the test programme. From the beginning, the Ka-50 development programme attracted a great deal of high-level interest, though, as will be seen, the aircraft remained virtually unknown outside official Soviet circles. Air forces Commander-in-Chief, Marshall of Aviation P. S. Khutahov, himself a former ground attack pilot, took particular interest in the programme and was a frequent visitor to the various test airfields being used. In October 1986 a complete firepower demonstration was organised at the behest of Minister of Defence Marshal S. V. Sokolov, as the culmina-

Left: A head-on view of the Ka-50 shows to advantage the semi-retractable nose gear in its retracted position, with the nosewheels just jutting below the level of the lower fuselage.

The fifth Ka-50 prototype is seen in flight with its undercarriage extended. The aircraft wears the same camouflage scheme as is currently carried by Russian army 'Hinds'.

tion of the competitive flyoff, involving two fully-equipped and fully-armed prototypes of the Ka-50 and the Mi-28.

The competing Mi-28 was revealed at the 1989 Paris Air Salon at Le Bourget, and was displayed again at the 1990 Helitech exhibition at Redhill, Surrey. Some observers took this as indicating that the Mi-28 had been rejected by the Soviet armed forces, and was now being offered for export on a private venture basis, an opinion apparently confirmed by vehement denials from Kamov that any new coaxial rotor attack helicopter even existed, this being taken to indicate that the Ka-50 was still in the running for a Soviet order, and thus still secret. In fact, Kamov's reticence in talking about the Ka-50 may well have indicated that the project was behind schedule, and seemed to be on the verge of losing the competition. Denials at Redhill virtually coincided with the release (by the US DoD) of a front view photograph of a Ka-50 prototype, which was published in the 1989 edition of *Soviet Military Power*. Additional clandestinely taken photos were published by *Jane's Defence Weekly* in September 1991, although the existence of the aircraft was not formally revealed until January 1992, when Sergei V. Mikheyev addressed the London Fighter Helicopter Conference.

Later in 1992, British Aerospace admitted that it would consider outfitting a Russian airframe with Western avionics and weapons to meet the British Army Air Corps requirement for an attack helicopter, as a means of becoming a prime contractor in the project. The possibility of offering a version of the Ka-50 with Western avionics and weapons to meet the Army Air Corps requirement was also examined by Kamov and its US agent, Group Vector, and

this effort is believed to have been behind the aircraft's appearance at the 1992 Farnborough SBAC show. Surprisingly, the Ka-50 did not fly at Farnborough, but while some Kamov officials muttered darkly about visa problems for the aircraft's pilots, some analysts suggested that the non-appearance of tie-rods linking upper swashplate and rotor head on the aircraft when displayed statically might have offered a more likely (but more embarrassing) explanation. A single early prototype had flown during the massive Moscow Aeroshow in August 1992, but Farnborough marked the formal public unveiling of the aircraft and afforded the first opportunity to see the aircraft up-close.

For its appearance at Farnborough, the Ka-50 '020' received an overall matt black colour scheme, with the name 'Werewolf' and a striking logo. A similar colour scheme was worn by '021', which accompanied 'Werewolf' to Paris in 1993, where both aircraft made display/ demonstration flights. This aircraft wore a different logo, reflecting its 'Black Shark' name. This was applied for a major motion picture whose production was reportedly held up 'on several occasions' due to the lack of an airworthy Ka-50 for filming.

The early aircraft

The exact number of Ka-50 prototypes produced is uncertain, with estimates varying from six to 12 At least seven aircraft can be identified from photographs. The first prototype, 010, was black, and differed from later aircraft in lacking PZU engine intake dust filters. It also had smaller fairings on its wingtips and its nose lacked any EO or command guidance equipment. 012 was finished in silver (or was left in natural metal) and had a large circular port in an overnose fair-

ing, together with a box-like undernose sensor housing. The aircraft has been photographed carrying enormous slab-sided boxes (perhaps containing test equipment) underwing, and with a variety of test cameras filming the rotors. A camouflaged aircraft coded '014' appears to have the later standard nose, with a rectangular window in the forward face of the undernose box fairing, and with prominent upward-pointing exhausts. No gun was fitted, but a fairing on the starboard side closely followed the contours of the cannon installation, perhaps simulating the weapon aerodynamically. '015' and '018' were finished identically in Mi-24-type green and stone camouflage, and both were of similar configuration, with an enlarged window in the pilot's hatch, and with a fully operational cannon installed on the starboard fuselage side. They were otherwise similar to '014'. The Werewolf ('020') and Black Shark ('021') differed externally from '015' and '018' only in having simpler engine exhausts. The description that follows applies to these latter two.

The Ka-50 is designed around a coaxial main rotor, based on that used by other Kamov helicopters. It has been refined for extra strength, with the blades attached to the semi-rigid rotor hubs by steel plates. The blades are of composite construction, with a new high-speed section and swept tips. Since they are aerodynamically symmetrical, coaxial rotors give no cross-channel control influences, simplifying handling and allowing a 'pedal turn' to be made throughout the speed envelope, with yaw control provided by differential collective pitch, rather than by

Kamov Ka-50 'Hokum'

The main tactical CRT display screen of the Kamov Ka-50 'Havoc' is designed to display FLIR or TV imagery, but does not have multiple input buttons to allow it to be used for navigation and other displays. The small, rubber-hooded screen dominates the narrow instrument panel, and is located directly below the head-up display. Other instruments are entirely conventional analog dials, and the overall 'feel' of the cockpit is similar to that of the Mil Mi-24 and other earlier attack helicopters. Only the pilot's rocket-powered Zvezda K-36 ejection seat strikes a dramatically new note.

altering tail rotor rpm. Kamov claims that the coaxial rotor gives 12 per cent greater lift than a conventional rotor asembly on a helicopter using the same engines. The controls are actuated via a four-channel digital autopilot.

Structurally, the Ka-50 is built around a torsion box beam, 1 m (3.3 ft) high and 1 m (3.3 ft) wide, to which the armoured cockpit is attached at the front, the rotor gearbox above, and the engines on each side. The wing centre-section passes through the beam, just below the engine nacelles. The Ka-50 uses a semi-retractable tricycle landing gear, with single wheels on the main units, and twin nosewheels. This reduces drag and fuel consumption, and the

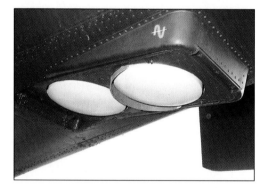

Above: Doppler antennas are housed below the tailboom of the 'Havoc'.

Below: One of the Ka-50 prototypes is seen with all its various access panels open. The engine covers double as servicing platforms.

hydraulically retracted undercarriage also serves to protect equipment lying behind it. These factors more than compensate for the increased weight and complexity. All four wheels are shod with low-pressure tyres, and the nosewheels are fully steerable. The tailboom provides a large volume for equipment and systems, which are located behind easy-access panels with different systems located in different locations, allowing simultaneous access or maintenance by different

Specification
Kamov Ka-50 'Hokum'

Powerplant: two Isotov (Klimov/Leningrad) TV3-117 turboshafts, each rated at 2,200 shp (1641.2 kW)
Rotor diameter: 14.430 m (47 ft 5¼ in)
Rotor area: 165.13 m² (1,777 sq ft) each
Fuselage length: 15.000 m (49 ft 2½)
Overall length, rotors turning: 15.960 m (52 ft 4½ in)
Wheel track: 2.670 m (8 ft 9 in)
Wheel base: 4.910 m (16 ft 1 in)
Wingspan: 7.34 m (24 ft 4½ in)
Normal take off weight: 9800 kg (21,604 lb)
Maximum take off weight: 10800 kg (23,810 lb)
Maximum level speed: 310 km/h (167.4 kts; 193 mph)
Maximum speed (shallow dive): 350 km/h (189 kts; 217 mph)
Sideways speed: 80 km/h (43 kts; 50 mph)
Rearward speed: 90 km/h (49 kts; 56 mph)
Hover ceiling (outside ground effect): 4000 m (13,123 ft)
Rate of climb at 250m: 10 m/s (1,968 ft/min)
***g* limit:** +3 *g*
Estimated combat radius: 250 km (135 nm; 155 miles)
Weapon load: 12 AT-9 Vikhr ATGMs and two S-8 20-round 80-mm rocket pods, with 2A42 cannon and 500 rounds.

specialist ground crew. Generous built-in test facilities, sensible access arrangements and engineering features which minimise the need for external equipment make the Ka-50 highly maintainable, able to operate autonomously away from its home base for periods of up to two weeks. The empennage has a fixed tailplane with endplate fins and a central tailfin with trailing edge rudder. The rudder incorporates a yaw damper.

The aircraft is powered by a pair of 1640-kW (2,200-shp) Isotov TV3-117K turboshafts, the same as those which power the competing Mi-28. These are mounted on the sides of the upper fuselage, adjacent to the main rotor shaft. The exhausts on some aircraft have upswept triple IRCM mixers. The high level of installed power gives the Ka-50 excellent performance characteristics, and also allows the carriage of external loads of up to 3000 kg (6,613 lb). An internal APU allows autonomous engine starting at altitudes up to 4000 m (13,123 ft) and supplies electrical and hydraulic power during ground checks.

Mikheyev saw the main task of the Ka-50 as being the destruction of enemy armour, which might be protected by escort helicopters and ground-based air defences, which would thus be the Ka-50's priority targets. Simulations showed that such targets would best be engaged by a helicopter using external target designation,

Kamov Ka-50 'Hokum'

1 Rudder
2 Fixed tab
3 Tail navigation light
4 Radar warning antenna
5 IFF aerial

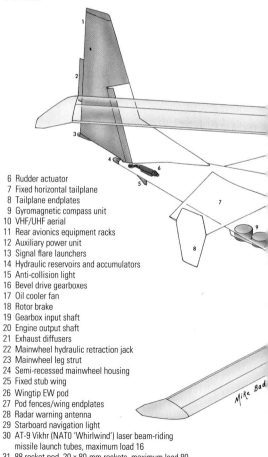

6 Rudder actuator
7 Fixed horizontal tailplane
8 Tailplane endplates
9 Gyromagnetic compass unit
10 VHF/UHF aerial
11 Rear avionics equipment racks
12 Auxiliary power unit
13 Signal flare launchers
14 Hydraulic reservoirs and accumulators
15 Anti-collision light
16 Bevel drive gearboxes
17 Oil cooler fan
18 Rotor brake
19 Gearbox input shaft
20 Engine output shaft
21 Exhaust diffusers
22 Mainwheel hydraulic retraction jack
23 Mainwheel leg strut
24 Semi-recessed mainwheel housing
25 Fixed stub wing
26 Wingtip EW pod
27 Pod fences/wing endplates
28 Radar warning antenna
29 Starboard navigation light
30 AT-9 Vikhr (NATO 'Whirlwind') laser beam-riding missile launch tubes, maximum load 16
31 88 rocket pod, 20 x 80-mm rockets, maximum load 80
32 Wing stores pylons
33 Ventral HF aerial
34 2A42 30-mm cannon

Left: A cluster of six ZT-3 Vikhr ('Whirlwind') laser beam-riding anti-tank guided missiles is fixed to the outboard underwing pylon of a Ka-50. The launch tubes can be depressed by 10°, as seen here.

Right: The cannon installation on the Ka-50 allows the gun to be depressed through 30°, elevated through 15° and traversed through 15°. Access for maintenance personnel is unrivalled.

either from an observation helicopter or from a ground-based team. The commander of Russian army aviation, Lieutenant General Vitalii Pavlov, has pointed out that reliance on an external source for preliminary targeting is not the disadvantage it might seem: "An autonomous target search by a combat helicopter in a strong air defence environment, or against a target using modern camouflage methods, is a fiction. Preliminary external designation, handed off to attack helicopters ensures a covert attack and allows a high level of group co-ordination, essential to the success of the attack mission."

The keys to success lay in being able to approach the fire position without being seen, and in then having weapons with a longer reach than those of the enemy. Thus, the most important system to be automated on the Ka-50 was the weapons system. The first generation of anti-tank guided missiles (Falanga, Milan, SS-11, etc.) relied on manual guidance, which limited missile speed and firing range. The second generation (Shturm-V, TOW, HOT) introduced semi-automatic guidance, with the operator manually tracking the missile. Such systems tended to limit range to about that of the shoulder-launched SAM, or that of the main armament of a typical tank target. This gave the heli-

copter only about 10 seconds to aim and fire at ranges of less than 3 km (1.86 miles), or between 15 and 20 seconds at ranges of between 5 and 6 km (3.1 and 3.7 miles). Increased range would give greater time to acquire a target, aim, fire and guide the weapon, and was clearly necessary. Such ranges demanded a missile with supersonic speed and this, in turn, demanded a fully automatic guidance system. A true fire-and-forget, launch-and-leave capability would obviously be the ideal solution, but was not felt to be possible within the timescale envisaged.

The primary armament chosen was the

35 Cannon barbette, able to move in azimuth
36 Ammunition feed chute, 500 rounds
37 Armoured fuselage fuel tank
38 Engine oil tank
39 Klimov (Isotov) TV3-117VK turboshaft engines
40 Engine accessory equipment gearbox
41 Main rotor combining gearbox
42 Rotor head hydraulic actuators
43 Lower rotor pitch control mechanism
44 Swash plate mechanism
45 Main rotor mast
46 Pitch control rods
47 Upper rotor pitch control mechanism
48 Semi-rigid rotor heads
49 Blade root attachment with emergency explosive separator
50 Composite rotor blades
51 Engine air intake dust/debris filter
52 Intake filter spill duct
53 Control linkages
54 Fuselage flank avionics equipment bays
55 Cockpit armour
56 K-37 ejection seat
57 Outside air temperature probe
58 Port side entry door
59 Rear-view mirror
60 Port side collective pitch control lever
61 Port cockpit hatch
62 Side console panel
63 Semi-recessed nosewheel housing
64 External cable duct
65 Nosewheel leg strut
66 Nosewheel hydraulic jack
67 Yaw control rudder pedals
68 Cyclic pitch control column
69 Instrument panel
70 Instrument panel shroud
71 Windscreen wiper
72 Pilot's head-up display
73 Armoured cockpit glazing

74 IFF aerial
75 Swept blade tips
76 Forward avionics equipment bay
77 Temperature probe
78 Nose electro-optical sensor housing
79 Radar warning antenna
80 Electro-optical sighting window
81 Radar equipment
82 Terrain-following radar
83 Radome
84 Air data booms
85 Yaw vanes

Above and left: The sixth Ka-50 received a sinister black colour scheme and the werewolf logo for use in an ill-starred Russian feature film, but this was retained for the aircraft's starring role as Ka-50 demonstrator. Tie rods between the upper and lower rotors are missing on the aircraft above, and are perhaps the real reason it did not fly at its Farnborough debut.

PTUR Vikhr ('Whirlwind'), known to the US DoD as AT-9. The missile is a beam-rider, following a laser beam generated by the launch aircraft. This form of guidance is jam-resistant and gives the target minimal warning of attack, even if it has laser warning devices. The supersonic missile weighs only about 60 kg (132 lb) and has a range of between 8 and 10 km (4.9 and 6.2 miles), exceeding most ground-based air defence systems. A shaped-charge warhead with proximity and contact fuses ensure maximum lethality, by allowing the weapon to penetrate up to 900 mm (35.4 in) of reactive armour. Up to 16 Vikhrs can reportedly be carried, in clusters of eight, although the maximum number seen on a Ka-50 so far has been 12, with the clusters consisting of a lower side-by-side row of four missiles, with two in an upper row. They appear to be limited to the outboard underwing pylon only, leaving the inboard pylon clear. The Vikhr reportedly has a formidable air-to-air capability.

Other weapons that can be carried by the Ka-50 include the B-8 rocket pod (containing 20 S-8 80-mm rocket projectiles), the older UV-32-57 rocket pod (containing 32 57-mm rockets), FAB500 500-kg bombs, Kh-25 ASMs or even twin-barrelled 23-mm cannon pods. All

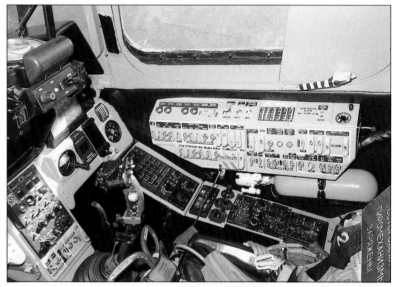

The cockpit of the sixth Ka-50 prototype is close to that of the intended production configuration. The starboard part of the panel is dominated by a primitive moving map display, with the TV screen and MiG-29-type HUD in the centre and conventional flight and engine instruments on the left. It has been reported that the pilot would usually wear a helmet-mounted target designator, but since this could not cue the cannon (which is effectively fixed) or the laser designator, its use would be restricted to cueing AAMs. Visibility from the heavily armoured cockpit is surprisingly poor, a function of the sheets of armour plate surrounding the pilot's shoulders, and the need for all of the switches, instruments and controls to be within reach of the single pilot.

four underwing pylons are 'wet' to allow the carriage of external fuel tanks for ferrying. The wingtips house launchers for a total of 128 26-mm chaff/flare cartridges. For self-defence or in the anti-helicopter role, the Ka-50 can carry R-60 (AA-8 'Aphid') or R-73 (AA-11 'Archer') IR-homing AAMs. The Ka-50 can launch the latter missile at off-axis targets, using a helmet-mounted target designator similar to that used by MiG-29 pilots.

Primary gun armament

From the start, it was realised that the Ka-50 would need a built-in cannon for use against soft targets, or those whose value did not warrant using a rocket or missile. The gun also offered excellent potential as an air-to-air weapon. Combat experience with the Mi-24 had shown the traditional Soviet helicopter gun, the 12.7-mm machine-gun, to be ineffective against many targets, even in its four-barrelled form. A weapon with a calibre of more than 20-mm was clearly preferable. The development of a brand new weapon was not practicable and, for one reason or another, many existing aircraft guns had to be ruled out. The eventual solution proved to be adoption of the Shipunov 2A42, a weapon originally developed for armoured fighting vehicles and used on the well-known BMP. The same weapon was selected for the Mi-28, and both Mil and Kamov claim credit for its selection. Whoever suggested the gun, it was an excellent choice, a 30-mm cannon with variable rates of fire and the option of selective feed from separate ammunition boxes which could house different types of ammunition (e.g. armour-piercing and high explosive). Remarkably resilient to jamming and dust, and with a high muzzle velocity (980 m/3,215 ft per second) the weapon promised accuracy and a devastating punch. Moreover, at 116 kg (256 lb), it was lighter and simpler than equivalent aircraft weapons.

Weapons up front

While Mil designed an unusual nose turret, in which the ammunition boxes traversed and elevated with the gun itself, Kamov initially decided on a fixed mounting on the fuselage side, close to the centre of gravity, as in the Mi-24P. This location minimised the effect of recoil and gave a strong and rigid location for the mount, and did not demand local strengthening of the airframe, thereby saving weight. The ammunition boxes (containing 500 rounds) could be installed in the fuselage, with short feeds to the breech. It was soon decided to give the gun a degree of movement (using an electro-hydraulic drive) with 30°/15° of depression/elevation and 15° of traverse. The limited travel of the gun was compensated for by the agility of the helicopter itself, whose high side slip, pitch and yaw rates made it fast and easy to point the gun by pointing the aircraft. The only weakness of the gun mounting was the proximity of some sensitive avionics items to the barrel, vibration and 'noise' leading to some problems before anti-vibration mountings solved the problems. Even with the hydraulic drive and ammunition feed system, gun weight is only 250 kg (551 lb).

Apart from its coaxial rotor configuration (with its attendant performance advantages) and its weapons system, the key to the Ka-50's success lies in its high degree of survivability over the battlefield. This is partly a function of its long reach (conferred by the Vikhr missile), partly a function of its speed and agility, and partly a function of its resistance to battle damage. The Ka-50 needed to be particularly well protected against battle damage because of its single-seat configuration, since some two-seaters have a second set of (emergency) flying controls in the gunner's cockpit, which may allow the aircraft to be flown safely home, or at least to make a controlled landing.

Coaxial benefits

By comparison with a helicopter of conventional configuration, the Ka-50's coaxial rotor configuration offers some survivability advantages. There is no tail rotor, tail rotor driveshaft or gearboxes, and the transmission system is small, compact and easy to protect. This reduces the likelihood of a fatal hit on the transmission system. The rotor disc is smaller in area than that of a conventional helicopter of similar weight, and the tailboom can be severely damaged (or even shot off completely) without causing catastrophic loss of control.

The cockpit is lightly pressurised to prevent NBC contamination, even if its integrity is breached, and is armoured against ground fire. The cockpit itself incorporates more than 300 kg (661 lb) of steel hybrid armour, in two layers, while the transparencies are of toughened glass. Steel armour, integrated with the primary airframe structure, was chosen after careful study of all the alternative options, including ceramic armour, which was rejected due to its low durability, difficult reparability and high cost. The cockpit armour is proved against direct hits by 20-mm rounds. Inside the cockpit, the Ka-50 pilot wears a flak jacket over his water survival suit, giving further protection and confidence. In the event of a crash, the cockpit will not be penetrated by other elements of the helicopter, and internal volume will not change by more than 10-15 per cent, minimising deformation. Furthermore, the undercarriage and fuselage are designed to offer maximum energy absorption, with main gear oleos giving three times the usual energy absorption.

Vital systems are as well protected as the cockpit, and duplication gives a high degree of redundancy. The hydraulic system compartment, for example, is surrounded by steel armour, while the fuel tanks, hidden in the main box-beam and filled with reticulated foam, have self-sealing linings, effective extinguishers and some armour protection. A hit by a 20-mm or 23-mm round will not cause an explosion, and fires are extinguished within five seconds. Because the tank is of composite structure, there is little chance of burning metal being injected into the fuel even if the tanks are hit.

Control rods are enclosed within the armoured cockpit as far as possible, and are of increased diameter. Composites form 35 per

cent of the airframe by weight, and are used in the rotor blades, control rods wings and fuselage. Seventy m² (753.5 yd²) of the surface of the Ka-50 is covered by more than 100 three-layer honeycomb panels, 40 per cent of which are load-carrying structural elements. The three layers consist of a Kevlar or Kevlar/carbon skin, a nomex core and a metal frame. The use of such panels reduce weight by about 25 per cent by comparison with conventional alloy structures, increase airframe fatigue life by a factor of two or two and a half, reduce manufacturing complexity, and improve battle damage tolerance. The rotor blade spars are of two-contour structure. The transmission system is designed so as to continue running for 30 minutes after the oil

supply has been severed, while the aircraft can continue flying on one engine.

If the worst comes to the worst, the Ka-50 pilot can abandon his aircraft with relative ease, since it is the first helicopter to be equipped with an ejection seat. The provision of an ejection seat is an excellent boost to pilot morale, and is said to "embolden the pilot, when there is insufficient time to bail out conventionally in very low-level flight." The ejection system consists of a Zvezda (Severin) K-36 ejection seat. When the pilot actuates the seat the rotor blades are automatically jettisoned, as is the upper hatch of the canopy. Arm and leg restrainers simultaneously pull the pilot back into the seat, whose back is pulled into alignment with the rotor mast as the rocket pack fires. This then tows the seat out of the helicopter using a cable. The pilot separates from the seat conventionally. A SAR radio beacon is activated during ejection, and the seat pack includes a dinghy and a

NAZ-7M survival kit. The ejection system does impose a minimum separation distance of 150 m (492 ft) in formation flight, since within this distance a wingman could be damaged by jettisoned rotor blades in the event of an ejection.

Despite many announcements to the contrary, it seems premature to regard the Ka-50 as having been selected for full production. Development of both Ka-50 and Mi-28 continues apace, and the recent development of the better-equipped, all-weather Mi-28N might suggest that the baseline Mi-28 and Ka-50 may have already been sidelined. Whether a similarly improved Ka-50 could be developed as a competitor to the Mi-28N (Colonel Novikov, of the Directorate of Ground Forces Aviation, claimed that such an aircraft was under development, along with a trainer in January 1994), or whether the Russian army sees a need for two complementary helicopter types, remains uncertain. Certainly statements put out by the Kamov

Left and right: The seventh (and final?) prototype Ka-50, 021, received an overall black finish and a stylish black shark logo for the same motion picture for which the sixth prototype received its werewolf logo. The aircraft acted as a demonstrator at the 1993 Paris air show, where these photos were taken, but may have lost its logos since then, and is now believed to be testing advanced sensors and systems intended for any production Ka-50.

OKB that the Ka-50 has won the Soviet/ Russian army competition (such statements have been made, and denied by Mil and sometimes the Russian government at regular intervals) should be taken with a pinch of salt, and at best the Ka-50 remains some years from true service entry. For the record, Kamov claims that the Ka-50 was selected in preference to the Mi-28 because it was 'superior in all respects', most notably in having superior flight performance, longer-range anti-tank missiles (the Mi-28 using the older 9M117 Shturm V (AT-6 'Spiral') ATGM), greater ammunition capacity (500 rounds rather than 250), heavier armour and greater accuracy. Kamov further claims that a recommendation to place the Ka-50 in production was made by the Ministry of Defence in October 1984, and then again in 1986, at the conclusion of the competitive evaluation (prototype flyoff).

Marketing difficulties

During 1993, *Flight International* reported a strange row between Kamov and Group Vector, the US company apparently acting as its worldwide Ka-50 marketing agent. Steve Stylianoudis, President of Group Vector, accused Kamov of claiming that 30 aircraft were ready for delivery to the Russian armed forces when it had not even been put into limited production, of claiming victory in the competition with the Mil Mi-28 when the Ka-50 was "never competitive with the Mil Mi-28," and of claiming a night-attack capability that the aircraft was lacking. Stylianoudis further accused Kamov of writing contracts with foreign companies which it then subsequently cancelled without cause, merely to sign a contract with a third party under more favourable terms. These 'totally untrue' claims emerged in August 1993, when Stylianoudis asked Kamov to provide technical details for two potential customers, and to release airframes for 1994 delivery to one of them, the US Special Forces, which had funds for eight aircraft for evaluation. The other potential customer was rumoured to be the Greek army.

At a time when fixed-wing types are starting to relinquish the close air support role to helicopters, and when the development of increasingly effective SAMs and AAA make the battlefield an ever more dangerous place to operate, it seems clear that the attack helicopter must become more sophisticated and more complex, in order to undertake the new tasks demanded of it, to engage its targets at greater ranges with fire-and-forget missiles, and simply to survive. All of these factors seem to mitigate against a single-pilot aircraft. An extra pair of eyes is becoming increasingly invaluable in all military aircraft, and in an attack helicopter it seems essential to be able to split the workload between at least two crew members. It is unrealistic to expect the pilot to designate targets, launch (and guide) weapons and select the next target while simultaneously hovering in a confined area, keeping an eye out for threats, manoeuvring the aircraft as necessary, and communicating with his commander or with other aircraft in the flight.

Even with the most advanced avionics and automated systems, the attack helicopter role seems to be one in which two crew members are essential, and in which the peak workload is simply too much for a single pilot to cope with. Even if such an assumption is incorrect, it is so widely held as to render the Kamov Ka-50 virtually unsellable, at least in the anti-tank role. Perhaps as a dedicated escort helicopter, where compact size, agility and low cost are critical factors, the Ka-50 could have a role to play, or in roles such as drug interdiction or special forces support. The Kamov Design Bureau can only hope that in the post-Cold War world funding for such a narrowly specialised machine might still be forthcoming.

Falcon, Thunderbolt & Lightning

Known by three separate names in IDF/AF service, the F-16 Fighting Falcon forms the backbone of Israeli air power, and has notched up an impressive service record. The baseline F-16A or Netz (Falcon) serves primarily in the air defence role, while the F-16C or Barak (Lightning) and F-16D or Brakeet (Thunderbolt) have an air-to-ground commitment. The later variants serve in mixed squadrons, but the F-16Ds are much more than two-seat trainers, having special equipment for the defence suppression role accommodated in a distinctive extended fuselage spine.

Like 105 Squadron, with whom it shares Hatzor, 101 Squadron operates a few examples of the single-seat F-16C alongside a larger number of two-seat F-16Ds. The squadron's badge is a winged skull. and diagonal red and white rudder stripes are an extra traditional adornment that date back to the Avia S199 and Spitfire era.

The yellow falcon on a green disc adorning the fin of this F-16A is believed to mark it as an aircraft of 253 Squadron based at Ramon.

The scorpion tail marking identifies this F-16D as belonging to 105 Squadron at Hatzor. This aircraft carries three long-range fuel tanks and has an unidentified targeting or FLIR pod on the starboard side of the engine intake. This may be an AAQ-13 or AAQ-14 LANTIRN navigation or targeting pod. A single AIM-9L Sidewinder is carried on the port wingtip. Israeli F-16Ds may have an entirely new, indigenous radar. The appearance of these photos should not be misconstrued; Israel takes its security extremely seriously and aircraft spotting or photography is likely to be interpreted as spying, which carries a severe penalty.

190 Squadron at Ramon decorates its F-16As with an insignia which combines an F-16 silhouette with a hawk's head, all superimposed on a red disc. A further 50 F-16As (surplus to USAF requirements) may soon be procured from US sources.

An F-16D of 101 Squadron, Israel's premier fighter squadron, is seen landing at Hatzor carrying a variety of weaponry underwing. The huge weapon below the starboard wing appears to be an inert wingless training round for some kind of electro-optically guided and perhaps rocket-propelled glide bomb. World Air Power Journal is currently gathering material for an Israeli Air Power Analysis, so readers with photos of IDF/AF aircraft or information about the Israeli air force are invited to contact the editors.

Lockheed F-117
The Black Jet

An extraordinary shape, revolutionary radar-defeating features and a top secret, yet highly glamorous development have combined with a star appearance in Desert Storm to make the Lockheed F-117 the best-known warplane in the world. Able to penetrate hostile airspace without being seen by radars or infra-red sensors, the F-117 can then use its sophisticated target acquisition and designation system to score strikes against vital targets with pinpoint accuracy.

The first flying aircraft to validate the revolutionary concept of facetting was the second *Have Blue* experimental machine, which was completed with full stealth coatings and no excrescences. Results from the *Have Blue* programme left Lockheed and the *US Air Force* in no doubt as to whether to build a full-scale operational warplane.

Cruising high over Nevada, a pair of F-117 pilots enjoy their new-found freedom to train in daylight hours. For the first seven years of its operational career, the F-117 had flown almost exclusively at night to protect the secrets of its amazing shape.

At 2:51 a.m. on 17 January 1991, an F-117 dropped the first bomb of the Gulf War, a laser-guided GBU-27 which destroyed half of the Iraqi air defence center at Nukayb. A second F-117 blew away the other half. Ten more F-117s, the rest of the coalition's first wave, headed downtown to Baghdad. Thirteen minutes earlier, a daring raid – known in American parlance as Objective Oklahoma – by US Army Apache helicopters had unleashed Hellfire missiles to take down a segment of Iraq's air defence radars at pivotal location, opening a passageway for coalition warplanes to attack Saddam Hussein's forces without being detected early, en route. By then, the 12-aircraft first wave of F-117s was already 50 miles (80 km) beyond Oklahoma. The US Air Force insists that this first wave of F-117s reached Baghdad while Saddam's radars were still up and running, and without being detected.

Major Jerry Leatherman was in F-117 number 85-0816, one of those first 10 over Baghdad. Leatherman's job, like that of another F-117 pilot ahead of him, was to bomb the Baghdad International Telephone Exchange, known to the F-117 pilots as the AT & T building because its real Arabic

name was unwieldy. Leatherman followed the night eastward at 480 kt (551 mph; 886 km/h). He skirted the capital to attack from the north, seeing city lights, neon signs and the snake-like Tigris River winding through the city. Sixty SAM sites and 3,000 anti-aircraft guns encircled Baghdad on this night, almost all of them shooting as he overflew. Only later would Leatherman learn that, panicked, they were shooting 'blind' and not at him.

Stealth attack

At exactly 3:00 a.m., H-Hour, the F-117 in front of Leatherman hit the AT & T building with a GBU-27. On Leatherman's scope, the target abruptly glowed, hotter than adjacent office towers and the nearby, tulip-shaped Iraqi Martyrs Monument. Leatherman pickled one minute later, splitting the crosshairs on his display and blowing out the upper four floors of the building. Leatherman peeled away to the west, for the safety of the desert, and turned for home, switching on heavy metal music from Def Leppard on his Walkman. Behind him, Captain Marcel Kerdavid swooped down through a sky alive with fire and pickled a

GBU-27 through the Al Khark communications tower, to blow the 370-ft (112-m) spire in half at its mid-point.

"My biggest fear was that I would survive," said Major Mike Mahar, pilot of an F-117 in the second wave assaulting Baghdad. "'They're all dead,' I told myself. 'All the guys who went in ahead of me have been shot down. If I live through tonight, I'll be the only F-117 pilot who survived. Everybody will ask why.'

"Twenty minutes away from Saddam Hussein's presidential retreat at Abu Ghurayb, I saw what looked like red-orange explosions from bombs filling the landscape ahead. But we didn't have any aircraft up there. I know, now, I was looking at muzzle flashes from anti-aircraft guns."

The sky around Mahar seemed to be full of fire. Flak detonated above and below him, buffeting the F-117. "No one had ever seen such a nocturnal display of pyrotechnics," he remembers. "With no spatial reference, it was impossible to tell how far some of it was from my aeroplane. But it seemed very close."

There are those who believe Major Mike Mahar (today a lieutenant colonel) will be chief of staff of the United States

Perhaps the most memorable images of the 1991 Gulf War were those taken from infrared sensors used to guide laser weapons. This remarkable still comes from an F-117's DLIR turret, with the cross-hairs firmly aligned over an air shaft on the roof of a building in downtown Baghdad. Moments after this, the bomb is seen entering the building, and the ensuing blast is seen erupting out of the side windows.

Above: F-117s make their way to Saudi Arabia during the Desert Shield build-up, supported by KC-10 tankers. In the war which followed, the F-117s usually flew to the Iraqi border with the tankers, which waited at the border until the Nighthawks returned from their secretive forays into hostile airspace.

right way. Today, we know that no Iraqi bullet ever touched it – Mahar and everyone else who took the 'Black Jet' into combat did survive.

Two years earlier in Panama, the F-117 had been introduced to combat the wrong way. It was an uncharacteristic hiccough in a story that has been mostly smooth and seamless. On balance, very little has gone wrong in the design, development, and operational and combat employment of the mystery aircraft from the Lockheed Advanced Development Company's 'Skunk Works', headed by Ben R. Rich.

'Black' project

Rich's motto is "make things black and skunky," meaning secretly and smartly. His patron saint is Clarence L. ('Kelly') Johnson. Johnson, who died in 1990, founded the 'Skunk Works' at Burbank, California, in 1943, and was the moving force behind its products from the XP-80 Shooting Star to the SR-71 Blackbird. The nickname was originally 'Skonk Works' from a foul-smelling whiskey still in Al Capp's 'Li'l Abner' comic strip. Lockheed engineer Irv Culver, who worked with Johnson on the XP-80, thought the place smelled like the moonshine beverage, Kickapoo Joy Juice, created in the cartoon from old shoes, skunks and high-octane rubbing alcohol. Culver thought up the name because of the reek from a plastics factory across the street. The 'Skunk Works' has since relocated to a less odiferous setting and today employs 4,500 people working at Palmdale, 35 miles (56 km) west of Edwards Air Force Base in the California high desert.

The 'Skunk Works' was very much like the 4450th Tactical Group created at Groom Lake, Nevada, on 15 October 1979 under Colonel Robert A. Jackson. The cover story was that the group was formed to test A-7 avionics. In fact, the Vought A-7D, the US Air Force's version of the Navy Corsair II, was leaving the active-duty inventory (although some years of Air National Guard service lay ahead) and represented an available, credible airframe which a test/trials unit might usefully and realistically use. Pilots were told not to give out the cover story, not to say anything. The real purpose of the A-7D at first was simply to keep the men flying while their actual aircraft evolved. Later, the A-7D would be useful for cover purposes, for flying time and as a chase aircraft, known to the 4450th as a 'companion' aircraft to the new flying machine taking shape.

The real purpose of the 4450th TG was to bring into the world a new kind of warplane, so revolutionary that not

Air Force by 2010. He seems easygoing, devoid of fear. "But that first night over Baghdad, the sky itself seemed to be on fire as I turned south-east toward my target, a biological weapons bunker at Salman Pak. Another F-117 banked toward Saddam's retreat.

"I needed to get my mind away from that firestorm outside the aeroplane. I reached for a switch located on a console to my left and electrically lowered the seat of my F-117 as far as it would go. I hunkered down. I peered straight into my instrument panel and my multi-functional display. To distract myself, I muttered a song I'd often enjoyed with my children: 'Heigh-ho, heigh-ho, it's off to work we go...'

"I reached my aiming point, illuminated the target with my laser designator – we don't talk a lot about the details of that – and went down in a dive, looking into the crosshairs of my display. I dropped a laser-guided bomb [GBU-27] and banked to get out of there.

"A quick movement above my F-117 caught my attention. I looked up to see a missile streak past my canopy and explode in a brilliant flash of yellow. My aircraft shook and faltered.

"I thought, 'Maybe I won't have to explain surviving, after all...'"

The F-117 had now been introduced to combat the

The 37th TFW (Provisional) was established at King Khalid Air Base, Khamis Mushait, to control all F-117 operations in Desert Storm. Despite the high-tech nature of their charges, the 37th ground crew kept alive the traditions of wartime humour.

The cockpit of the F-117 is perhaps the most sought-after seat in the Air Force. However, the acceptance process is rigorous, and candidates must show the right mix of attitude, ability and experience.

even its existence was admitted. Both the 'Skunk Works' and the 4450th TG, which owned no aeroplanes for its first years of existence, were small, tightly integrated, relaxed and very secret.

History

Starting with the U-2 in the 1950s and continuing with the SR-71 Blackbird in the 1960s, Lockheed's 'Skunk Works' embarked on a concerted effort to become the industry authority on foiling radar. The company was first to become deeply involved with what is known today as 'stealth' or very low observables (VLO) techniques.

Recognising the company's quiet way of accumulating expertise, the Defense Advanced Research Projects Agency (DARPA) found a place for Lockheed in a generously-funded, scientific review of LO principles. Almost nothing has been disclosed about this study, which was codenamed Harvey after the invisible rabbit of a James Stewart film.

Today's 'Black Jet' owes its origins to a subsequent study, a 1974 DARPA investigation into making fighters less detectable by radar. This time, it was more than just theory. And this time, for reasons unclear, Lockheed was not at first invited to participate. To appeal the snub, 'Skunk Works' boss Ben Rich obtained CIA permission to discuss the SR-71's low-observables characteristics. With its blended wing/fuselage join and small frontal profile, the SR-71 and its Oxcart civilian counterpart properly deserved to be called the world's first stealth aircraft; Rich was promptly invited to join the DARPA study.

Soon afterward, the programme took on a status like no other in history. It became SAR (Special Access Required) and, not merely top secret, it was compartmentalised. People working in some 'compartments' had no idea what others were doing. Only a handful were 'read in' on the whole story. Later, the term 'black programme' came into vogue to describe this kind of undertaking, which was also kept secret from all but a few Congressmen. The US Air Force, which took over from DARPA, would not even acknowledge that the programme existed.

XST programme

In August 1975, Lockheed and Northrop were invited to develop and test an aircraft known as the Experimental Survivable Testbed (XST). Years later, still in the shadows and groping, an inquisitive press picked up the term and reported that it meant Experimental Stealth Testbed. This was the first of many speculations which were to prove wrong.

Both manufacturers designed small, single-seat aircraft. Northrop's XST air vehicle used a combination of rounded and angular surfaces to achieve its lowered radar cross-section. Some have referred to Northrop's design as 'Shamu' because it resembled the famous orca whale at San Diego's Sea World.

Lockheed mathematician Bill Schroeder developed a computer programme called Echo 1 that made it possible to predict the radar signature of an aircraft shaped with flat panels, or facets. This in turn led to design of a pole mode called 'the hopeless diamond', which helped Lockheed win the Have Blue stealth demonstration programme in April 1976.

Have Blue

Schroeder's research led to an aircraft concept in which individual surfaces and edges were orientated to reflect incoming radar energy into narrow beams aimed away from the radar detector. In addition to shaping, the external surface of the aircraft then being designed was to be covered with radar-absorbent material (RAM). In time, the aircraft would have canopy windows with special coatings to make the panels appear as metallic surfaces to radar.

Despite the capabilities of radar-predicting computers, there is no substitute for live testing to find radar 'hot-spots'. Pole-mounted models on outside ranges provide the best means of measuring radar cross-sections, and there have been many tests throughout the Have Blue/Senior Trend programme. Shown here is a quarter-scale model of an F-117, mounted on a pole at Lockheed's own Helendale facility in the Mojave Desert.

Have Blue testing – an early small-scale model is tested for radar cross-section in Lockheed's anechoic chamber (right) at Rye Canyon, while above a full-scale model is tested on the White Sands Ratscat Backscatter Range in New Mexico.

Lockheed built two Have Blue sub-scale proof-of-concept demonstrator aircraft, completed at Burbank within months. Have Blue was a subsonic, single-place aircraft so ugly that it was disturbing to look at, powered by two 2,950-lb (13.12-kN) thrust General Electric J85-GE-4A engines. The engines came from the government after being removed from a North American T-2B Buckeye trainer.

The sharp-nosed, bent-tail Have Blue aircraft was 47 ft 3 in (14.62 m) in length, 7 ft 6.25 in (2.33 m) high, and had a wing span of 22 ft 6 in (56.97 m) and a wing area of 386 sq ft (36 m²). The unorthodox Have Blue configuration was designed to provide a highly manoeuvrable fighter aircraft with, as they were now called, VLO characteristics. The shape of the aircraft evolved from VLO and controllability considerations. This resulted in a relaxed static stability (RSS) aircraft which necessitated a quadruply-redundant, fly-by-wire (FBW) flight control system to provide handling qualities throughout the flight envelope.

The meaning of RSS, and the remarkable instability of this aircraft and of the production warplane which followed, are highlighted in a Lockheed document: "Since this was the first aeroplane designed by electrical engineers, it is not surprising that a number of aerodynamic sins were committed. The unaugmented airframe exhibits just about every mode of unstable behaviour possible for an aircraft: longitudinal and directional instability, pitch up, pitch down, dihedral reversal, and various other cross-axis couplings. The only thing it doesn't do is tip back on its tail when it is parked."

Aerodynamic configuration

As for the aeroplane's flight surface, the wing planform was a modified delta with a dramatic sweep of 72.5°. There were no flaps, speed brakes or high lift devices. The structure was aluminium alloy with steel and titanium utilised in the hot areas. The control surfaces were elevons, located inboard on the wings, and two all-moveable fins at the wingroot that were swept back and canted inboard. A side stick controller (taken from an F-16) and conventional rudder pedals operated the control surfaces through a Lear-Sei-

gler FBW command and stability augmentation system without mechanical backup, also taken from an F-16. Elevon nose-down pitch control was augmented by a large, two-position flap called the 'platypus', which was deflected downward automatically whenever 12° angle of attack was exceeded. The unique aerodynamic configuration and complex flight control system necessitated a sophisticated and highly accurate flight test instrumentation system, and as a result a long boom was added to the nose. This carried pitot static pressure sources, angle of attack and side split vanes, and an accelerometer.

Have Blue was longer than many fighters but otherwise extremely small. Gross weight of this bizarre new aircraft ranged from 9,200 to 12,500 lb (4173 to 5669 kg). Even for an aircraft with no payload, this made it a true bantamweight. Perhaps logically, Have Blue's landing gear came from a Northrop F-5 Freedom Fighter, the only lightweight fighter then in service.

Stealth is everything

Have Blue was like nothing that had ever flown. Restrictions imposed on its designers by VLO requirements – that is, by the goal of attaining stealth – were unprecedented. "Stealth was not just part of this story," said Rich later. "It was everything."

These constraints demanded new approaches to assuring engine performance. Each inlet duct was equipped with a flat, RCS-treated grid whose porosity was sized for the cruise condition. Air flow was augmented at take-off with blow-in doors mounted on the upper fuselage surface. There was concern that the inlet grids would impair operation of the J85 engines (this was similar to a problem that later arose with the production aircraft), but these worries proved unfounded. In fact, the grids had a beneficial side effect: they helped straighten the vortex-disturbed inlet airflow from the highly swept wing leading edges, especially at high angles of attack.

Design of the exhaust system for the J85 engines, like everything else, was driven by VLO requirements. To prevent radar energy from penetrating to the turbine face, the tailpipe was transitioned from a round duct to a 17-to-1 flattened slot convergent nozzle. The trailing edge of each nozzle was terminated on a 54° scarf angle to correspond to the airframe aft closure. Vanes which were interposed and angled in the slot exit helped straighten the exhaust flow back to the longitudinal axis, although some thrust vector 'toe-in' remained. Sufficient bypass air was passed over the tailpipe to cool the aft fuselage structure.

A one-third scale RCS model of the Have Blue aircraft was tested in December 1975 at the Grey Butte Microwave Measurement facility. A smaller model was tried out in the Lockheed anechoic chamber. A second series of one-third scale model tests was conducted at Grey Butte in January 1976, confirming that minor changes in configuration had brought about considerable RCS improvement. Subsequently, a full-scale RCS model was constructed and used at the Ratscat Backscatter Measurement Range at White Sands to further develop Have Blue's VLO characteristics.

Initial engine runs were accomplished on Have Blue on 4 November 1977 at the Lockheed Burbank facility. To maintain security, the aircraft was parked between two semi tractor-trailers over which a camouflage net had been drawn. The runs were performed at night after the airport was closed. A local resident telephoned to complain about the noise, but Have Blue's secret remained intact.

The Have Blue aircraft, known as HB 1001, was taken to remote, concealed Groom Lake on a C-5A Galaxy on 16 November 1977. This was the first time a C-5A had operated from Burbank, and morning traffic was congested as people strained to see the giant transport.

At Groom Lake, engine thrust runs were performed and four low- and high-speed taxi tests conducted. During the third taxi test, a problem developed that would become a

nuisance throughout the programme: overheated brakes caused the wheel fuse plugs to melt. These tests verified the working of the drag chute and, following the fourth taxi test, HB 1001 was cleared to fly.

Lockheed test pilot Bill Park made the first flight not in January or February 1978, as widely reported, but on 1 December 1977, just 20 months from contract award. This first ship was not intended to be flown against radars but

A rare inflight photograph of HB 1002 shows the aircraft's extraordinary shape, highlighting the dramatic sweepback angle of the leading edge. Noteworthy are the facetted elevons, moving platypus tail surface and retractable blade aerial under the starboard leading edge.

The completed HB 1002 awaits a ground test prior to its first flight. This aircraft had the full-up stealth treatment, lacking the nose probe of the first aircraft and being fully covered with radar absorbent material. Construction was largely of aluminium.

Lockheed XST #1 Have Blue HB 1001

Configuration
The XSTs validated the facetting concept, and the basic aircraft shape. Key differences were the inward-canting of the fins, which were mounted on the outside of the main fuselage body and much further forward than on the production aircraft. The all-important leading edge was set at the very sharp angle of 72.5°.

Systems
The XST utilised many off-the-shelf systems from other aircraft, including the fly-by-wire system from the F-16. The aircraft also had the F-16's sidestick controller, while the undercarriage came from the Northrop F-5. The engines were government-furnished equipment – two General Electric J85-GE-4A turbojets each rated at 2,950 lb (13.13 kN) thrust taken from the US Navy's stock for the Rockwell T-2B Buckeye.

Platypus exhaust
The exhaust slot for the XST's engines had a greater extension on the lower lip than for the F-117, and the two slots met at a common point on the centreline. The lower portion of the nozzle, known as the platypus, formed a two-position flap which automatically deflected downwards when angle of attack exceeded 12°.

HB 1002
The second Have Blue aircraft flew on 20 July 1978, some weeks after HB 1001 had crashed. By that time sufficient of the flight envelope had been explored to allow HB 1002 to progress straight to RCS testing. Consequently it lacked the test instrumentation boom from the outset, and did not have an anti-spin parachute. It also featured other differences such as nosewheel steering, which made ground handling easier.

Pole testing
The flying of HB 1002 against real radars in an operational environment was the culmination of a long RCS trials programme, which began with testing of small, third-scale and full-scale models on poles. These tests showed the radar 'flare-spots' – areas of too much reflectivity – which allowed the designers to refine the design to a truly stealthy shape.

Flight control sensors
The Have Blue's flight control system was served by three static pressure sensors on the forward fuselage, and three total pressure probes, one on the nose and two on the cockpit windscreen post. HB 1001 also had the instrumentation boom which correlated data from the primary system. The correct alignment of the flight control system proved to be one of the greatest challenges to the design team.

This three-view depicts the first of the two Have Blue experimental test-ships, which paved the way for the design of a full-scale tactical stealth fighter. The aircraft was first flown by Lockheed test pilot Bill Park on 1 December 1977, and was intended purely as an aerodynamic test vehicle. It wore this strange scheme to hide its unique facetted surface, although the second Have Blue was finished in an all-over grey. HB 1001 also differed by having a decidedly non-stealthy nose instrumentation boom, whereas HB 1002 had a more refined nose sensor group for feeding the flight control system. HB 1002 was the aircraft involved in all the low-observables tests. Both aircraft crashed during the flight test programme, HB 1001 being lost on 4 May 1978 after 36 flights when a high sink rate and low landing speed resulted in damage to the undercarriage while landing at Groom Lake. Park took the aircraft to altitude and ejected, but was badly injured in the process. HB 1002 was lost in early 1980 when an engine fire forced Ken Dyson to eject.

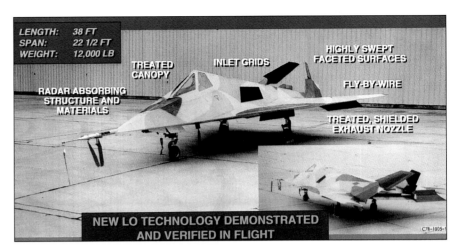

LENGTH: 38 FT
SPAN: 22 1/2 FT
WEIGHT: 12,000 LB

TREATED CANOPY
INLET GRIDS
HIGHLY SWEPT FACETED SURFACES
FLY-BY-WIRE
RADAR ABSORBING STRUCTURE AND MATERIALS
TREATED, SHIELDED EXHAUST NOZZLE

NEW LO TECHNOLOGY DEMONSTRATED AND VERIFIED IN FLIGHT

This is how Lockheed revealed the Have Blue design to the world, two photographs showing the aerodynamic test vehicle HB 1001 outside the Groom Lake test facility. HB 1001 arrived at the remote Nevada site inside the hold of a C-5 Galaxy on 16 November 1977, was reassembled, ground-tested and then flown on 1 December. Funding for the entire XST programme, one of the most important in military aviation history, totalled just $43 million, of which $10.4 million was put up by Lockheed with the remainder coming from DARPA and the US Air Force.

Handling idiosyncracies

The XST's handling was largely as predicted, but there were some notable discrepancies. The aircraft was found to be directionally unstable above Mach 0.65, but an increase in the yaw gain in the FCS software solved the problem. Heating in the platypus area caused an asymmetry of the airframe which induced a side-force. The FCS would correct this with ruddervator inputs, resulting in the aircraft crabbing. This was solved by the substitution of a side-slip angle detector in place of a lateral accelerometer for feeding the directional stability augmentation system. Finally, an asymmetric thrust situation caused roll and yaw towards the good engine rather than away from it, and the roll moment was surprisingly greater than the yaw.

In 1979, before Senior Trend production could begin, a full-scale wooden mock-up was constructed so that the assembly line could be planned. This provides an excellent illustration of the internal structure of the real aircraft.

Aircraft 780 in its original guise seen either on, or shortly after, its June 1981 first flight. At the time the aircraft still had the three-tone camouflage, and the small vertical fins which were found to be inadequate.

was to demonstrate loads/flutter, performance, handling qualities, and stability and control.

HB 1001 accomplished 36 flights over the next five months, and expanded the flight envelope to pave the way for RCS testing to be carried out by the second aircraft, HB 1002. The concept of a warplane capable of defeating an enemy's air defence radar was now alive and flying, but HB 1001 never saw it.

Loss of XST-1

On 4 May 1978 during HB 1001's 36th test flight, Bill Park attempted to make a landing at just a few miles per hour less than optimum setdown speed, a grim reminder of the XST's difficult handling qualities and general instability. One of the Have Blue's main landing gears hit the runway too hard, and the impact caused it to move into a half-extended, half-retracted configuration. Park made several attempts to free the jammed gear by pounding the other main wheel on the runway. As his fuel supply waned, he was ordered to make a climb to 10,000 ft (3048 m) and bail out, leaving the aircraft to its fate.

In the process of blowing the canopy and ejecting, Park hit his head and was knocked unconscious. He was still unconscious when his chute lowered him to the ground, and sustained back injuries severe enough to dictate an early retirement from flying. Park stayed on at Lockheed as director of flight operations.

HB 1002 flew on 20 July 1978, not in March or April as widely reported, apparently piloted by Lieutenant Colonel Norman 'Ken' Dyson. Like its predecessor, the No. 2 Have Blue resembled the operational warplane which was to follow. It differed from the first ship in having a 'real' air speed system fed by flush pitot static ports on the upper and lower surfaces of the nose and by three total pressure probes (thus, it required no nose boom), and did not have an anti-spin chute installed. It also incorporated nosewheel steering and was adorned with the coatings and materials needed for VLO work. Following early airspeed-calibration flights, HB 1002 made 52 flights in the next 12 months and completed the low observables testing. Final testing against mock air defence radars was in progress in July 1979 when the second XST ship was lost in a mishap.

The demise of HB 1002

One of HB 1002's hydraulic fluid line welds cracked, spraying fluid on the hot section of an engine. The fluid caught fire and flames became intense. With a fire on board that could not be extinguished and with no hydraulic power, Lieutenant Colonel Dyson was told to abandon the aircraft. He ejected safely (and later, as a civilian, became Rockwell's test pilot on the X–31A project) but the second Have Blue ship was a total loss. As they had done with the first ship, workers hauled the wreckage to a remote spot in the desert and buried it deep beneath Nevada's sagebrush and mesquite.

Even though both aircraft were lost, the Have Blue flying effort was deemed a success. The US Air Force moved quickly to the next step, a stealth fighter engineering full-scale development (FSD) contract on 16 November 1978. The original order was for 20 (five FSD and 15 production) aircraft. The effort to produce an operational fighter was codenamed Senior Trend. The aircraft had no other name.

This programme remained hidden beneath a blanket of

security rivalling the Manhattan Project, the top-secret programme during World War II under which Brigadier General Leslie Groves (architect of the Pentagon building) sequestered a small army of scientists in the remote New Mexico village of Los Alamos to design and build the first atomic bomb. Like that programme, this one moved quickly. Lockheed met wind-tunnel, pole model, and wooden mock-up milestones in record time.

Playing politics

In 1980, Presidential candidates Jimmy Carter and Ronald Reagan accused each other of risking national security by talking too much about a mysterious thing called stealth. Both talked too much about both talking too much. In fact, press leaks about a future stealth bomber forced incumbent Carter and Defense Secretary Harold Brown to acknowledge that an unnamed secret aircraft (Have Blue) had been tested. Nothing was disclosed about Senior Trend or the future bomber project. A promise to rearm America (using unprecedented public debt to pay for it) planted Reagan in the White House the following year. The new chief executive's emphasis on a military build-up went hand-in-hand with a love of secrecy which fit well with the stealth effort. Once Reagan was sworn in, no one was in any mood to disclose anything further about phantom warplanes flying in Nevada.

The separate effort aimed at developing a stealth bomber took on its own momentum and (as we know today) led to Northrop reviving its flying wing designs of the late 1940s. Early in the Reagan years, a budget item associated with this project was listed in Congressional documents under the word Aurora. The word was never intended to disguise anything: it was merely inter-office shorthand never meant to appear on a budgeting document. It referred to a component of what, in later years, became the Northrop B-2 Spirit stealth bomber. The word Aurora never did, then or later, refer to any other aircraft or 'black' programmes and, contrary to widespread rumour, no aircraft named Aurora has ever been conceived, designed, built or flown.

To set the record straight, there was one other air-breathing stealth vehicle developed during the Reagan years. It was not named Aurora, and it was unmanned. A prototype made a few test flights, crashed, and was broken up, carried to a remote stretch of desert, and buried in a deep hole. Contrary to the legend created by a misguided model-maker and others, there was never a 'black' programme for an aircraft named Aurora and there was never a 'black' reconnaissance aircraft known as the Northrop TR-3 Manta. The only manned warplanes developed in these secret programmes were the Lockheed stealth fighter and the Northrop flying-wing bomber, the future B-2 which during this era was designated Senior C. J.

Flight testing of the Lockheed's Senior Trend aircraft was preceded by a series of flights in the Calspan (Cornell Aero Labs) Lockheed NT-33 aircraft where suitability of PA (power approach) flight control laws was checked. The variable-stability NT-33 – which even then, a decade before its retirement, was the oldest aircraft in Air Force inventory – was employed primarily to simulate aircraft response to a pilot control input; with minor exceptions, it had no capability to simulate the actual performance of the subject aircraft.

First flight

Lockheed test pilot Hal Farley made the first flight of the Senior Trend aircraft on 18 June 1981, less than 31 months after go-ahead for the project. The first aircraft was serial number 79-10780, usually referred to as ship 780; it was painted light grey initially, and subsequently in disruptive camouflage (like the Have Blue) to conceal its contours and facets, and blur its general configuration, from the eyes of prying Soviet satellites. This apparently proved ineffective and the aircraft was again painted light grey, which had been the intended production colour.

Ship 780 had its V-shaped vertical fins canted exactly opposite from the inverted V-shape of the Have Blue ships, but of smaller size than later appeared on the second and subsequent aircraft. Contrary to reports, flight testing was done not at night but during daylight at Groom Lake.

It appears that the first aircraft to contain a full avionics

F-117 Weapons

Above: 'Bombs R Us' – despite many reports of missile armament, the laser-guided bomb is the only weapon so far confirmed for the F-117.

Left: A 57th Fighter Wing F-117 at Holloman carries an SUU-20 practice bomb and rocket dispenser. The rocket option is not used, but the underside of the pod carries six BDU-33 practice bombs which simulate the ballistics of full-size weapons. Just forward of the bomb bay are the four retractable perforated baffles which improve airflow for bomb release.

Above: The standard weapon of the F-117 is the GBU-27, seen here in its penetration version with a straight-sided, thick-cased BLU-109 warhead. The bomb combines the guidance section of the Paveway III with the smaller fins of the Paveway II.

Above: An inert GBU-10 LGB carried by a 410th TS aircraft displays the rounded Mk 84 warhead profile. A good comparison is provided between the gimballed Paveway II seeker head and the fixed head of the GBU-27 Paveway III in the other bomb bay.

Below: For deployments away from home the F-117 can carry the ubiquitous MXU-648 baggage pod, an empty case of a BLU-1/27 fire-bomb provided with a door. All weapons are carried on the retractable trapeze with 30-in lug spacing.

Right: Colonel Al Whitley inspects a GBU-27A prior to a Desert Storm mission. The Paveway III uses proportional guidance rather than the 'bang-bang' guidance of earlier Paveway II bombs, conferring greater range and accuracy.

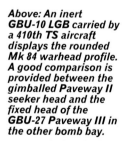

Powerplant and fuel

Buried deep within the F-117's fuselage are two General Electric F404-GE-F1D2 engines, each rated at approximately 10,800 lb (48 kN) thrust. Developed especially for the F-117, this engine is derived from the standard F404-GE-400 used by the F/A-18 Hornet, itself a derivative of the YJ101 employed by the Northrop YF-17. The engine is a compact low bypass ratio turbofan, with a diameter of approximately 35 in (890 mm). In the standard Hornet version, the front fan is a three-stage unit, with the outer flow diverted to the bypass duct at a ratio of 0.34. Downstream from the fan is a seven-stage high-pressure compressor with a compression ratio in the region of 25:1. Aft of the single-piece annular combustion chamber are the high-pressure and low-pressure turbines, each consisting of a single stage of blades. The engine is aspirated through the four-sided intakes which are covered with a fine mesh. At low speeds these are augmented by large suck-in doors of six-sided shape situated in the top of the intake trunk. In order to vastly reduce the infra-red signature, the F-117 has a novel slot exhaust. Jet efflux from the circular-section jetpipe is mixed with the cold bypass air to cool it, and then widened and flattened to exit the slot exhaust in a plume some 4 in (100 mm) deep and 5 ft (1.5 m) wide. The exhausts, designed by Astech/MCI, incorporate an extended lower lip to shield the main heat source from sensors below, a series of guide vanes along the slot to maintain thrust direction, and ceramic heat tiles similar to the re-entry heat shields fitted to the Space Shuttle. Large access doors between the undercarriage and weapons bay allow the engines to be easily dropped out for maintenance.

Fuel is held in large tanks situated in the main fuselage body, filling the vacant upper areas fore and aft of the weapons bay. This can be augmented by fuel tanks in the weapons bay for ferry flights. Inflight refuelling is accomplished via a receptacle aft of the fuselage apex, normally covered by a six-sided door. The receptacle and toughened slipway rotates to stand proud from the fuselage, so aiding the boom operator. At the apex of the fuselage above the cockpit is a small 'pimple' which houses a floodlight for illuminating the receptacle area.

Laser-guided bombs

Although the USAF claims that a "full range of USAF tactical fighter ordnance" can be carried, and reports abound as to the use of AGM-65 Maverick, AGM-88 HARM and AIM-9 Sidewinders, the 2,000-lb class laser-guided bomb remains the F-117's main weapon. There are four main versions, consisting of combinations of two warhead types and two seeker heads. Warhead options are the standard Mk 84 high-explosive (GBU-10C/D/E/F and GBU-27) and the BLU-109 penetration warhead (GBU-10G/H/J and GBU-27A), which has a thick 4340 steel alloy case, low explosive/weight ratio (30 per cent) and tail-mounted FMU-143 fuse to ensure that it explodes after having punched through a hardened structure, thereby destroying the contents. A penetration of up to 6 ft (1.83 m) of reinforced concrete has been demonstrated. The seeker heads, or CCG (computer control and guidance) units, are either Paveway II (GBU-10) or Paveway III (GBU-27) units. The Paveway II CCG has a gimballed seeker whereas the Paveway III has an enclosed head. The Paveway II CCG uses full-deflection guidance, moving the front fins fully to alter the bomb's path. This 'bang-bang' guidance causes the bomb to lose a great deal of energy and some accuracy as it 'bounces' from one edge of the laser 'basket' to the other. When using Paveway IIs, crews tend to leave the laser 'sparkle' to the last possible moment so that the bomb does not lose too much energy under guidance. This requires a good level of normal ballistic bombing accuracy. On the other hand, the Paveway III uses proportional guidance, with only small deflections of the fins to control the bomb. This allows the bomb to retain most of its kinetic energy, and flies it in a much straighter attitude, vastly increasing penetrative power. Another advantage is a much greater range and improved accuracy as the bomb does not 'flap' during the final phase of its trajectory. Paveway III CCGs can also be programmed to give an optimum strike angle against differing targets. However, the Paveway III seeker does come at a much greater price, and so its use is restricted to high-value targets. The standard Paveway III bomb is the GBU-24, as used to devastating effect by the F-111 during Desert Storm. This has the full-spec features, with much larger control fins and pop-out wings for vastly increased range. However, these fins are too big to fit the confines of the F-117's bomb bay, so the short-range Paveway II wings are fitted and the front fins cropped accordingly.

Weapons are held on a retractable trapeze, which swings down and forward from the bomb bay. This is of inestimable value for ground crew loading the weapons, allowing easy all-round access to the bomb carriage mechanisms. With laser-guided weapons, the warhead and fin assembly is loaded using a standard trolley, which can get under the aircraft and then offer the bomb up to the shackles. The delicate CCG section is fixed with the bomb *in situ*, followed by the forward control fins. The trapeze, with bomb, is then slung back up into the bay for flight. Whether the trapeze is deployed for bomb release has, at the time of writing, not been ascertained, but the provision of two small perforated baffles which deploy from the front of the bay to disrupt airflow either side of the trapeze may suggest this is the case. If missiles are employed, the trapeze would certainly be lowered to put the weapons into clear air for launch. However, the opening of the bay doors and the extension of the trapeze would seriously harm the low-observable properties of the aircraft while the weapon is being released. It is likely that a timed mechanism opens the door, releases the bomb and then snaps the door shut in as short a time as possible.

Inside the F-117

Left and right: Two shots of the standard F-117 cockpit prior to the final OCIP improvements which add a moving map display and replace the Texas Instruments displays with Honeywell colour units. Underneath the HUD is a large screen for displaying infra-red imagery, beneath which is the main comms panel. Either side of the IR screen is an MFD for aircraft systems. Beneath the right MFD is a radar altimeter and attitude instruments, and to the right of this are the engine instruments. Below the left MFD is the weapons control panel, with standard flight instruments to the left. The left-side console has aircraft system controls, while the right-side console has the nav/comms control panel. The two side handles on the seat initiate the ejection sequence.

Lockheed F-117

1 Air data sensors
2 Nose avionics equipment compartment
3 Air data computer
4 Starboard side downward-looking infra-red (DLIR)
5 Screened sensor aperture
6 Forward-looking infra-red (FLIR), to be replaced by Texas Instruments IRADS sensors in third phase update
7 Cockpit front pressure bulkhead
8 Nosewheel bay
9 Forward-retracting nosewheel
10 Canopy emergency release
11 Position light
12 Cockpit pressure enclosure
13 McDonnell-Douglas ACES II 'zero-zero' ejection seat
14 Instrument panel shroud, central infra-red video monitor and dual head-down multi-function CRT displays
15 Head-up display
16 Windscreen panels, gold film coated
17 Upward-hinging one-piece cockpit canopy

18 Apex-mounted refuelling floodlight
19 Starboard air intake
20 Flush HF aerials
21 Rotating flight-refuelling receptacle
22 Avionics equipment bay
23 Retractable ILS antenna
24 Retractable VHF COMM antenna
25 Port engine air intake
26 Intake screening
27 Intake lip spring-loaded secondary (cooling) air intake
28 Weapons bay doors, open
29 Retractable spoilers

30 Port weapons bay
31 Intake suction relief door aperture
32 Airframe-mounted accessory equipment gearbox
33 Engine bay bulkhead
34 Compressor intake
35 Engine fuel system equipment

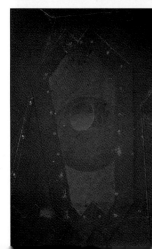

Details of the FLIR (above) and DLIR (left) turrets show the infra-red sensors and boresighted lasers. The turrets are often swivelled round when not in use so that the sensor windows are protected. The fine mesh acts like a flat surface when illuminated by radar.

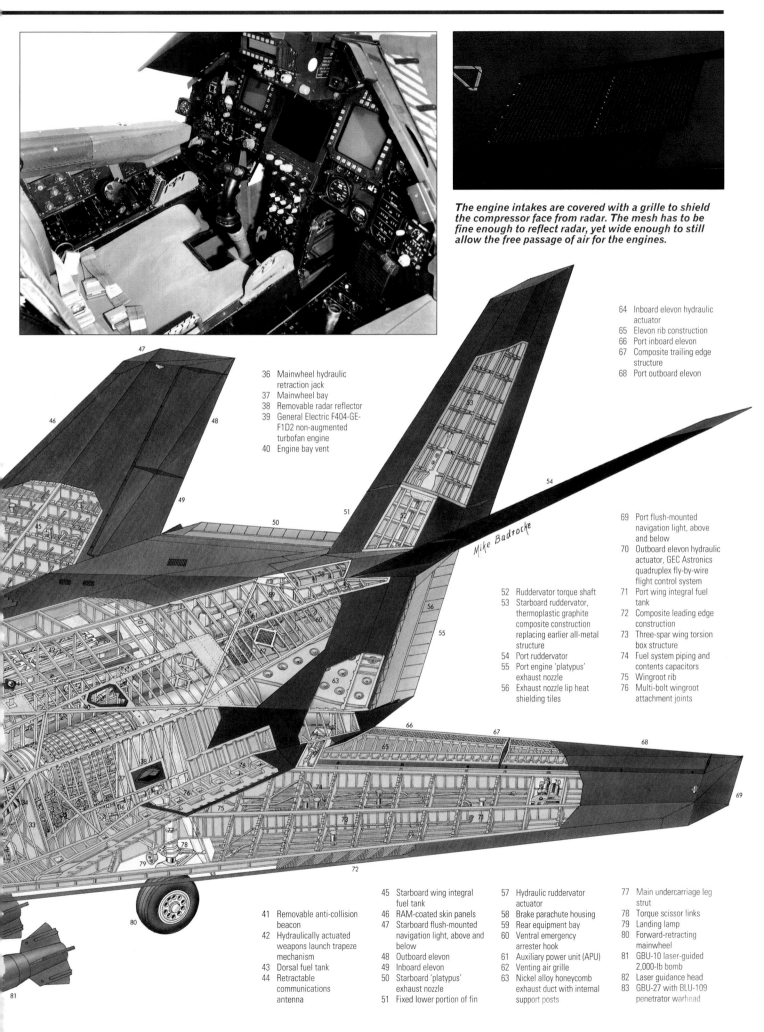

The engine intakes are covered with a grille to shield the compressor face from radar. The mesh has to be fine enough to reflect radar, yet wide enough to still allow the free passage of air for the engines.

Mike Badrocke

36 Mainwheel hydraulic retraction jack
37 Mainwheel bay
38 Removable radar reflector
39 General Electric F404-GE-F1D2 non-augmented turbofan engine
40 Engine bay vent

64 Inboard elevon hydraulic actuator
65 Elevon rib construction
66 Port inboard elevon
67 Composite trailing edge structure
68 Port outboard elevon

52 Ruddervator torque shaft
53 Starboard ruddervator, thermoplastic graphite composite construction replacing earlier all-metal structure
54 Port ruddervator
55 Port engine 'platypus' exhaust nozzle
56 Exhaust nozzle lip heat shielding tiles

69 Port flush-mounted navigation light, above and below
70 Outboard elevon hydraulic actuator, GEC Astronics quadruplex fly-by-wire flight control system
71 Port wing integral fuel tank
72 Composite leading edge construction
73 Three-spar wing torsion box structure
74 Fuel system piping and contents capacitors
75 Wingroot rib
76 Multi-bolt wingroot attachment joints

41 Removable anti-collision beacon
42 Hydraulically actuated weapons launch trapeze mechanism
43 Dorsal fuel tank
44 Retractable communications antenna
45 Starboard wing integral fuel tank
46 RAM-coated skin panels
47 Starboard flush-mounted navigation light, above and below
48 Outboard elevon
49 Inboard elevon
50 Starboard 'platypus' exhaust nozzle
51 Fixed lower portion of fin

57 Hydraulic ruddervator actuator
58 Brake parachute housing
59 Rear equipment bay
60 Ventral emergency arrester hook
61 Auxiliary power unit (APU)
62 Venting air grille
63 Nickel alloy honeycomb exhaust duct with internal support posts

77 Main undercarriage leg strut
78 Torque scissor links
79 Landing lamp
80 Forward-retracting mainwheel
81 GBU-10 laser-guided 2,000-lb bomb
82 Laser guidance head
83 GBU-27 with BLU-109 penetrator warhead

Markings

In keeping with the covert nature of its operations, the F-117 is painted the same all-over matt black as worn by the SR-71 and U-2R, rendering the type virtually invisible at night. Tanker boom operators report that the aircraft simply appears under the boom during night refuellings, despite the use of floodlighting. Apart from the emergency canopy release triangle below the cockpit, all markings are in low-visibility grey, consisting of national insignia on wings and fuselage, tail markings representing the last three digits of the aircraft serial, Air Combat Command badge and 'HO' tailcode for Holloman AFB. The 49th Fighter Wing badge is worn on the intake sides, this comprising a winged helmet and a covered wagon separated by a lightning bolt, and the motto 'Tutor et Ultor' ('I protect and avenge') beneath.

Lockheed F-117A Nighthawk
49th Fighter Wing
Holloman AFB, New Mexico

Along with the B-2 bomber now entering service, the Nighthawk is the USAF's prime attack weapon, the F-117 force being able to exert an influence on an air campaign that far outweighs its meagre size. As was seen during Desert Storm, the F-117's primary role is to attack high-value command, control and communication targets to, in effect, 'decapitate' the enemy's ability to control its forces. Such targets include leadership bunkers, command posts and air defence and communications centres. Most of these types of targets are well-defended, usually hardened against normal attacks and often in down-town areas. Many may have only one or two small weak spots, such as air shafts, where a bomb will do any damage at all. The need to deliver a high-energy penetration weapon with the least-possible collateral damage requires the utmost accuracy and high survivability. By using stealth, the F-117 can cruise into the target area unmolested, relying on its extensive low-observables properties for protection and putting the aircraft into the optimum position for an accurate attack. Whereas the crew of a conventional aircraft has to fly low and fast while dodging defences to penetrate the target area, leaving them little time to concentrate on accuracy, the F-117 pilot can take his time to use the sophisticated weapons system to ensure a pinpoint strike. If the strategic targets run out, the F-117 is a valuable weapon in a standard interdiction role, being able to hit bridges, railroad depots, airfields and industrial complexes with ease.

Having started life in a 'black' world of nocturnal flying and a secret base, the Nighthawk force has now virtually completed its move into the public glare, although many key technological areas remain under wraps. Following the public unveiling at Nellis AFB, NV, in April 1990, the F-117 began a round of air show appearances throughout the United States, and occasional appearances in Europe, including the 1991 Paris air show. The move from Tonopah Test Range to Holloman AFB was accomplished from May 1992 with a change in wing designation from 37th TFW to 49th FW. The three old squadrons of the 37th TFW renumbered in mid-1993 as the 7th, 8th and 9th Fighter Squadrons. Of these, the 8th and 9th are the operational units with an authorised strength of 18 aircraft each, the 7th being the training squadron (ex-417th FS) operating about 16 F-117As and a handful of T-38s. Since the end of the Gulf War, a detachment of F-117s has been maintained in Saudi Arabia as a deterrent to further Iraqi aggression. The test and trials fleet consists of one F-117A alongside three FSD YF-117As with the 410th Test Squadron, 412th Test Wing. Although wearing 'ED' codes, the 410th TS actually operates from the Lockheed/AF plant at Palmdale. At least one F-117 is at Holloman for operational test and evaluation purposes with a detachment from the Nellis-based 57th Fighter Wing.

Weapons system

The F-117's weapon/nav system is designed to allow the pilot to concentrate on scoring a precise hit with the weapons. The system virtually flies the aircraft to the target area without any input from the pilot, while taking the optimum route to avoid any threat areas. A moving-map display allows the pilot to monitor precisely the aircraft's path. Prior to any F-117 operational mission, the aircraft's central computer is programmed with the mission profile. Ground-based mission planning computers are used to plan the precise parameters of the mission, which are then downloaded on to the EDTM (electronic data transfer module). This cartridge is then plugged into the aircraft's IBM AP-102 computer. Once loaded, the computer uses the EDTM data to integrate the navigation and flight management system to allow a hands-off approach to the target area through a complicated set of turnpoints, altitude changes and airspeed adjustments. The principal en route aid is the Honeywell SPN-GEANS INS, which allows the aircraft to be positioned accurately in the target area.

Once within sensor range, the pilot resumes control of the system, using the infra-red acquisition and designation system (IRADS). This is integrated with the weapon release system and consists of the FLIR and DLIR. These two sensors are boresighted on the ground by raising the nose of the aircraft and then using each in turn to sight on the same object. Due to its look angle, the FLIR is the principal search sensor, a zoom function allowing early identification and lock-on. The target and lock-on is handed off electronically to the DLIR as the downward look angle increases. The pilot uses the image, presented on a large central cockpit TV display, to fine-tune the lock-on before initiating weapon release. The DLIR turret also contains a boresighted laser designator, which fires a coded burst of laser energy at the locked-in aim point at some point during the bomb's trajectory. The bomb then follows the 'sparkle' to a direct hit. Flying at medium altitude, the F-117's stealth properties allow the pilot to make slow and deliberate approach runs, giving him greater time for accurate attacks. However, the current FLIR/DLIR system is often hampered by cloud and smoke. The third phase of the current OCIP programme aims to improve the performance of the F-117's IRADS with a new Texas Instruments sensor.

Stealth origins

Remarkably, the history of the F-117 and its revolutionary 'stealth' technology began in 19th century Britain, where Scottish physicist James Clerk Maxwell derived a set of mathematical formulae to predict the manner in which electromagnetic radiation would scatter when reflected from a given geometric shape. The equations were further refined by famed German electromagnetic scientist Arnold Johannes Sommerfeld. In the 1960s the chief scientist at the Moscow Institute of Radio Engineering, Dr Pyotr Ufimtsev, revisited the Maxwell-Sommerfeld work and simplified it to concentrate on the electromagnetic currents at the edge of geometric shapes. In Moscow Ufimtsev published a paper in 1966 titled 'Method of Edge Waves in the Physical Theory of Diffraction', but at the time this was thought to only have applications to very simple two-dimensional shapes. Nevertheless, the work was there, and along with the earlier Maxwell-Sommerfeld work, could provide the basis for a mathematical model of a stealthy aircraft. The USAF's Foreign Technology Division regularly gathered and translated foreign scientific documents, so they were available to Lockheed engineers.

In 1974 DARPA invited five aircraft companies (not including Lockheed) to study the potential for a stealthy aircraft. In early 1975 Lockheed's 'Skunk Works' heard of the studies, and sought permission to use data from the SR-71 programme to submit their own study. The Advanced Development Projects organisation had been concerned with low radar cross-section for some time, with work on shaping and radar-absorbent material. However, to produce an aircraft with a very low radar cross-section would need a quantum leap in technology. Enter Bill Schroeder, a retired Lockheed mathematician. Using Ufimtsev's simple formulae for two-dimensional shapes, Schroeder proposed that by reducing a three-dimensional body to a finite number of two-dimensional surfaces, the overall radar dissipation patterns could be forecast, and kept to a mangeable number. Armed with this information, the individual surfaces could then be angled in such a way that radar energy could be reflected away from its source (and hence the receiver) from virtually any aspect. If such a shape could then be fashioned to create lift, then a stealthy aircraft could be possible, especially since the need for natural stability in an aircraft shape had been removed by computer-controlled fly-by-wire control systems. The concept of facetting was born.

With other companies also examining stealth, Lockheed could waste no time in attempting to turn Schroeder's idea into workable technology. Led by Denys Overholser, a Lockheed ADP software team worked closely with Schroeder to produce a computer programme that would accurately predict the radar scatter patterns of a facetted shape. In just five weeks the programme Echo I was produced, a remarkable achievement by Overholser and Schroeder. To validate the software a simple, idealised aircraft model was produced, nicknamed the 'Hopeless Diamond'. This was tested in an electromagnetic facility, and was found to have a much lower radar cross-section than any previous shape tested by the company. Now known as 'Have Blue', the programme moved to larger-scale tests with pole-mounted shapes, all of which exhibited extremely low cross-sections. In April 1976 DARPA declared Lockheed the winner of the competition, the Echo I programme having proven to be the key breakthrough in achieving a practical aircraft with true low-observable properties. Lockheed's technology was such an advance that the originally-unclassified DARPA project was rapidly submerged into a deep 'black' status, with very limited access. Work then began on the two XST technology demonstrators, the first of which flew in December 1977.

With the F-117 in service, Dr Ufimtsev later said that he had devised a method of detecting stealth aircraft. Basing his thoughts on the fact that "all this dissipated radar energy has to go somewere", he proposed the use of bistatic radars, with receivers in different locations to the transmitter. These would detect the radar refelctions which were angled away by the F-117's shape. However, the time and processing power needed to accurately compute the position of the aircraft from these deflected returns is potentially so enormous as to render the scheme unfeasible. Certainly with current technology the F-117 would have long vacated the area by the time its previous position had been fixed.

Lockheed F-117A

This five-view illustration depicts an aircraft marked for the commander of the 49th Fighter Wing, complete with non-standard fin legend and coloured wing badge on the intakes. It is shown carrying a standard GBU-10 bomb in the port weapons bay and a GBU-24A in the starboard.

Fin alignment
The fins were carefully positioned to keep radar reflections to a minimum, and also to help shield the engine exhausts from infra-red sensors, especially those carried by a chasing fighter.

Cockpit
The original cockpit features Texas Instruments monochrome displays surrounded by standard off-the-shelf flight instruments from other aircraft, notably the F/A-18. In the centre of the dashboard is a large TV screen which displays imagery from the IRADS, with two smaller multi-function displays on either side for aircraft information. Above the dashboard is a Kaiser head-up display based on the AVQ-18. The new OCIP cockpit replaces the TI displays with Honeywell full-colour screens, and adds a large colour moving map for improving situational awareness. The pilot sits on a McDonnell Douglas ACES II ejection seat under a heavy-framed canopy with five flat glazed panes made by Sierracin/Sylmar Corporation.

RAM
Radar-absorbent material was originally applied to the aircraft surface in sheets, but is now available as a spray. Operational alert aircraft are regularly kept in full stealth status with regular visits to the RAM spray facility to maitnain the coating in top condition.

OCIP I and II
Since 1984 the F-117 has been the subject of an Offensive Capability Improvement Program (OCIP) which further eases the pilot's workload while improving the aircraft's ability to undertake pinpoint strikes. The first phase of the OCIP involved the replacement of the original three Delco M362F mission computers with the IBM/Loral AP-102, a repackaged version of the Shuttle computer offering 1 million instruction per second capability. The second phase, also known as Offensive Combat Improvement Program, completely revises the cockpit layout, adding Honeywell multi-function displays and a large Harris Corporation moving-map display. A 'four-dimensional' flight management system controls an autothrottle in addition to autopilot and is designed to put the F-117 at a desired location with +/- 1 second time tolerance. Another feature of the second phase is the Pilot-Activated Automatic Recovery System (PAARS), which rights the aircraft to straight and level flight from any attitude with a flick of a switch, a useful aid for an aircraft which flies its operational missions mostly in darkness. The first OCIP aircraft flew on 1 December 1988, with service redeliveries commencing in November 1990. All F-117s have the first phase, and Lockheed is redelivering the second phase at the rate of about one a month. By mid-1994 about 40 had gone through second phase modifications.

OCIP III
Portions of the third phase of the Offensive Combat Improvement Program are currently under flight test with the 410th Test Squadron at Palmdale. The key components of this are a new Honeywell ring-laser gyro inertial navigation system in place of the same company's SPN-GEANS unit, originally produced for the B-52 and which is now out of production and expensive to maintain. The INS receives updates from a new Rockwell Collins global positioning system for highly accurate navigation. The GPS requires a stealthy satellite-receiving antenna. The INS/GPS system is due for flight test in late 1994. The main IR sensors are replaced with new thermal imagers, still made by Texas Instruments, doubling the effective acquisition range of the FLIR and prolonging laser life.

Visibility
The pilot sits high in the cockpit, and has a good view forwards, sideways and downwards across the sharply sloping nose. However, the view to the rear is virtually non-existent due to the broad fuselage and engine trunks.

Lockheed F-117

Stealth features
Apart from the flat facets making up its exterior, the F-117 exhibits many other features for a low radar cross-section, notably in the front hemisphere. The straight line running from nose to wingtip (swept at 67.5°) and similar sharp sweep-back on the fins is a major dissipator of radar energy away from its source. Every door or surface excrescence has diagonal patterns on the fore and aft edges, while the whole surface is sprayed with radar-absorbent material. The glazed panels are coated with gold to conduct radar energy into the airframe. Necessary holes in the overall shape for the engine intakes and two IRADS sensors are covered with a grille. This has a fine mesh much smaller than the wavelengths of detection radars, and consequently would appear as another facetted surface.

Weapons bay
The bomb bays are located side-by-side, with one-piece doors opening inwards from a hinge on the centreline. Each bay is 15 ft 5in (4.7 m) long and contains a trapeze for stores carriage. Bay doors and weapon arming is accomplished on a control panel immediately below the left-hand multi-function display.

IRADS
The infra-red acquisition and designation system consists of the forward-looking infra-red (FLIR) in front of the cockpit, and the downward-looking infra-red (DLIR) mounted to the starboard side of the nosewheel bay. Both are mounted in swivelling turrets, which can rotate to the rear when not in use to protect the delicate optics. The IR sensors employ a wide-angle function for initial search and target acquisition, followed by closer target designation using a zoom function. Both turrets also incorporate a laser designator.

Specification
Lockheed F-117A
Powerplant: two General Electric F404-GE-F1D2 non-afterburning turbofans, each rated in the class of 10,800 lb (48 kN) thrust

Wing span: 43 ft 4 in (13.20 m)
Length: 65 ft 11 in (20.08 m)
Height: 12 ft 5 in (3.78 m)
Wing area: 1,140 sq ft (105.9 m²)

Empty weight: approx 30,000 lb (13608 kg)
Maximum take-off weight: 52,500 lb (23814 kg)
Internal weapon load: 5,000 lb (2268 kg)

Maximum speed: 561 kt (646 mph; 1040 km/h)
Normal operating Mach number: 0.9
Take-off speed at normal combat weight: 165 kt (190 mph; 306 km/h)
Landing speed: 150 kt (172 mph; 227 km/h)
Unrefuelled combat radius with 5,000-lb (2268-kg) load: 600 nm (690 miles; 1112 km)
g limits: +6

Undercarriage
The F-117 has a Menasco tricycle undercarriage, all units retracting forward into bays covered with sawtooth doors. Loral steel brakes were originally fitted but are being replaced by carbon-carbon brakes, which improve cross-wind capability and may allow the deletion of the Pioneer Aerospace brake chute which deploys from between the fins. An emergency airfield arrestor hook is located under the rear fuselage, covered by an explosively-jettisoned cover.

Structure

Due to its unorthodox shape, the F-117's internal structure is considerably different to standard construction techniques. The central carapace, including the engine trunks but minus the nose section, is constructed as a skeleton of ribs and stringers with larger members running through the key load routes. To this skeleton is attached the facetted panels, separate nose section and fins. The wings are constructed separately around a two-spar box. The rear spar forms the trailing edge of the fixed wing, and therefore the attachment point for the elevons. A leading-edge member runs the full span of the wing, curving round to form the main wingtip attachment. The wing is mated to the central structure just outboard oif the engine trunks, using five main bolts along the inter-spar interface, three bolts forward of the front spar and an angled attachment strut attaching the rear spar just forward of the exhaust slot. The majority of the structure is of aluminium, although nickel alloy is used in the jetpipes, and the original metal ruddervators have recently been replaced by thermoplastic graphite composite structures.

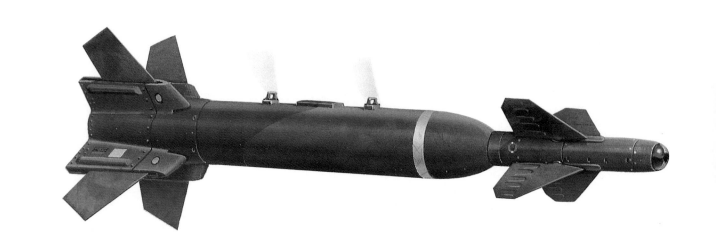

Flight control system

Designing an aircraft with true stealth properties and relaxed stability was deemed virtually impossible, so the F-117 uses a fly-by-wire system to maintain stability. This is almost certainly based on the GEC Astronics quadruplex unit employed very successfully on the F-16. Providing precise air data for the system posed Lockheed designers with a problem in maintaining stealth properties. The result is a group of four air data probes projecting from the nose, each being facetted to defeat radars and with multiple ports for taking differential pressure readings. These are heated to prevent ice fouling the ports. Comparison of the readings from each probe gives adequate data for the flight control system.

Aerodynamically the F-117 relies on many vortices created by the sharp surfaces to form a lifting airflow pattern. The wing forms a simple airfoil by having three flat sections above and two below. The underwing flat surfaces blend into the underfuselage surfaces to create a whole lifting surface below the aircraft. Contrary to some press opinion, which gave rise to the 'Wobblin' Goblin' nickname, the F-117 has more than adequate handling characteristics and considerable agility for an aircraft of its size and power, although landing speeds are high.

The F-117 has just six moveable control surfaces, consisting of four trailing-edge elevons which provide both pitch and roll control, and two ruddervators which work in opposition for yaw control and in unison for pitch control. Like the rest of the aircraft, the control surfaces are made up of flat facets, the ruddervators exhibiting a flattened diamond cross-section. An unusual feature of the control surfaces, also seen on the YF-22, are small flat-sided cut-outs along the gaps between the surfaces and the main structure. The gaps are obviously a great source of radar reflection, especially when the control surfaces are deflected. The notches reduce this to a great extent.

49th Fighter Wing

The 49th FW was established as such on 10 August 1948, and activated on 18 August at Misawa AB, Japan, with Mustangs and F-80s. It fought with F-84s in the Korean War. In 1953 the fighter-bomber mission was moved to France and Germany with, successively, the F-86, F-100, F-105 and F-4. The wing moved to Holloman in 1968, and flew combat missions in Southeast Asia in 1972. In October 1977 the wing began receiving F-15A Eagles, which served with the 7th, 8th and 9th TFS until 1992, when the F-117 arrived.

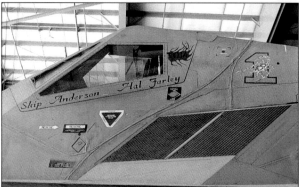

system was 79-10781, a.k.a. ship 781, which flew on 18 December 1981. VLO requirements shaped the design and development of the aircraft, while other features, particularly avionics, had to be 'made to fit' once the needs of stealth were satisfied. The result was to be an aircraft in need of avionics improvements almost from its first day of service.

The Baja Scorpions

The US Air Force had decided there would be no prototypes. The first five aircraft, the FSD vehicles, were to carry out the flight test programme. Owing to their desert home, these test aircraft were designated 'Scorpion' 1 through 5. The name comes from the decision by the Lockheed-USAF team to adopt the Baja Scorpion as its symbol after a terrifying incident in which one of the creatures – more successful than any Soviet spy – penetrated to the very heart of the 'black' programme by showing up on a desk in the team's office area. This deadly member of the *Arachnida* class, with its pincers, nipper and poisonous sting, which also kills by sucking body juices its prey, is nothing to fool with. But once they survived the office mishap without being injected with lethal venom, pilots and maintainers got their zoology mixed up and began referring to the scorpion as a 'cockroach'. Because of the ungainly shape of the aircraft, the Lockheed stealth fighter is still referred to, today, by many who fly and work on it, as the 'Cockroach'. Many

other names which appeared in the press, for example 'Wobbly Goblin', have never been used in real life at all.

The 'Scorpion' full-scale development airframes contributed to design changes that were implemented even as succeeding aircraft were rolling down the production line. From mid-1981 through early 1982, four FSD Senior Trend aircraft (ships 781 through 784) were successfully flown at Groom Lake.

MiG neighbours at Groom Lake

Groom Lake was, throughout those early days of Have Blue and Senior Trend, the most secret military airfield in the United States. In addition to the five FSD Senior Trend aircraft, Groom Lake was home of the 4477th Tactical Group 'Red Hats', equipped with Soviet aircraft as part of several compartmentalised programmes, among them Have Doughnut (for exploitation of the MiG-17), Have Drill (MiG-19), and Have Rivet (MiG-21), plus programmes for the MiG-23 and Su-7, the names of which remain undisclosed. Like Senior Trend, these were 'black' programmes, hidden from press, public and most legislators. Some reports also say that a Northrop stealth prototype flew at Groom Lake, possibly the company's XST vehicle, although (since the XST probably was never built) it was more likely a scaled-down prototype for what became the Advanced Technology Bomber (ATB), later the B-2.

Security at Groom Lake was incredible. Aircraft were kept indoors during the known overflight times of Soviet reconnaissance satellites. Weapons, including surface-to-air missiles, were available to use against any intruder who broke widely-published rules and flew within visual range of the base. There was no town adjacent to the airfield – people came and went by air – but anyone for miles around who asked questions about the Senior Trend or 'Scorpion' aircraft (still not, so far, designated F-117) was hustled into an interrogation with federal officers and, as one put it, "frightened half to death." The federal officers, themselves, did not know what was going on at Groom Lake. One of them thought the Air Force was developing a time machine.

Early in the hush-hush programme, Lockheed was pro-

Stealth on a stick: F-117s have been mounted on poles several times, but usually on a remote range for RCS testing. After a productive test career, Aircraft 780 now takes pride of place in an impressive display of pole-mounted aircraft at Nellis AFB near the Red Flag headquarters at the southern end of the base.

ceeding with the original grey paint scheme when the USAF ordered all Senior Trend aircraft painted black. This appears to have bothered no one, since the 'Skunk Works' believes in Ben Rich's version of the Golden Rule: "He who has the gold sets the rules."

For the first few years of the programme, pilots had no simulator. They trained on a no-motion, no-feedback cockpit procedures trainer (CPT) at Lockheed's Burbank facility. No two-seat model of the Senior Trend warplane was originally planned, nor was one ever built, although, even after a simulator came on line, there was a proposal to construct a two-seater using a damaged airframe, much as had been done with the Oxcart. In due course, a visual-feedback 'dynamic' simulator was installed at the Tonopah, Nevada, operating base.

The Senior Trend aircraft were built at Burbank. The wings were then removed and the aircraft crated for transport to their base (the ultra-secret Groom Lake at first, later Tonopah), where they were assembled by both Lockheed and USAF technicians. In transit, the aircraft was covered by curtains and a deceptive over-frame to hide its true shape.

On 20 April 1982, in preparation to fly the first produc-tion Senior Trend, company test pilot Robert L. Riedenauer lined up for take-off at Groom Lake. Unknown to him or anyone else, flight-control wires had been plugged incorrectly into actuators: coded in reverse so that pitch was yaw, and vice versa. Riedenauer advanced the throttles, released the brakes and rotated for take-off. The aircraft rotated as planned but, immediately after lift-off and just after its main landing gear cleared the runway, it went berserk. Instead of its nose pitching gently upward, it yawed horizontally then pitched up violently. Loss of control was instantaneous. The aircraft hit the runway inverted, going backwards.

The 'lost' F-117

Riedenauer was seriously injured and had to retire from flying. The first production Senior Trend aircraft was damaged beyond repair and, since it had crashed prior to delivery, was not accepted by the US Air Force. Although it fell between the final FSD ship (79-10784, alias 'Scorpion 5') and the machine which took its place as the first production craft (80-10785), Riedenauer's ship was never assigned a serial number. This was the aircraft Lockheed proposed to rebuild as a two-seater, an offer that was not accepted. Parts

Aircraft 784 ('Scorpion 5') was the last of the FSD aircraft. Here it is seen dropping a GBU-27A/B Paveway III laser-guided bomb during weapon separation trials. The large red fairings under the wing, and a small fairing under the nose, house TV cameras to record the weapon falling from the bay. Freefall weapons are believed to drop straight from inside the bay, as to extend the weapon trapeze would severely affect radar cross-section.

Exhaust slot shingles
The platypus exhaust area caused some problems during the flight tests, as this area often went out of shape as it heated up, so destroying the precisely-calculated facetted shape and consequently increasing radar cross-section. Lockheed engineer Henry Combs solved this by introducing 'shingled construction', much like a tiled roof, which allowed panels to slide over each other as they expanded and contracted while still preserving the aircraft's shape.

Original colour scheme
The main three-view depicts Ship One in its first colour scheme of a disruptive blue, grey and sand pattern. This was primarily intended to hide the facetted nature of the aircraft's shape from prying eyes, especially as the early flight tests were undertaken in daylight. This was worn only by the first aircraft, and only for a few months. The later grey scheme proved far more effective in camouflaging aircraft either in the sky or against a concrete ramp should they inadvertently be caught in the open by a Soviet satellite.

F-117 FSD #4

This aircraft is one of three YF-117As still flying with the 410th Test Squadron at Palmdale. It wears an 'F-117A Flight Test' badge on the intake, and the 'ED' tailcodes and white cross fin-stripe of the 412th Test Wing, headquartered at nearby Edwards AFB.

Aircraft fates

All five FSD aircraft survived the test programme. Three are still in use with the 410th TS (782, 783 and 784) at Palmdale, while 'Scorpion 2' (781) is preserved at the USAF Museum, Wright-Patterson AFB, Ohio. Aircraft 780, now in almost full production configuration, has pride of place in a long line of pole-mounted displays at Nellis AFB, Nevada.

Flight tests

The five FSD aircraft explored the full spectrum of the aircraft's operations, including much work on weapon release and radar cross-section. The latter involved flights against captured Soviet air defence radars, and a wide variety of fighter aircraft.

Lockheed YF-117A FSD #1

Aircraft 780, or Ship One, was the first of five full-scale development examples of the F-117A, also known as YF-117As. The five aircraft (79-10780/1/2/3/4) were flown from the works at Burbank to the secret test airfield at Groom Lake in C-5s and reassembled for the first flight. 780 took to the air with Hal Farley at the controls on 18 June 1981, and by early 1982 all five FSD aircraft were helping the flight test programme. The tests ran fairly smoothly, although the first production aircraft (intended to be Aircraft 785 but never assigned a serial) crashed on its first take-off on 20 April 1982 due to a cross-wiring in the flight control system. Another FSD F-117 lost a rudder during high-speed tests, but the pilot remained unaware of his predicament until he was informed by the pilot of a chase plane. The aircraft landed safely. FSD testing continued apace, as production aircraft were being manufactured concurrently, and the need to spot faults early, so that remedies could be incorporated on the production line, was paramount.

Flight control system

The FSD aircraft featured a different nose air data sensor configuration to production aircraft, with one large central probe and four smaller probes feeding the flight control system.

FSD differences

In addition to the air data probes, there were other minor differences between FSD and production aircraft. The most notable was the almost rounded apex to the fuselage behind the cockpit. Later this would be the location of the refuelling light.

Later colour scheme

After a short period in a three-tone camouflage, Ship One was repainted in an all-over grey scheme (depicted below) which was highly effective both in the air and on the ground. This was applied to all five FSD aircraft and was Lockheed's intended service colours. Later the USAF decreed that all F-117s should be black, including the FSD aircraft.

Tailfins

Aircraft 780 was initially built with small tailplanes but these were found to provide insufficient stability and control authority. The fins were subsequently enlarged by the addition of chord to the leading and trailing edges, and lengthening.

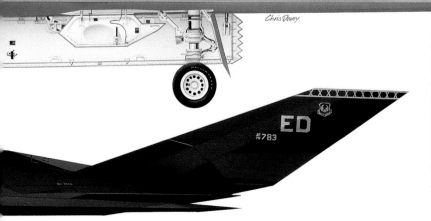

The Baja Scorpions

When the FSD F-117s arrived at Groom Lake, the ground crew quickly nicknamed them 'Scorpions' on account of their strange shape. The Baja Scorpion, a creature of the American south-west, was soon adopted as the unit's insignia, while the aircraft were named 'Scorpion 1' through 'Scorpion 5'. In addition to the large badge behind the cockpit (illustrated right), the aircraft also wore a similar marking, complete with the individual aircraft's number, on the inside of the weapon bay door. Further individual markings were Lockheed's trade-mark skunk on the fins of 'Scorpion 3' and '4', while 'Scorpion 4' wore the name 'The Dragon' on the weapon bay doors. This aircraft was painted with a drawing of the dragon Elliott from the film *Pete's Dragon*, this in tribute to Colonel Pete Winter who commanded Groom Lake. In the movie, the dragon had been invisible to everyone apart from Pete.

Lockheed F-117

Aircraft 783 is still used by the 410th Test Squadron for trials work. Here the aircraft demonstrates the braking parachute, and the large suck-in auxiliary air intakes. Testing by the 410th TS of new brakes may lead to the deletion of the brake chute altogether.

of the aircraft were later used in a mock-up.

In May 1982, Colonel James S. Allen assumed command of the 4450th Tactical Group. Soon afterward, it was time to move. Groom Lake was the ideal location for a 'black' programme, but it lacked facilities for an operational unit. Additionally, at Groom Lake people on one secret project often caught glimpses of another, taking in more than they were supposed to see. Among black-world specialists this was tolerable, but an operational unit would bring in too many people with too many questions.

Move to TTR

The 4450th TG relocated to the Tonopah Test Range (TTR) airfield 140 miles (225 km) north-west of Las Vegas. The site was little known. Airmen had trained in P-39 Airacobras at Tonopah early in World War II, and Airacobra pilots shared a taxiway which encircled the field with automobiles; at traffic lights, pursuit ships had the right of way over Chevrolets. Later in the war, Tonopah was a B-24 Liberator training base. The TTR airfield has almost nothing in common with the wartime Tonopah base, which was at a different location, but the military tradition in the sparsely-populated Tonopah area is deeply rooted.

The Tonopah range lies astride the north-western corner of the Nellis complex and, throughout the Cold War, had been used for drop-tests of nuclear weapon 'shapes'. The nearest town, Tonopah itself, was 32 miles (51 km) north-west of the TTR airfield. At the field, a new control tower and other new facilities were soon joined by guard posts, revetments and security fences.

Some of the security features at the base seemed to come out of a science fiction film. As with any good security arrangement, this one existed in layers, with some people having a little knowledge of what was going on, and very few knowing all. Barbed wire appeared atop double-row fences, like those at a penitentiary. Badges were colour-coded, to indicate how deep into the layers an individual was allowed to go. Those in the inner sanctum reached the

most secure areas of the base only by gaining entry with number codes and palm prints. A special unit of security personnel was heavily armed and ready to repel an assault on the base by protesters or terrorists, if the need arose.

The cloak of secrecy hanging over the Senior Trend stealth fighter was so tight that even some visitors to the TTR airfield never learned what was going on there. One pilot, who travelled to Tonopah but was not selected for the programme, was flown there in a 'Huey' helicopter with one side of the aircraft blacked out: no windows of any kind. The flight path of the UH-1N was arranged to keep the window side of the aircraft facing away from the Tonopah airfield at all times.

Colonel Allen subsequently became the first commander to fly the Senior Trend aircraft, taking delivery of the first aircraft (counting Riedenauer's, the second production example) on 23 August 1982. This turnover appears to have taken place at Groom Lake, although by 1983 the move to Tonopah was virtually complete. At the latter airfield, a handful of Senior Trend aircraft were flying regularly. At Tonopah, initial operating capability (IOC) in Senior Trend was attained on 28 October 1983 with the delivery of aircraft 82-0799. It appears the term IOC was defined rather loosely, with less than a squadron on hand at the time.

Stealth commuters

Security dictated that only people working on Senior Trend be housed at Tonopah. There was no provision for families. Pilots were housed with their families at Nellis AFB, 190 miles (305 km) away. They commuted by air to work on Monday and returned home on Friday, an unusual transport job handled by Boeing 727s belonging to civil contractor Key Airlines. The 4450th TG also flew a Mitsubishi MU-2 turboprop aircraft to carry small groups between Tonopah and Nellis. The security force at the base operated UH-1N helicopters.

As the 4450th TG took shape, its support elements were

given short nicknames which concealed their purpose. The group itself was usually called the A-Unit. The 1880th Communications Squadron became C-Unit, Detachment 8 of the 25th Air Weather Squadron was D-Unit, and the 4450th Combat Support Group was E-Unit. The 4450th Test Squadron (which had been established on 11 June 1981) was the I-Unit. The term P-Unit was used to refer to the A-7D flying detachment, which at this point, like group HQ, remained at Nellis. Detachment 1 of the group, at Tonopah, was the Q-Unit.

Nellis 'SLUFs'

The Vought A-7Ds of P-Unit remained at Nellis and the detachment was by 1987 commanded by a pilot who was not checked out in the Senior Trend aircraft. The underlying concept was that even in a secure area, even among comrades with 'compartmented' clearances – even, for example, in the hangars at Tonopah (for the aircraft were never kept outdoors) – the men of Senior Trend never allowed their small talk, or even their shop talk, to become an outlet for terms that described their secret. "Over the Coke machine or in the cockpit, the word stealth was never mentioned," says one. A pilot was not allowed to tell his family about the 'bandit number', a secret identity awarded to each man who had flown the Senior Trend. On papers which required an entry for 'aircraft type', such as the Form 5 which listed flying hours, pilots jotted down 117, a meaningless number. No one has revealed when the US Air Force adopted this figure and made it the designation for the Senior Trend aircraft, which was never called the F-19 (as widely reported).

Senior Trend also was never known as the RF-19 or AR-19, despite reports; in fact, the aircraft had no designation for years. Nor does the F-117 appellation have any connection with the Pentagon's system for numbering fighter types, which back in 1962 jumped from F-111 to F-1.

When the 'Black Jet' was revealed in later years, all kinds of nonsensical explanations for the F-117 designation were proffered by aviation editors. Although, as already explained, the designation has no connection of any kind with fighter numbers that stopped at F-111, the rumour persists (fed, in one instance, by an air traffic controller, quoted in Aviation Week & Space Technology) that 'Red Hat' Soviet MiGs concealed their real identity by using as radio callsigns terms such as F-112, F-113, and so on. This preposterous bit of fancy has absolutely no basis in truth.

As for the 'gap' in the designation system caused by the missing F-19 designation, the hoopla about its absence

Final assembly of Aircraft 780 at the Burbank factory is shown just after the wings have been mated to the central fuselage structure. Engine systems, nose and flight control surfaces will be added next.

A pair of Palmdale-based FSD F-117As displays the large one-piece bomb bay doors. The leading and trailing edges of the doors (and of virtually every other door or excrescence on the aircraft) has a sawtooth pattern to trap or disperse radar energy. Presenting a sharp-lined opening perpendicular to the source of radar energy would reflect a massive 'flare-spot' back to the radar.

Transporting the finished F-117 from Burbank to Groom Lake provided some security problems. With wings removed, the F-117 was given a wooden frame on the nose to disguise its true shape and covered with a shroud. The aircraft was then transported by C-5 Galaxy to Groom Lake (or later Tonopah) for reassembly.

would make sense only if the Department of Defense properly followed its own system for designating aircraft, which it does not. It has been reported that an F-19 was skipped (F-18 to F-20) to give the Northrop F-20 Tigershark a nice, even number. It is indisputable that the absence of a real F-19 enabled the US Air Force to deny that any F-19 existed. None of this has anything to do with the F-117 story, and never did.

Operational planning

Even as they became operational, while the existence of their aircraft remained a dark secret, the 4450th TG commander and others made plans for how their warplane would be used. The stealth fighter had always been seen by American warfighters as a 'silver bullet'. Only a few existed, and they would be used against high-value assets (HVAs), the Pentagon's term for an enemy's leadership structure and for his central nodes of communication and transportation. A warfighting plan known as Downshift 02 provided for deployment of Senior Trend aircraft to Europe for 'decapitation' strikes against leadership targets such as the Soviet premier's dacha.

Washington intelligence agencies heaped upon the 4450th TG reams of briefings, satellite photos, and maps to use the group's handful of very secret warplanes to lop off the heads of any foreign adversary. Downshift 02 and other warfighting plans envisioned the secret warplanes operating without large support packages of electronic jammers,

'Wild Weasel' and other aircraft, and involved conventional munitions.

Senior Trend was considered for use in Operation Urgent Fury, the United States' combined arms invasion of Grenada in October 1983, but the 4450th TG was deemed not ready, and the F-117 not needed. When other trouble spots flared up – Beirut, the Bekaa Valley – Colonel Allen's F-117 pilots expected to be tapped. It was not until 1984 that they were reaching IOC with a second squadron, and there were more years of seclusion ahead.

F-117 description

With its clandestine stealth fighter becoming operational, the US Air Force now had a warplane which was settled into service and beginning to mature. A 'walk-around check' of the wedge-shaped, V-tailed 'Black Jet' – still performed indoors, to foil reconnaissance satellites – revealed an aircraft indisputably based upon the earlier Have Blue platforms, but different from anything else in the military's arsenal. In contrast to the Have Blue configuration, the production aircraft had a more dramatically notched leading edge and rudders which were canted outward. The aircraft was about 60 per larger than the Have Blues.

The F-117 has a modified delta planform with small wings mated to a broad lifting body, with leading edge sweep of 67.5° (or just slightly less than its Have Blue precursors). The aircraft comes close to being a flying wing with this highly-swept shape, very small vertical fins, and no horizontal tail. Stealth, or VLO, dictated every aspect of the F-117 and is the reason why the modified delta, which offers no aerodynamic advantages, was chosen. Its shape makes the aircraft not merely unstable, as been noted repeatedly, but potentially a troublemaker in the airfield pattern. Early in the test programme, the F-117 was tested with outboard leading-edge slats to reduce its landing approach speed, but it was deemed that the reduction in speed was not significant enough to warrant installing the slats on the entire fleet, and the aircraft retains its high approach speed of around 138 mph (222 km/h).

The aircraft employs RAM on external surfaces and chisel-edge, angular features which contribute to reduced RCS. These facets reduce RCS by scattering radar returns back in multiple directions, but their sharp angles prevent the F-117 from being either aerodynamic or aesthetic. Use of radar-absorbent materials makes the aircraft dim to a radar, while the facets cause it to 'glitter' irregularly as its aspect angle varies.

As one of many features which contribute to stealth, the F-117 has three or four retractable antennas, radio aerials that pop in and out of the airstream when needed. The

Wearing 'LV' codes for Las Vegas, the A-7Ds of the 4451st Test Squadron, 4450th Tactical Group operated openly from Nellis from 1981, being regarded as just another operational trials unit. Its true task was somewhat different – in the early days it provided flight time for prospective F-117 pilots, and later used the A-7s as chase planes on F-117 training sorties.

largest, a retractable blade antenna, is on the back of the aircraft on the starboard side of the refuelling receptacle. The stealth qualities of the aircraft are enhanced by engine exhaust nozzles located atop the fuselage along the wing-root just ahead of the tail surfaces. The exhaust bleeds over the aft fuselage to screen the heat emissions from detection below.

It is worth noting that stealth does not refer only to eluding radar detection. To quote Lockheed, "The F-117A employs a variety of design features to significantly reduce aircraft signature. There are seven different types of observable signatures of concern: radar, infra-red, visual, contrails, engine smoke, acoustics and electromagnetic emissions. The three signature characteristics providing the greatest potential for exploitation by threat systems are radar, infra-red, and electromagnetic emissions. The F-117 is designed to minimise these signatures."

In the cockpit

Pilot of the F-117 sits on a McDonnell Douglas ACES 2 ejection seat in a small cockpit which features a windshield arrangement with a separate panel in front and two different-sized windows on each side. The pilot has a conventional HUD (head-up display) for basic flight information and infra-red imagery, with an up-front control panel beneath it for radio and display mode selections. On the main panel, two MFDs (multi-function displays) flank a large monochrome CRT and IRADS (infra-red acquisition and detection system) video screen. The MFDs can present the pilot with a variety of imagery, mission data and diagnostic information. Between the HUD and the display screens is a console embracing small warning lights which come on to indicate which, if any, part of the aircraft has 'gone dirty' and lost its radar-evading LO properties. Four protruding spikes on the aircraft's nose are air data probes for air speed and altitude sensing. The F-117 has quadruply-redundant fly-by-wire flight controls.

To reduce development risks and maintain security, the F-117 was created, in part, as a hybrid of components from other aircraft types. The cockpit included dials, lights and switches which date to the analog features of the century series of fighters. Many of the cockpit systems are derived from the FA-18 Hornet, including stick grip, throttles, engine instruments, fuel gauge and HUD. The F-117 has at least one minor component from each of a dozen aircraft types including the P-2 Neptune, F-104 Starfighter, T-33 Shooting Star, C-130 Hercules and SR-71 Blackbird. The sensor display is provided by Texas Instruments and borrows heavily from the OV-10D Bronco and P-3C Orion programmes.

Avionics

The F-117's original avionics architecture was a real-time processing system employing three Delco M326F computers from the F-16 Fighting Falcon interconnected with a dual redundant MIL-STD-1553 databus. These computers interfaced with the displays, controls, Honeywell SPN-GEANS INS (inertial navigation system, originally developed for the B-52 Stratofortress's Offensive Avionics System upgrade programme), automatic pilot, stores management system, and sensor systems. The aircraft computer system was administered by a weapons delivery computer which serviced and updated cockpit displays, performed weapons delivery ballistics projections, interfaced to the various sensor systems, and controlled the data distribution. The navigation control computer performed all navigation and control functions including the inertial measurement unit, the control display unit, navigation steering, flight director steering, position update, attitude heading reference system integration, and the TACAN (tactical aid to navigation) and ILS (instrument landing system) interface. The third computer provided control and data processing for an additional sensor system and was used as a back-up computer if one of the other two should fail. A data transfer module interface unit was provided to load pre-flight mission data via a data transfer module from the missing data planning system. At the root of all this was the concept that the avionics system would drive the cueing of the sensor to the target via a precision navigation system, thus providing updated target information for accurate weapons release. Development of the F-117's avionics was very much a second cousin to the prime goal of achieving stealth capability, and at every turn in the design of the aircraft VLO came first. The avionics system was always adequate at best, went through an early upgrade effort beginning in the mid-1980s, and is receiving attention today as the subject of a more ambitious upgrade programme.

As the F-117 was conceived, its ability to carry out a precision bombing relied upon accurate target information and the effective working of the onboard inertial system.

The 4450th Tactical Group moved to Tonopah Test Range airfield in 1982, and the F-117 force built up slowly from just two or three aircraft. This is one of the early aircraft, seen during the 'Tonopah Years' when the aircraft flew without tailcodes and almost exclusively at night.

Lockheed F-117

Target information was not always readily available, even to a great nation with enormous technical resources, and given the value of the F-117 no mission was likely to be launched without it. Given the information and an inertial system performing well enough to find the target at night looking only through a small IR window, the F-117's computer system cued the infra-red (IR) system to the target. Everything had to come together: the target had to be within the field of view of the IR system, the pilot had to

see it on his sensor display, and the pilot had to refine the aiming, designate the target, and act to release a weapon, which would occur through the stores management system.

The Texas Instruments IRADS was an off-the-shelf, single turret system adapted to a twin turret configuration due to the VLO external contour requirements. Since there was a need to see from just above the horizon to well behind the aircraft, a FLIR (forward-looking infra-red) turret and DLIR (downward-looking infra-red) were deemed neces-

sary. Because of the mounting arrangement in the aircraft, the DLIR is inverted relative to the FLIR and thus required the video to be inverted electronically when displayed to the pilot. Although this meant alignment and calibration problems, any turret may be mounted in either position. Both FLIR and DLIR have proven to need screens to maintain their VLO signature and to prevent damage from acoustical effects.

Beginning in 1984, a WSCS (weapon system computer sub-system) upgrade was begun to replace the merely satisfactory (at best) M326D computers. The AP-102 MIL-STD-1750A computer package developed by IBM was chosen. This was developed from the computer installed by Rockwell in the space shuttle orbiter vehicle. Three AP-102 computers were used, each controlling a dual redundant MIL-STD-1553 bus, one set of each being a spare. The WSCS upgrade effort also gave the F-117 the capability to drop two bombs at once, where in the past the aircraft had been restricted to releasing from one of its two bays at a time. This required changes to cockpit controls, bomb bay doors and hydraulics.

Two aircraft were modified for testing during the WSCS upgrade programme. The first, 'Scorpion 3' or FSD-3 (79-10782), was modified for the computer change only and did not receive the full weapon bay upgrade. As such, it was precluded from performing dual bay bomb drops. A second aircraft, 'Scorpion 5' or FSD-5 (79-10784), later joined the test force with all capabilities. This aircraft required a significant lay-up to install the bomb bay modifications and to relocate its instrumentation package (see section on bombs, below) from the bay to a fuel tank area. Seventy-five sorties were flown in connection with the WSCS programme.

F-117 bomb

The F-117's primary weapon is the laser-guided bomb (LGB), part of the 'smart' family of ordnance known to the USAF as precision-guided munitions (PGMs).

The F-117 has a slender, centre-hinged bomb bay with two weapon-bearing hoists, or trapezes, which lift weapons up into the bay. Because the F-117 is directionally unstable over large parts of its operational envelope, it is of interest that opening the weapon bay makes the aircraft more unstable than it is already. In lieu of conventional bomb

racks such as those on the B-52, which would be inconsistent with design constraints (which required the bay to be sandwiched between the engines), the trapezes offer the most efficient way for armourers to load up the 'Black Jet'. The hoists can be lowered below the fuselage silhouette to release a bomb. The bay is too confined and too short for the GBU-24 series of bombs used by other fighter-bombers.

Trapeze drops

The requirement for weapons to be dropped with the trapeze down resulted from early concerns about possible damage to the aircraft and bay doors from fin-equipped bombs, but lowering the trapeze spoiled the F-117's VLO characteristics. Although initial certification of the F-117 with various types of ordnance was accomplished with trapeze-down launches, later efforts by Lockheed's aerodynamics department found that adequate clearance could be maintained with the trapeze up.

The F-117 is fully capable of level, loft, dive, dive toss, and LADD (low-altitude drogue delivery) weapon release manoeuvres, but usually uses straight and level overfly delivery. When weapons delivery work was carried out (by the 4450th TG during the 'black' days), early tests were restricted by the need for one of the two bomb bays to carry instrumentation. Progress was further impeded by

Lockheed F-117

Top and above: 'Cockroaches' at Tonopah – the 1988 revelation of the F-117 allowed the 4450th TG to begin daylight operations, greatly easing the fatigue factor which had afflicted the unit through its first five years of F-117 operations.

each aircraft exhibiting its own personality due to equipment installation tolerances. BDU-33 training shapes were used in lieu of actual bombs for weapon baseline testing, and the difference between simulated and real bombs became one of several factors which caused delays. During the developmental period, the F-117 dropped 500-lb (227-kg) Mk 82 bombs. These drops caused Lockheed's Richard Silz to recommend, "Always do accuracy testing with the weapons fully combat-configured with all fuses, wires and lanyards." The BDU-50, a training version of the Mk 82,

could not be used because the weapon cannot be configured exactly like a real Mk 82.

On most missions, the F-117 carries one or two thin-skinned GBU-10 series bombs, which are in general use among USAF strike aircraft, or more thickly encased GBU-27 series bombs, which are unique to the 'Black Jet' and were developed from the wrongly-sized GBU-24. Both GBU-10 and GBU-27 employ distinctive canards and tail fins.

These bombs rated at 2,000 lb (907 kg) employ either the Mk 84 explosive warhead employed throughout the USAF's inventory, or the BLU-109B (Lockheed designation I-2000) deep-penetrating warhead designed specifically for the F-117.

The GBU-10, as employed on the F-117, combines either Mk 84 or BLU-109B warhead with a Vietnam-era Paveway II guidance kit. (The generic term Paveway comes from the acronym PAVE (precision avionics vectoring equipment), while the GBU designation means guided bomb unit.) The version employing a BLU-109B warhead is designated GBU-10I. The relatively thin casing of the GBU-10 is intended for enhanced blast effect.

Paveway III

The GBU-27, unique to the F-117 (but based on the GBU-24 in general use, but with the canards on the front clipped and the rear fins based on the Paveway II, rather than Paveway III, configuration) came with the 1984 WSCS upgrade effort and employs the more recent-technology Paveway III guidance kit. The version using a Mk 84 warhead is designated GBU-27/B; the version equipped with BLU-109B warhead is designated GBU-27A/B. The bomb is designed to be dropped from medium altitude, although its shorter wings (as compared with the GBU-24 series) degrade some of its stand-off capability.

When the GBU-27 series was being developed, there was concern whether the bombs would separate cleanly from inside the F-117's bomb bay. The bomb was nearly as long as the bay itself. As already noted, one problem was that a trapeze lowered to guarantee hazard-free release would give the 'Black Jet' a non-stealthy face to enemy radars. The changes which came with the WSCS upgrade, including changes to the twin bays, trapezes and doors, resolved this and made it possible to drop the GBU-27 with the trapeze up. The F-117 bay also has four perforated baffle plates which deploy ahead of, and flank, the bomb being released, apparently both to interrupt air flow and to minimise the unstealthy effect.

The GBU-27 offers two guidance modes, each optimised to achieve the best penetration angle for horizontally or vertically orientated targets. For a horizontal target such as a bunker, the GBU-27 flies a commanded pitch down after release to strike the target in an attitude as nearly vertical as possible. The trajectory for a vertical target such as a high-rise building is essentially the ballistic path. In early development trials, on the second occasion when a Senior Trend aircraft dropped a GBU-27, the bomb hit a target barrel and split it in half, testimony to bombing accuracy and a memento which has been kept by the 'Skunk Works'.

One report has said that F-117s carried 500-lb GBU-12 bombs (Mk 82 bombs with Paveway II kits) in attacks on the fire trench system along the Kuwaiti border during Operation Desert Storm.

Boosted bomb

In 1992, Lockheed proposed a Boosted Penetrator conventional bomb to be carried by the F-117. Like the current GBU family, the bomb would glide to its target after release (although from greater range, introducing a stand-off capability). Just before impact it would be boosted by a rocket motor to increase its velocity and kill power. Lockheed indicated that it had completed preliminary work on the booster, the warhead, the fuse and the tail airfoil group. The weapon was said to have been inspired by the GBU-

Below left: Although initial training on the F-117 could be undertaken in daylight, the aircraft was always envisaged as a nocturnal predator, and night flying continued. Throughout the 1980s there were several proposals to use the F-117 in surgical strikes, targets in Lebanon, Grenada, Libya and Nicaragua being discussed but all being rejected as a waste of the years of security.

Below: With the need for a cover story removed, the A-7 companion trainers were replaced by Northrop AT-38Bs in September 1989. These offered better economy and reliability. The base ops buildings, flightline and aircraft barns formed the inner sanctum of the Tonopah base, and the entire area was encircled by a double cordon of fencing protected by constantly-manned security posts and sturdy gates at access points. Aircraft had to taxi through these gates to gain access to the runway.

Lockheed F-117

Above and right: Two views of F-117s refuelling highlights the facetted shape of the aircraft and the rotating refuelling receptacle. Radio-silent refuellings are regularly practised, and at night the only illumination comes from the small light above the cockpit and a floodlight on the tanker's tail. Noticeable on the aircraft are small blade antennas which serve the communications suite. On operational missions these are retracted to maintain full stealthiness.

28, a 4,700-lb (2133-kg) gravity bomb with BLU-113 warhead that was fabricated quickly during Desert Storm and rushed into use aboard the F-111F in the final days of the war in an apparent attempt to reach Iraqi command bunkers and, perhaps, Saddam Hussein. Nothing further has been disclosed about a Boosted Penetrator bomb for the F-117, but development may be proceeding quietly.

Although it is called a fighter, the F-117 has no capability for air-to-air combat. The aircraft has no gun and is not known to have ever carried air-to-air missiles. In fact, the 'Cockroach' carries no external weapons at all, and has very little flexibility with its internal bomb load – all of which eased, to some extent, the demands on aerodynamicists who initially conceived the F-117. Although warfighters wanted the aircraft to 'decapitate' an enemy's C3I assets (command, control, communications and intelligence), no-one ever expected the F-117 to carry nuclear weapons, making it perhaps the only tactical warplane designed without this capability. Without nuclear capability, the F-117 was never part of the SIOP (single integrated operations plan) for the initial phase of a nuclear war with the Soviet Union and its Warsaw Pact allies.

The F-117 is theoretically capable of employing air-to-air missiles such as the AIM-9 Sidewinder or air-to-ground types such as the AGM-65 Maverick, but only with its weapon-bearing hoists (trapezes) extended, again defeating the purpose of stealth. It is not clear whether the F-117 has ever been 'wired' for these weapons.

The USAF intended the F-117 to be readily deployed to trouble spots. When details about the aircraft were still 'in the black', rumours persisted that C-5A/B Galaxy airlifters were hauling the stealth fighters to various locations around the world, where they were flying clandestine night missions. Most or all of this hearsay proved to be inaccurate. The F-117 can be carried on board a Galaxy with its wings removed, but the process is not effective as a rapid response to a crisis because of the time consumed by disassembling, spraying joints, packaging and reassembling. Maintenance of the F-117 can be performed out of vans which can be moved overseas aboard C-130, C-141B or C-5A/B transports. In real life, self-deployment works faster and easier, and if indoor facilities are available at the other end, so much the better.

Propulsion

The F-117 is powered by two 10,800-lb (48.05-kN) thrust General Electric F404-GE-F1D2 engines without afterburners. After flight icing trials, the engine installation team had to resort to a wiper system to keep the F404 inlet grids free from ice; designers had rejected a plea from the airframe development team which had said it would "welcome any change of shape as it could only make [the aircraft] better." Regarded as responsive, reliable and with more than adequate thrust for the Nighthawk's high-subsonic speed regime (Mach 0.8), these engines give the aircraft a low noise signature and produce no visible exhaust. In later years, plans to retrofit the General Electric F412 engine developed for the defunct A-12 Avenger 2, or to install the newer F414 which delivers 37 per cent more thrust, were bogged down by financial constraints. Plans for

the latter engine are still being put forth by the manufacturer, in a non-afterburning form.

Only recently were full details of the F-117's stealthy exhaust tailpipe revealed. ASTECH/MCI Manufacturing of Santa Ana, California, achieved a method of reducing infrared signature without reducing thrust, by transitioning the F404 exhaust from a circular pattern to a flattened-out, louvre-type duct. A honeycomb sandwich of nickel alloy reshapes the flow of exhaust gases and absorbs much of the heat and pressure of the design.

The F-117 has "a very special nozzle" in the back, as described by Lockheed's Jack Gordon. "It uses a Coanda effect to turn the flow back into the axial direction, but from the waterline of the trailing edge of the aeroplane and below, you cannot look up into the nozzle and into the engines, so it helps very much in controlling the signature."

Pilots describe the F-117 as pleasurable and smooth to fly, if not entirely forgiving. Its characteristics are not unlike those of other deltas, like the F-106. Landing and take-off speeds are quite high (a parachute is always used on landing) and the aircraft flies nose-high at low speeds and decelerates rapidly in a sharp turn. The thrust-to-weight ratio at maximum take-off weight is 0.4:1, which is not generous, especially in hot climates.

When the F-117 was still in the 'black', refuelling operations were carried out primarily by KC-135 crews from

A 37th TFW F-117 manoeuvres over the Nevada desert. The aircraft picked up its nickname in the early days so that crews could easily distinguish between the 'camo jets' (A-7s) and 'black jets' (F-117s) without having to use the classified designation. Later the AT-38s became the 'gray jets'.

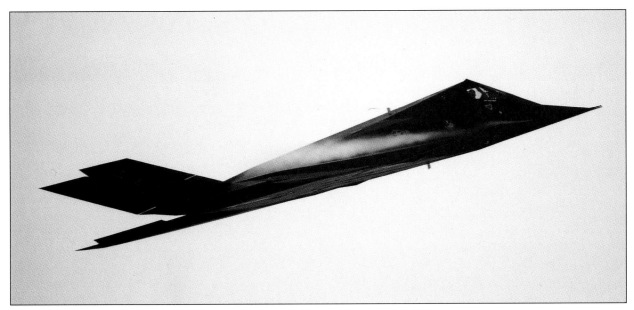

Vortices stream from the leading edge as a 49th FW F-117 pulls up sharply (note the deflection of the elevons). Despite reports to the contrary, the F-117 handles well at all speeds, although exhibiting the normal disadvantages associated with a delta. These include high landing speed and swiftly-bleeding energy in a tight turn. The low thrust/weight ratio precludes traditional fighter-style flying, but the aircraft is surprisingly agile considering its size.

Lockheed F-117

Beale AFB, California, known as the 'Beale Bandits'. The USAF's hard-working boom operators reportedly were nervous about 'gassing up' the 'Black Jet', fearful that the flying boom would damage RAM material on the aircraft exterior. The F-117 is apparently no more or less stable when being refuelled than any other warplane, and the early skittishness seems to have gone away.

4450th TG progress

On 15 April 1984, Colonel Howell M. Estes III became the third commander of the 4450th Tactical Group. Estes led the group through its first ORI (operational readiness inspection), which was deemed a success. During his tenure, weapons delivery tactics for the Senior Trend aircraft were standardised.

In 1984, the Lockheed F-117 was still 'in the closet' and reporters and aircraft spotters were still wondering what kind of mysterious apparition was cavorting about in Nevada skies. A tragic fluke in May 1984 stirred conjecture about the Senior Trend stealth programme for the wrong reason. Lieutenant General Robert M. ('Bobbie') Bond, vice commander of Air Force Systems Command and a decorated Vietnam-era A-7D pilot, was killed attempting to eject from an aircraft while flying in the Nellis area. A joyride, some said. Outside the inner sanctum, it was mistakenly thought that Bond was flying the mysterious stealth fighter. Only much later has it become clear that the general was piloting a Soviet-built MiG-23, a Russian warplane employed in unrelated 'black' programmes at Groom Lake.

The secrecy of the F-117 programme actually helped the manufacturer to deliver on time, at cost. Later, however, Congress was to ask whether the USAF concealed teething troubles. USAF acquisition chief John Welch was to acknowledge some technical problems which delayed the

programme by nearly two years. Welch identified problems with correlating the upper and lower FLIR systems, as well as fuel leaks and exhaust gas leaks.

Potential debut over Libya

Secretly but vigorously, the 4450th Tactical Group continued to thrive in the America of the mid-1980s, when a free-spending Reagan presidency created many secrets, and many weapons, and plunged the nation into crippling debt to pay for them. At the White House, advisor Marine Lieutenant Colonel Oliver North cooked up schemes for American intervention in Lebanon and Nicaragua. Twice, North recommended using the F-117 against high-value assets. By 1986, Reagan, North and others were focusing on Libya's Colonel Muamar Khadaffi, hardly the world's worst terrorist but surely its most convenient. Almost everything, from the bombing of a discotheque to the trade deficit, could be blamed on Khadaffi, who had no defenders in the American press.

In early 1986, commanded now by Colonel Michael W. Harris (who took the helm on 6 December 1985), the 4450th TG was alerted for a secret mission to 'decapitate' Khadaffi. A grave question arose. Khadaffi was small stuff – had the Americans really been hell-bent on punishing terrorists, they would have gone after Syria's Haffez Assad – but the F-117 was big time, a crucial 'hold card' in a war with the Soviet Union. Was it worth unwrapping the secret of stealth, merely to bomb, or even to kill, Khadaffi? One officer warned, "We've worked too hard on stealth and laser-guided bombs to use them to blow up a pile of camel shit." What's more, one necessity for a successful F-117 operation – good target information – may have been lacking. The attack on Libya's capital, Tripoli, by the F-117 was called off. Instead, US forces carried out Operations Prairie Fire and Eldorado Canyon, using carrier-based warplanes and Britain-based F-111 'Aardvarks'.

Handling a loss

The F-117 fighter remained unknown to the outside world. The US Air Force was not fully comfortable keeping it that way, but decision-makers in the Reagan and Bush administrations wanted the lid to remain clamped. Plans were readied to deal with the unexpected, one of the worst scenarios being: what would happen to the secret if one of the stealth fighters crashed?

The first loss of an operational aircraft occurred at 2:00 a.m. on 11 July 1986 on a hillside along the Kern River

near Bakersfield, California, killing pilot Major Ross E. Mulhare. Mulhare was flying aircraft 81-10792, callsign ARIEL 31. There is evidence that fatigue – which was chronic among the stealth pilots, who flew only at night – caused him to become disorientated and plunge into the slope. A fire started by the crash burned about 150 acres of dry grass and brush and was not extinguished for 16 hours. The immediate crash site was cordoned off by battle-garbed Security Police toting M16 rifles, and fire-fighters were not allowed within that area. London's Sunday Times reported that US officials had thrown a "ring of steel" around the "crashed bomber". Air traffic controllers were told that Mulhare's aircraft was an A-7D. Only reluctantly was the pilot's affiliation with the 4450th Test Group made public.

Model furore

That same month, legislators in Washington were up in arms when Testor Corp. of Rockford, Illinois released a $9.95 plastic kit model of the F-19 'Stealth Fighter'. Congressman Ron Wyden complained that, "What I, as a member of Congress, am not even allowed to see is now ending up in model packages." Editorials warned that 'foreign spies' might grab up the hobby kit and exploit its enclosed F-19 'Stealth Fighter' Profile. The biggest nonsense in all this was a report that Russian agents had scarfed up cartons of the new model and shipped them to Moscow via diplomatic pouch.

None of this uproar took into account the incompetence of Testors, which seemed to know less than anyone else speculating about the secret of stealth. The model-maker was completely wrong in every detail, as it has been consistently, before and since. In fact, the inability of the model-maker to come up with anything remotely like the real aircraft (or like its real designation) probably helped keep the real thing secret. The kit model was a smooth, sleek aircraft having nothing whatever in common with the faceted shape of the Senior Trend.

Others with keener minds were striving, hard, to unlock the secret of the hush-hush aeroplane flying over the Nevada desert. On 23 August 1986, in a landmark news story triggered by the Bakersfield crash the month before, the Washington Post's George Wilson peeled away layers of secrecy, disclosing that "several combat-ready squadrons of stealth fighters are reportedly hidden in hangars in the Nevada desert near Tonopah, south-east of Reno," to avoid detection. Wilson said that the new aircraft was known as the Covert Survivable In-Weather Reconnais-

A swirl of tyre smoke signals the safe return of a Tonopah 'Black Jet' after a training mission. The lack of a two-seat trainer version (proposed but turned down) has put great demands on the simulator for initial training. Once fully proficient in the sim, the new F-117 pilot takes his first ride accompanied by an experienced pilot flying chase in a T-38.

Above: With gear locked down, the 49th FW commander's aircraft turns over the snow-dusted New Mexico countryside for landing at Holloman. The landing gear retracts forward, this arrangement having the benefit of allowing the gear to fall under gravity and then be forced back to lock by aerodynamic pressure should power be lost.

Right: The 'Black Jet' is by operational nature a solitary beast, but the 410th Test Squadron put up this rare formation of three for the 1993 Edwards air show.

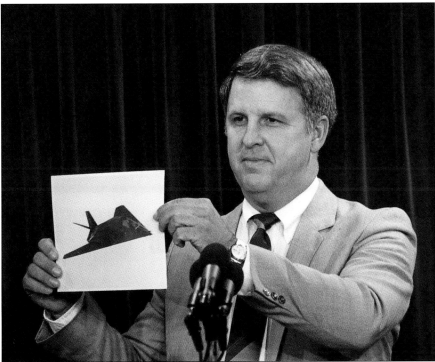

sance Strike (COSIRS) and also as the F-19. Wilson also said that "the fighter bears a top-secret, two-word code-name that replaced Have Blue, which was an umbrella term for early stealth prototypes." He meant Senior Trend.

On 14 October 1987 at a gunnery range at Nellis, another crash occurred, in which Major Michael C. Stewart died. Stewart was 40 minutes into a mission when his 'Black Jet' (85-01815, callsign BURNR 54) crashed into the gentle, sloping high desert 65 miles (105 km) east of Alamo, Nevada. The aircraft struck the earth at a steep angle, digging a hole into the powdery sand. As with Mulhare's crash the year before, insiders speculated on fatigue – an ever-present companion to men flying at night, their mental time clocks out of sequence – and resulting spatial disorientation. Again, Security Police cordoned off the crash site and covered everything beneath a cloak of secrecy.

When Colonel Michael C. Short became the fourth commander of Tonopah's 4450th Tactical Group on 3 April 1987, there was still talk about using the F-117 in

This was how the Department of Defense finally revealed the F-117 to the world, Assistant Secretary of Defense J. Daniel Howard holding a Pentagon press conference on 10 November 1988 at which this one photograph was released. The illustration was deliberately grainy to hide the details of the aircraft's facets, and taken from an intentionally misleading angle to make it look much shorter and wider than is the case.

'Black Jet' and 'Gray Jet' during initial training at Holloman. The Talon sticks close to the F-117, with experienced pilots calling out instructions and monitoring the performance of the trainee 'Bandit'. The AT-38 wears markings for the 417th Fighter Squadron, which undertook the training mission for several years. In 1993 the three F-117 squadrons eventually took up the numbers of the 49th Fighter Wing's traditional units (long after the move to Holloman), the 417th FS becoming the 7th FS 'Bunyaps' in December.

Over 17 months elapsed from the first Pentagon press briefing to the final public unveiling, which took place on 21 April 1990. Two aircraft, one marked for the 37th TFW commander and one carrying 415th and 416th Squadron markings on either side of the fin, flew in to Nellis from Tonopah for the occasion, which was attended by thousands.

Opposite page: F-117s trail behind a KC-135 prior to refuelling.

The final F-117 was delivered to the Air Force in a ceremony at Palmdale on 12 July 1990. Adhering to true 'Skunk Works' philosophy, Lockheed delivered the 59 aircraft on time and within a surprisingly low budget for such a sophisticated aircraft.

said nothing to the contrary. Some Congressmen were infuriated by the timing of this very first release of any information. The release, including the first, fuzzy photograph (of "a black bat," said George Wilson), was delayed until 10 November 1988, one week after voters had picked Bush.

New companions

In September 1989, the Vought A-7D 'companion' aircraft operated by the 4450th TG were replaced by Northrop T-38 Talons; the former were no longer needed for cover purposes and the latter were far more economical to operate. The A-7D had some commonality with the F-117 in terms of size and handling characteristics, but was no longer employed elsewhere in the active-duty inventory and was increasingly costly to maintain and operate. The T-38A (followed, in due course, by a few armed AT-38Bs) was more than adequate for training. The A-7D aeroplanes had worn a unique 'LV' tailcode, for Las Vegas, which never had been painted on the F-117 itself. The T-38s adopted the stealth fighter's 'TR' tailcode, for Tonopah Range.

The 'coming out' of the Lockheed F-117 was welcomed by Air Staff officers and others, eager to strip away the barriers which prevented them from including the aircraft in everyday operations. No longer was it necessary for the F-117 unit to shield its purpose behind an ambiguous name. In October 1989, the 4450th Tactical Group was redesignated 37th Tactical Fighter Wing. Colonel Anthony J. 'Tony' Tolin (who had taken over from Short on 10 August 1988) was commander of the 4450th-cum-37th during its most difficult period, namely its emergence from the closet, its introduction to combat, and (later) the first few days of Operation Desert Shield.

Another year was to pass, together with a war in Panama, before any further details of the hush-hush F-117 would come out.

December 1989 saw US forces deployed for Operation Just Cause, the combined arms assault on Panama aimed at ousting strongman Manuel Noriega, who had made the mistake of tweaking American noses. These were always combined arms exercises because every branch of service and every kind of military unit had to be given a role; inefficient as this was, Congress would have it no other way. With the F-117 public knowledge now, the Pentagon's Joint Staff could no longer deny a 'silver bullet' opportunity to the Tonopah-based stealth fighter. On the night of 19-20 December 1989, two F-117s were launched to support a never-disclosed Special Operations 'snatch' of Noriega, which was called off only as they approached Panamanian airspace. Two other F-117s were back-ups, and two flew a bombing mission intended to 'stun, disorient and confuse' Panamanian Defense Forces (PDF) at Rio Hato. As unlikely as it sounds, their target was a large, open field alongside a barracks housing 200 elite PDF troops, and not the barracks itself.

Just Cause mission

The six F-117s flew from Tonopah and refuelled five times during the round trip to Panama. The two Rio Hato F-117s dropped two 2,000-lb (907-kg) GBU-27A/B bombs with BLU-109B/I-2000 warheads, both of which exploded several hundred feet away from their intended target. Lead pilot for this attack was Major Greg Feest, who later dropped the first bomb on Baghdad. Four of the six F-117s returned to Tonopah with their bombs on board.

In Congress, a critic argued that the mission "could have been flown with an Aero Commander," a twin-engined, propeller-driven business aircraft. Time magazine asserted that the USAF "unleashed its F-117s not to scare Manuel Noriega, but to build a case that high-tech aircraft have a role even in a low-tech war." At the time the press was referring to the F-117 as the 'Wobbly Goblin', a term

Nicaragua. Those with a compartmentalised clearance known as Veil (pertaining to US covert operations in Central America) knew of a plan to use the F-117 to attack specific buildings in Managua to take out the Sandinistas' leadership. A contingency plan called for basing Senior Trend warplanes temporarily in Honduras for this purpose. The plan was never activated.

A-7D accident

On 20 October 1987, attention was abruptly focused on the 4450th TG when one of the group's Vought A-7D aircraft lost engine power and crashed into the Ramada Inn hotel near the Indianapolis, Indiana, airport. Pilot Major Bruce L. Teagarden ejected safely but the A-7D struck the hotel and erupted in flames, killing nine people. Judged blameless in the mishap, Teagarden was publicly acknowledged as a member of the 4450th TG; the mainstream press never picked up on his connection with a mystery plane flying in Nevada.

The F-117 nose-dived into election politics again in 1988. In a move certain to boost George Bush's campaign against Michael Dukakis, the Pentagon scheduled what the Boston Globe called a "coming out party" for the as-yet unacknowledged stealth fighter for 9 October 1988, a month before American voters were to choose their next president. Press and public still thought the mystery debutante was called the F-19, and the Reagan administration

Right: Some two weeks after the Iraqi invasion of Kuwait, the 415th TFS dispatched 21 aircraft (including three spares) on 19 August 1990 for the long journey to Khamis Mushait in Saudi Arabia. One stop was made, at Langley AFB, Virginia, where this aircraft is seen rolling out with its black brake chute. After one night's rest, the F-117 pilots continued to Saudi Arabia in a marathon flight which took over 14 hours.

Below: Three 'Black Jets' bask outside their shelters at King Khalid Air Base. The aircraft in the foreground is notable for carrying the name of Sqn Ldr Graham Wardell, the first RAF exchange officer. He had left the 37th TFW by the time hostilities began.

never used by those who worked on and flew the aircraft. It was the worst time that the US Air Force could have chosen to reveal that it would be seeking 132 Northrop B-2 stealth bombers.

On 21 April 1990, thousands witnessed a public unveiling of the F-117 stealth fighter at Nellis AFB, Nevada. That month, Colonel Ber Reiter, who had been the USAF's F-117 programme director since July 1987, acknowledged that F-117s were being upgraded with graphite thermoplastic fins. Reiter said that Lockheed and the USAF had "recently produced and flown" an F-117 vertical fin made of the composite material and that the fin was "the first primary structural component" made of "this exceptionally strong, light, damage-tolerant material." Reiter confirmed that the F-117 fleet would be upgraded with the new fins, and this apparently happened over the following two to three years.

On 12 July 1990, three weeks before an Iraqi invasion of Kuwait, the US Air Force took delivery of its 59th and last F-117 aircraft (87-0843) in a ceremony presided over by chief of staff General Michael Dugan.

Desert build-up

Almost immediately after Saddam Hussein invaded Kuwait and the military build-up known as Operation Desert Storm was launched in August 1990, the 37th Tactical Fighter Wing dispatched its 'Black Jets' on a journey halfway around the world, to King Khalid air base at Khamis Mushait in mountainous south-west Saudi Arabia near the Red Sea, 1,000 miles (1610 km) from Baghdad. It was the first overseas deployment for the Nighthawk. The journey was made via a stop at Langley AFB, Virginia, where observers were treated to the spectacular sight of 22 F-117s lined up along a flight line in broad daylight. The trip from Langley to Khamis involved 14 to 16 hours in the cockpit, and four to six aerial refuellings en route.

'Tonopah East'

The Saudi air base, elevation 6,776 ft (2065 m), quickly became known as Tonopah East. At the start of the deployment, Colonel Alton C. ('Al') Whitley, Jr (who in the distant past had been the first operational pilot to fly the F-117) took command from Tolin.

Within the 37th TFW, weaponeering and targeting officers began plotting how the F-117 would be used against Iraq if diplomacy failed and war came. Although it took

three air refuellings per sortie and inflicted much pilot discomfort – almost every 'Black Jet' pilot had a Sony Walkman rigged to his helmet earphones to listen to his music of choice while in the cruise mode – the F-117 could fly 1,000 miles (1610 km) and deliver a 2,000-lb (907-kg) laser-guided bomb with pinpoint accuracy. This accuracy was important. In the 1990s, with the merciless eye of television shining on Operation Desert Shield, American plan-

ners no longer lived in a world where 'collateral' civilian deaths and injuries were acceptable.

On 12 September 1990, the well-liked chief of staff, General Dugan, visited Khamis, where the F-117 force was now on alert. A week later, Dugan described exactly what coalition air power would do to Saddam Hussein if necessary, and was fired for doing so. Dugan said that "the cutting edge" of an air campaign "would be in downtown

Above and below: Accommodation at King Khalid AB was superb, with hardened shelters each housing two aircraft. In addition to reinforced concrete, the shelters were protected and disguised with a top cover of rocks.

Baghdad." Dugan was sacked for predicting exactly what occurred months later.

Computer war

In a command facility named the 'Black Hole' at Riyadh, Lieutenant General Charles Horner's air staff worked out all the details of a possible air campaign against Iraq, such as refuelling tracks, jamming, countermeasures and air rescue, at a time when almost nobody believed there would really be a war. On 3 October 1990, Colonel Whitley began a series of 'mirror image' combat rehearsals, named Sneaky Sultan, in which strikes on Iraq were practised, and in which computer modelling saw numerous 'Black Jets' shot down without reaching their targets. Still, everyone felt the situation would be resolved through negotiation. One day in October 1990, intelligence officer Michael P. Curphey sat in on a meeting where Horner and others confirmed that 'downtown' (Baghdad) would be set aside exclusively for unmanned cruise missiles and the 'Black Jet'. Curphey emerged shaking his head. "You know," he said, "that goddamned crazy man Saddam Hussein isn't going to back down."

The decision to set aside HVAs in Baghdad for the F-117 was reinforced as preparations continued. Even after experts reduced their estimate of Iraq's air defence network, a Studies and Analysis Agency team came up with computer models which projected extremely high losses if non-stealthy warplanes struck the capital. Baghdad belonged to the 'Black Jet'.

Eve of war

Whitley found himself in charge of the deployed version of his outfit, now known as the 37th TFW (Provisional). The designation was applied on 20 December 1990. Whitley's deployed wing included most of the 415th TFS 'Nightstalkers' under Lieutenant Colonel Ralph Getchell plus the 416th TFS 'Ghostriders', as well as a few members of the training squadron, the 417th TFTS under Lieutenant

Colonel Robert Maher.

On the evening of 16 January 1991, after a United Nations ultimatum to Saddam Hussein passed without result, the men of the 37th TFW (P) finally realised that they were going to war. Leatherman, Kerdavid and Mahar were among the pilots who flew those first missions. Each, later, admitted to the fear which gripped Mahar: each man was certain he would be the only member of the 37th TFW to live through the gauntlet of flak around Baghdad, and would be stuck with explaining to the widows and children of his buddies why he alone had survived.

Combat glitches

That eventuality was not realised, but problems arose throughout the campaign. It had been planned that follow-up F-117s striking the same target would arrive at one-minute intervals, to allow time for surface winds to push dust and smoke away from the aim points. This tactic did not work. It took at least 10 minutes for AAA (anti-aircraft artillery) gunfire to die down once the gunners had been 'excited' by the arrival of a 'Black Jet'. A second 'Black Jet' needed to arrive as much as 15 minutes after the first. The revised sequencing went into effect from the second night and may have saved some pilots' lives.

The first night, it was deemed a mistake when EF-111 Raven electronic warfare aircraft stirred up Iraqi gunners, seemingly making them more ready for the arrival of the F-117. After a second look at the tactic, it was determined that forcing the Iraqis to fire prematurely heated-up gun barrels had made the anti-aircraft batteries less accurate by the time the F-117s arrived.

Many F-117 strikes were postponed or cancelled because of the awful weather which plagued the air campaign. A adverse-weather situation highlights the lack of a radar on board the F-117, which essentially relies upon a clear air mass to carry out its mission.

As Desert Storm unfolded, F-117 pilots returned with undropped bombs because conditions would not permit the

Brothers in arms: a 'Black Jet' returns from a mission behind an F-15D of the Royal Saudi Air Force. No. 42 Squadron flew the Eagles from King Kahlid.

Infra-red film gives some idea of the eerie sensation experienced by KC-135 boomers as the F-117 loomed out of the dark as it approached the boom. During missions into Iraq the F-117 topped off its tanks just short of the Saudi/Iraq border before proceeding alone into hostile airspace.

standard of accuracy they were charged with meeting. At its best, the F-117 gave precision delivery of munitions, as when 'Black Jets' struck the main Baghdad telephone exchange without harming the Mustashfa Faydi hospital located just across a wide boulevard. Targets were taken out with surgical precision. A bomb from an F-117 destroyed an Iraqi Adnan-2, a Soviet-built Ilyushin Il-76 transport converted into an early warning aircraft with the addition of French-designed Tiger-G radars. Another, according to one report never confirmed, destroyed three of eight Tupolev Tu-16 bombers being readied at Al-Taqaddum for a chemical bombing raid. Strikes were mounted against surface-to-air missile sites containing American-made Hawk batteries, seized by Iraq during its invasion of Kuwait. As the campaign wore on, the F-117 force ran out of strategic targets; the Air Force's 'silver bullet' found itself being used much like any other fighter-bomber, taking part in the interdiction campaign against bridges and aircraft shelters.

Desert Storm statistics

The US Air Force later concluded that the F-117 represented only 2.5 per cent of the shooters in-theatre on the first day of the war, yet credited it with hitting over 31 per cent of the targets. During the war, 45 F-117s and about 60 pilots flew 1,271 combat sorties, dropped over 2,000 tons (1814 tonnes) of bombs, flew over 6,900 hours, and (said its supporters) "demonstrated accuracy unmatched in the history of air warfare." During the conflict, the F-117 had a mission-capable rate of 85.8 per cent, which was four per cent higher than in peacetime. GBU-10 and GBU-27

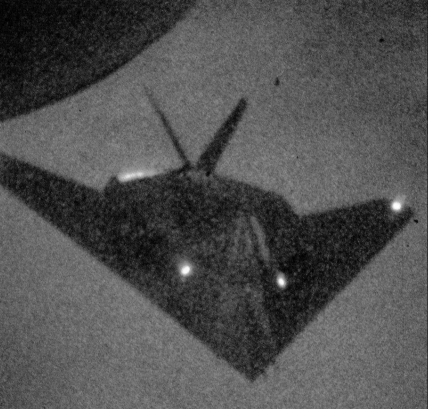

On 1 April 1991 Colonel Al Whitley led back the first F-117s from Saudi Arabia to Nellis AFB, where a tumultuous welcome from a crowd of 25,000 awaited the crews. Over the next three months the force at Khamis Mushait dwindled to a handful of aircraft, which have been maintained there ever since as a rotational deployment from the CONUS Nighthawk unit. Crew swap-overs are undertaken every three months.

Lockheed F-117

Opposite page: An F-117A of Det 1, 57th Wing, drops an inert GBU-27A/B 2,000-lb class laser-guided bomb, watched by a T-38A assigned to the 509th Bomb Wing, the operators of the Northrop B-2 at Whiteman AFB, Missouri. The 57th Wing is involved in operational trials and evaluation, and operates this aircraft (804) from Holloman AFB alongside the frontline Nighthawk force.

Opposite, below: With security restrictions removed, the F-117 became 'just another Air Force jet'. The tanking mission was spread to any unit, not just the classified mission specialists at Beale. Here a pair of 37th TFW 'Cockroaches' works with a KC-10 of the 22nd ARW from March AFB, California.

bombs dropped by the F-117 proved highly effective against aircraft shelters, bunkers and other strategic targets in Baghdad. Contrary to what Mahar and others expected, not a single F-117 was touched by Iraqi fire.

Proponents of other aircraft types argue that any warplane which can designate for its own laser-guided weapons can be similarly effective: the F-111F, which used hi-tech weaponry to 'plink' main battle tanks, performed well in the Gulf; the F-16 Fighting Falcon might have demonstrated a good record of precision bombing, too, if only LANTIRN targeting pods had been available at the time.

Attempt to revive production

In October 1991, there was a brief flurry of bureaucratic jousting as Washington insiders, glowing over hyped reports of the Nighthawk's success in Desert Storm, sought to revive production. Lockheed suddenly had a rare opportunity to lobby for business it had neither expected nor sought, but the US Air Force had other plans. Eager for funding for the B-2 bomber and Advanced Tactical Fighter (which turned out to be the Lockheed F-22), blue-suiters in the Air Staff made it clear that reopening the F-117 production line was an idea whose time would never come. As it did with a premature (and later cancelled) plan to retire the F-111F 'Aardvark', the Air Staff was prepared to sacrifice a proven asset (the 'Black Jet' had won the 1989 Collier Trophy for Rich and his design team, the 1989 David C. Schilling Award for the aircraft itself, and three outstanding unit citations for the men who flew it) to justify dollars for future projects.

In June 1991, General John Loh, head of Tactical Air Command, told the Senate that the F-117 had been eight times more efficient in delivering bombs against Iraq than 'non-stealth' warplanes requiring escort fighters, radar jammers and tankers. It was not true, but the success of the F-117 was becoming an embarrassment to the USAF. In 1991, the service wanted 72 more of the rather prosaic F-16 Fighting Falcons (still, at the time, manufactured by General Dynamics rather than Lockheed), and had "absolutely, positively, zero interest," as one officer puts it, in reopening the production line for the glamorous Lockheed F-117.

Congressmen were urging exactly that reopening. Senator Sam Nunn, the most knowledgeable defence figure on Capitol Hill, declared, "The Air Force already has more than 1,600 F-16s, and buying 72 more will provide only a marginal increase in capability. Buying 24 more F-117s for the same amount [as 72 F-16s] will provide a 50 per cent increase in the number of aircraft that proved to be the superstar of Desert Storm." The Senate voted to cancel the F-16s and called on the USAF to order the F-117s. Such a vote is over overtaken by some later vote and, in this case,

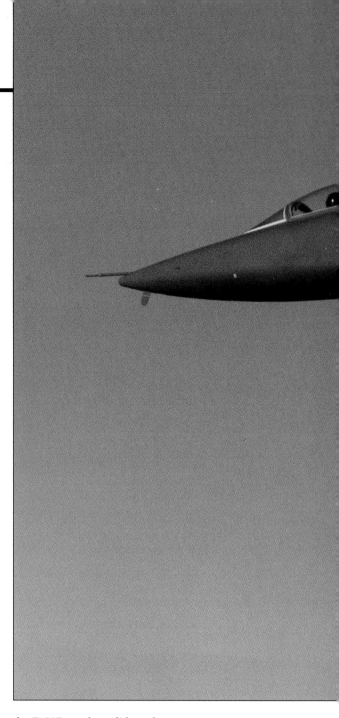

the F-117 purchase did not happen.

From early in the Nighthawk's history, Britain was made a partner in development of the stealth fighter, and Lockheed made proposals for an F-117 variant for the Royal Air Force. Early proposals to the RAF met with some interest from operators, but were thought to interfere with other procurement programmes that enjoyed a higher priority. Meanwhile, the F-117 community honoured a practice which has been part of the Anglo-American alliance since the 1940s, by inviting a British exchange pilot to serve as an operational member of a squadron. (In practice, Americans serving in the RAF get the better half of this exchange deal since their British hosts give them full opportunities for command and full disciplinary authority; Britons in the USAF perform the same job as their American colleagues but are treated more like guests.) The British F-117 pilot slot has been filled by Graham Wardell, Chris Topham and, later, Ian Wood. In the 1990s, Lockheed revived a plan to sell 'new-build' F-117s to Britain, but the RAF seemed to have no politically justifiable formal need and little money to spend.

Times were changing, and the revisionists were taking hold. They argued (truthfully) that the F-117 was not nearly as accurate as claimed (although extraordinarily precise when compared with any other strike aircraft). They said it was expensive to operate, which was true. They said it might stand in the way of funding for other much-wanted programmes, which was the only real concern. The party

Following their considerable successes in Desert Storm, the US forces put on an uncharacteristic display of power at the 1991 Paris air show. Dominating the impressive line-up was this F-117, giving the type its first public appearance outside of the United States (unless one counts Iraq!).

Lockheed F-117

was over, and it became the essence of Washington politics to display a lowered regard for the F-117. Lieutenant General 'Buster' Glosson, the Gulf War strategist who had become the USAF's top lobbyist, described the F-117 as "archaic, 15-year-old technology" that was "a nightmare to maintain."

Lockheed, whose F-22 had just been chosen as the USAF's Advanced Tactical Fighter (ATF), was told not to campaign for a new F-117 production contract. Push for more F-117 business, the manufacturer was told, and the F-22 will go down in flames. A company official said, "Lockheed's being terrorised."

Move to Holloman

The US Air Force had been ready to bring the F-117 out of the 'black' and was eager to take a further step to integrate it into everyday operations. A decision was made to move from sequestered Tonopah to readily-accessible Holloman Air Force Base at Alamogordo, New Mexico.

At Holloman, the F-15 Eagle-equipped 49th Fighter Wing was scheduled to give up its aircraft, but enjoyed a proud heritage which Air Staff officers wanted to preserve. Among its 43 air aces were Lieutenant Colonel Boyd D. 'Buzz' Wagner, the first American ace in the Pacific theatre, and Major Richard I. Bong, who racked up 40 aerial victories. The 37th's name was not associated with any such claim to glory. The number of tactical wings in the USAF was shrinking rapidly (from 40, the goal during the Reagan years, to 21 or fewer), so some squadron designations had to go. With the shift to Holloman, the F-117 establishment

took over the 49th designation. Plans to rename F-117 squadrons so as to align them with previous 49th associations (the 7th, 8th and 9th TFS) did not at first materialise, and were bitterly opposed by the pilots themselves, who wanted to keep the 415th, 416th and 417th squadron identities.

After the last F-15 Eagle departed Holloman on 5 June 1992 (ending 14 years of Eagle operations at the base), the 49th acquired the 415th, 416th and 417th Fighter Squadrons and their F-117s. The F-117 move from Tonopah to Holloman was carried out between 9 May 1992 and 7 July 1992. During this same period, the US Air Force dropped the adjective 'tactical' from the names of its fighter wings and squadrons. Only more recently have changes in squadron identity caught up with US Air Force tradition. On 30 July 1993, the 415th and 416th Fighter Squadrons were redesignated the 9th and 8th Fighter Squadrons, respectively. During December 1993, the training unit, the 417th FS, became the 7th FS. A detachment of the Nellis-based 57th Wing, known as the 'Dragon Test Team', intermittently operates two or three F-117s at Holloman after having been located at Tonopah since the F-117 came out of the 'black' world.

Readiness decline

The June 1992 move to Holloman was followed by a period of neglect when the US Air Force focused on other priorities and allowed F-117 readiness to decline. Some say that taking the 'Black Jet' out of its hush-hush environment and submerging it in the mainstream Air Force caused the drop in the number of war-ready F-117s from 37 (out of a fleet of 45) in 1992 to a mere 28 aircraft in 1994. Pentagon figures show that in May 1992 an average of 83 per cent of the fleet was ready for wartime operations, while in March 1994 the figure dropped to 62 per cent.

Holloman had no hangars to protect the fighters' radar-absorbing materials from sun damage, posing a new challenge to a maintenance force which had lost 70 per cent of its key people in the move. Holloman's maintenance force was further eroded by the deployment of members to the Middle East with those F-117s assigned to Operation Southern Watch, which monitors the 'No-Fly Zone' in southern Iraq. A funding shortfall led to a shortage of parts and forced F-117 maintenance workers to delay some avionics repairs.

On 4 August 1992, a nocturnal mishap claimed a third operational F-117 when Captain John B. Mills of the 416th Fighter Squadron at Holloman ejected while on a training mission. His aircraft (82-0802) struck a storage building, and no-one on the ground was injured.

In 1993, the USAF allocated an extra $12 million to cover the maintenance funding shortfalls, then assigned $174 million to the problem in 1994. An extra 143 maintenance personnel were put into training. Still, in mid-1994, actual flying by the 'Black Jet' had fallen to a new low. Each F-117 was flying an average of 11.3 sorties per month, about one per month fewer than the previous year.

The future

After being accused of neglecting its F-117 fleet for a couple of years, the US Air Force was embarked in 1994 on four major modification programmes for the stealth fighter:

The Offensive Capability Improvement Program (OCIP) began in 1990 and is aimed at making cockpit operations easier. It adds a moving-map display, an auto throttle, a liquid crystal display used as a data entry panel to communicate with the avionics system, a flight-attitude-awareness display, and (below) a system to automatically return a tumbling aircraft to level flight. The OCIP effort is claimed to improve pilot situational awareness by allowing the flight management system to fit complex profiles automatically. Cost: $191 million.

As part of OCIP and because of its unstable nature, the F-117 is equipped with a PAARS (pilot-activated automatic recovery system) which operates at all attitudes and speeds, gear up or gear down. Upon pilot command, the autopilot, even if not engaged, commands the flight control system and auto throttles to fly a pre-programmed set of manoeuvres, based on entry attitude and airspeed, to recover the F-117 to straight and level flight. The system was installed as a response to the fatal Mulhare and Stewart crashes where spatial disorientation was deemed a factor, and is the first auto recovery system installed for general use in a USAF fighter. Members of the F-117 community say that no one has had to resort to use of the PAARS system.

An IRADS modification is intended to upgrade the F-117's FLIR and DLIR retractable, steerable turrets. Goals for this programme are to double the acquisition range of IRADS and to increase the range and life of the laser. Cost: $144 million.

The MDPS (mission data planning system) modification will help pilots prepare for missions in less time and make it easier to execute missions. Cost: $18 million.

Differential GPS (global positioning system) navigation to replace the existing inertial navigation system. Cost $101 million.

New ideas

The 'Skunk Works' retains tools and jigs to put the F-117 back into production. Early in 1994, in the wake of cancellation of the proposed AF/X strike aircraft, Lockheed revived a longstanding proposal for a carrier-based version of the 'Black Jet'. As first conceived, this would have retained the basic F-117A structural design, altered only by the use of increased-strength materials for the carrierborne environment and the addition of an off-the-shelf ACLS (automatic carrier landing system). The US Navy, unflinching in stubborn pursuit of the McDonnell Douglas FA-18E/F as its next carrier-based strike fighter – a misguided pursuit, say some – told Lockheed that it had no interest in the F-117N and warned the manufacturer to back off.

For a time, Lockheed officials denied that they were proposing the carrier-based F-117N. Inside the Pentagon, however, a few upstarts convinced the US Navy's leadership that the seagoing 'Black Jet' could overcome political hurdles if Lockheed would leap over a few technical ones. 'Skunk Works' engineers made significant changes to their carrier-based stealth fighter, and renamed it the A/F-117X. Today, it is one of three new versions (below) being put forward by the manufacturer.

Paul Martin, F-117 Programs vice president, said in June 1994 that F-117A+, F-117B, and A/F-117X proposals were being briefed in Washington. Says Martin, "We're not gold-plated, we keep our team lean, and we work with the customer to provide the product he wants. We're the experts on low-rate production."

Rework proposal

The term F-117A+ applies to a proposed modification of existing Nighthawks belonging to the US Air Force. Lockheed proposes to turn out a prototype aircraft for $79 million. Details have not been released, although Martin says the upgrade involves "full-scale development of 18 advanced low-observables technologies." The US Air Force, which has resisted any major investment in new-build aircraft, is said to be interested in the F-117A+ and to be seeking funds to launch a programme.

The F-117B is the maker's proposal for a new-build US Air Force aircraft having some commonality with a Navy version to spread out costs if both were selected. The F-117B would have a maximum gross take-off weight of 73,200 lb (33203 kg) as compared with 52,500 lb (23813 kg) for the current aircraft. Combat radius would be

Experience with the F-117 gave Lockheed a tremendous boost when it came to development of the F-22, the winning design in the USAF's ATF next-generation fighter competition. The YF-22 showed some design concept similarities, notably in having a limited number of alignments of surfaces and sawtooth edges for doors, but it was a far more blended aircraft, and also attended to the operational requirement aspect more closely.

An artist's impression shows the A/F-117X proposal for the Navy, with folding wings, trapezoidal tailplanes, reworked exhaust area and a more extensively glazed canopy.

From head-on the huge bulk of the F-117 is apparent. Any new variant would feature a considerable improvement in weapons carriage.

only at night and only against HVAs in Desert Storm, the F-117, if it had been equipped with external racks, could have been employed as a very accurate 'bomb truck' during the day carrying weapons externally as a non-stealthy but highly accurate strike aircraft. The US Air Force has long stated its interest in increasing payload from two to four bombs internally, and possibly another four externally.

A new wing and tail would give the F-117B a distinct shape, and all-weather sensors (type not disclosed), advanced signature characteristics, improved aerodynamics, and two General Electric F414 engines with afterburners. Martin says these changes will "press the state of the art for low-observable aircraft."

Naval peculiarities

The A/F-117X would have the heftier weight, payload, engines and other characteristics of the F-117B, but would also have its fuselage and landing gear further strengthened for shipboard operations. This Navy aircraft would have a much-revised trapezoidal horizontal tail, a bubble canopy like that on the F-22, an arrester hook, folding wings and F-14 undercarriage. In a push for modular production and alleged cost savings, Lockheed is proposing that the US Navy and Air Force execute a joint programme to build both the F-117B and A/F-117X.

Lockheed documents credit the A/F-117X with AIM-120 AMRAAM and AIM-9 Sidewinder air-to-air missile capability. This is presumably a feature of the F-117B as well, but no one has said so.

increased to 980 nm (1,127 miles; 1813 km) from 570 nm (655 miles; 1055 km) and payload would be doubled to 10,000 lb (4540 kg).

While details have not been forthcoming, the latter change would overcome the F-117's principal weakness, namely its inability to carry more than two bombs. Used

Above: A 49th FW 'Black Jet' cruises serenely in the sunset over the White Sands National Monument near the unit's base at Holloman. The Air Force may expand the capabilities of the Nighthawk with the F-117A+ programme proposed by Lockheed, a rework of existing F-117As to improve operational performance, notably in the area of stealthiness.

Left: The immediate future of the F-117A is assured, but less rosy are the prospects of the F-117B, a much-improved new-build model with far greater bomb-carrying potential and systems. The naval A/F-117X is based on this aircraft, giving the Pentagon the opportunity of procuring both variants from the same production line, with a consequent saving in procurement and maintenance costs.

Individual Aircraft Details

The following table lists the complete XST/F-117 production run. Details of aircraft which participated in Desert Storm accompany the bomb bay door artwork.

XST-1 HB 1001 Ff 1 December 1977 (Bill Park). Crashed 4 May 1978 (Bill Park), W/O.

XST-2 HB 1002 Have Blue LO test aircraft. Ff 20 July 1978 (Lt Col Ken Dyson). Crashed July 1979 (Lt Col Ken Dyson), W/O.

79-10780 'Scorpion 1', full-scale development (FSD) aircraft. First flight 18 June 1981, Hal Farley. Listed by one source as YF-117A. Lost a tail fin during a side slip in 1987 but landed safely. Now preserved on display at Nellis AFB, Nevada.

79-10781 'Scorpion 2' FSD aircraft. First flight 18 December 1981. Listed one source as YF-117A. Now preserved on display at US Air Force Museum, Dayton, Ohio.

79-10782 'Scorpion 3' FSD aircraft. Listed by one source as YF-117A. First WSCS upgrade test aircraft. Considered as first OCIP upgrade test aircraft but rejected (in favour of 85-0831) because of expected delay in modification. 410th TS/412th TW Palmdale, 'ED' tailcode.

79-10783 'Scorpion 4' FSD aircraft. Listed by one source as YF-117A. Nicknamed 'Pete's Dragon' at Groom Lake. 410th TS/412th TW Palmdale, 'ED' tailcode.

79-10784 'Scorpion 5' FSD aircraft. Second WSCS upgrade test aircraft. Displayed for Secretary of Defense Caspar Weinberger during a secret visit to Groom Lake in 1984. Listed by one source as YF-117A. 410th TS/412th TW Palmdale, 'ED' tailcode.

—— Crashed 20 April 1982 prior to US Air Force acceptance (Robert L. Riedenauer), W/O; not assigned a serial.

79-10785 Possibly 79-0785

80-0786 Second operational aircraft delivered; used initially for weapons tests until reaching 4450th TG in September 1982. Desert Storm.

80-0787 First aircraft delivered to 4450th TG, 23 August 1982.

80-0788

80-0789 Desert Storm.

80-0790 Delivered to 4450th TG in Tonopah in December 1982 after trials at Groom Lake. Used for public unveiling ceremony at Nellis AFB, April 1990. Desert Storm. Suffered the most 'serious' damage of the Gulf War when it blew a nose wheel on landing.

80-0791 Delivered to 4450th TG in Tonopah in December 1982 after trials at Groom Lake. Desert Storm.

81-10792 Delivered to 4450th TG in Tonopah in December 1982 after trials at Groom Lake. Crashed 11 July 1986 (Major Ross E. Mulhare), W/O.

81-10793 Desert Storm.

81-10794 Desert Storm.

81-10795

81-10796 Desert Storm.

81-10797 Desert Storm.

81-10798 Desert Storm.

82-0799 Delivered to 4450th TG on 28 October 1983 enabling the group to attain IOC. Desert Storm.

82-0800

82-0801 Desert Storm.

82-0802 Desert Storm. Crashed 4 August 1992 (Captain John B. Mills, 416th FS), W/O.

82-0803 Desert Storm.

82-0804 Currently assigned to Det. 1/57th Wing at Holloman AFB for operational test and evaluation purposes.

82-0805

82-0806 Desert Storm.

83-0807 Desert Storm.

83-0808

84-0809 Desert Storm.

84-0810 Desert Storm.

84-0811 Desert Storm.

84-0812 Desert Storm.

84-0824

84-0825 Desert Storm.

84-0826 Desert Storm. (Captain Rob Donaldson).

84-0827

84-0828 Used for public unveiling at Nellis, 21 April 1990 marked for Colonel Tony Tolin and carrying '37 TFW' tail markings.

85-0813 Col. Alton C. ('Al') Whitley's wing commander's aircraft during Operation Desert Storm.

85-0814 Desert Storm. (Captain John Savidge).

85-0815 Crashed 14 October 1987 (Major Michael C. Stewart), W/O.

85-0816 Desert Storm.

85-0817 Desert Storm.

85-0818 Desert Storm.

85-0819 Desert Storm.

85-0820

85-0829 Desert Storm.

85-0830 Desert Storm. Made first overseas public display at Paris air show in June 1991. First on public display in the United Kingdom as TR (37th FW) at Mildenhall Air Fete '92.

85-0831 Third aircraft with WSCS upgrade. Chosen as first OCIP upgrade aircraft (and removed from the operational fleet for developmental work). 410th TS/412th TW Palmdale, 'ED' tailcode.

85-0832 Desert Storm.

85-0833 Desert Storm.

85-0834 Desert Storm.

85-0835 Desert Storm.

85-0836 Served as 37th TFW commander's aircraft before being deemed a 'bad actor' or 'hangar queen' at Tonopah. Desert Storm.

86-0821 Desert Storm.

86-0822

86-0823

86-0837 Desert Storm. (Captain Matthew Byrd).

86-0838 Desert Storm. (Lt. Col. Gregory ('Greg') Gonyea).

86-0839 Desert Storm. (Major Joe Salada).

86-0840 Desert Storm.

88-0841 Desert Storm.

88-0842 Desert Storm. (Captain Rich Cline).

88-0843 Delivered 12 July 1990. Final F-117 aircraft. Desert Storm.

Aircraft #786 – 'War Pig'
24 combat missions – 416th TFS

Aircraft #789 – 'Black Magic'
31 combat missions – 415th TFS

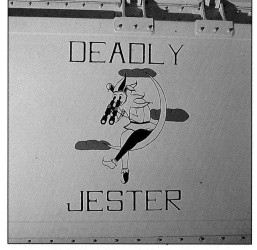

Aircraft #790 – 'Deadly Jester'
30 combat missions – 415th TFS

Aircraft #791 – 'Lazy Ace'
33 combat missions – 415th TFS

Aircraft #793 – 'Wiley E. Coyote's Tritonal Express'   33 combat missions

Aircraft #794 – 'Delta Dawn'
35 combat missions – 415th TFS

Aircraft #796 – 'Fatal Attraction'
29 combat missions – 415th TFS

Aircraft #797 – 'Spell Bound'
8 combat missions – 416th TFS

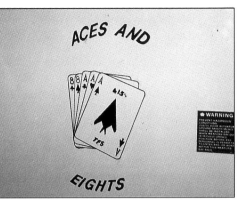

Aircraft #798 – 'Aces and Eights'
34 combat missions – 415th TFS

Aircraft #799 – 'Midnight Rider'
21 combat missions – 416th TFS

Aircraft #801 – 'Perpetrator'
38 combat missions – 415th TFS

Aircraft #802 – 'Black Magic'
19 combat missions – 416th TFS

Aircraft #803 – Unexpected Guest'
33 combat missions – 416th TFS

Aircraft #806 – 'Something Wicked'
39 combat missions – 415th TFS

Aircraft #807 – 'The Chickenhawk'
14 combat missions – 415th TFS

Aircraft #808 – 'Thor'
37 combat missions – 415th TFS

Aircraft #810 – 'Dark Angel'
26 combat missions – 416th TFS

Aircraft #811 – 'Double Down'
33 combat missions – 415th TFS

Aircraft #812 – 'Axel'
42 combat missions – 415th TFS

Aircraft #813 – 'Toxic Avenger'
35 combat missions – 416th TFS

Aircraft #814 – 'Final Verdict'
34 combat missions – 416th TFS

Aircraft #816 – 'Lone Wolf'
39 combat missions – 415th TFS

Aircraft #817 – 'Shaba'
18 combat missions – 416th TFS

Aircraft #818 – 'The Overachiever'
38 combat missions – 415th TFS

Aircraft #819 – 'Raven Beauty'
30 combat missions – 416th TFS

Aircraft #821 – 'Sneak Attack'
32 combat missions – 415th TFS

Aircraft #825 – 'Mad Max'
33 combat missions – 415th TFS

Aircraft #826 – 'Nachtfalke'
29 combat missions – 415th TFS

Aircraft #829 – 'Avenging Angel'
23 combat missions – 416th TFS

Aircraft #830 – 'Black Assassin'
31 combat missions – 416th TFS

Aircraft #832 – 'Once Bitten'
30 combat missions – 416th TFS

Aircraft #833 – 'Black Devil'
30 combat missions – 416th TFS

Aircraft #834 – 'Necromancer'
34 combat missions – 416th TFS

Aircraft #835 – 'The Dragon'
26 combat missions – 416th TFS

Aircraft #836 – 'Christine'
39 combat missions – 416th TFS

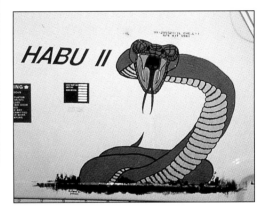

Aircraft #837 – 'Habu II'
31 combat missions – 416th TFS

Aircraft 838 – 'Magic Hammer'
36 combat missions – 416th TFS

Aircraft #839 – 'Midnight Reaper'
39 combat missions – 415th TFS

Aircraft #840 – 'Black Widow'
32 combat missions – 416th TFS

Aircraft #841 – 'Mystic Warrior'
18 combat missions – 416th TFS

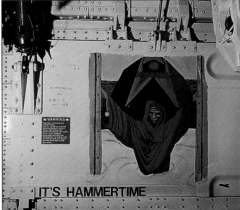

Aircraft #842 – 'It's Hammertime'
33 combat missions – 416th TFS

Aircraft #843 – 'Affectionately Christine'
33 combat missions – 415th TFS

F-117 Operators

4450th Tactical Group (A-Unit)

('TR'), Tonopah Test Range, Nevada

The 4450th TG was activated on 15 October 1979 with Colonel Robert A. Jackson as commander. The four-digit number beginning with '4' signifies a 'provisional' group not entitled to permanent military lineage or heraldry. The best-kept secret of the time was the development of a strike aircraft intended to be largely invisible to radar, and the 4450th – also known as the A-Unit, one of a series of designations devised for everyday use because they conveyed no meaning – began life at Nellis AFB, Nevada, awaiting the mystery aircraft. The group began rotating pilots and maintenance personnel through the super-secret Groom Lake, Nevada, facility in 1981, although the group's home was always meant to be the Tonopah Test Range (TTR) airfield, also in Nevada.

Although Colonel Jackson never flew the Senior Trend, he had a key role in hand-picking the field-grade officers who made up the initial cadre of stealth aircraft pilots. The group's Detachment 1, alias the Q-Unit commanded by Lieutenant Colonel Alton C. Whitley, set up shop at Tonopah, initially in mobile homes once operated by a Chevron oil drilling site, and was followed by the group headquarters. The group's Detachment 2, or R-Unit, activated with the group on 15 October 1979 and was a small flight-test detachment which apparently kept a handful of test pilots at Burbank (later Palmdale) and Groom Lake.

Lieutenant Colonel Whitley's Detachment 1, with the first operational pilots who flew the Senior Trend aircraft, evolved into 4452nd Test Squadron 'Goat Suckers', still called the Q-Unit, by September 1982.

The first squadrons in the group, however, were the 4450th and 4451st Test Squadrons, activated on 11 June 1981. The 4450th Test Squadron 'Nightstalkers', or I-Unit, was first commanded by Major William C. Helper, and the 4451st Test Squadron 'Ghostriders', alias the P-Unit, by Lieutenant Colonel Jerry Fleming. The P-Unit operated the Vought A-7D aircraft stationed at Nellis AFB, Nevada, which served at first to give pilots flying time and to cover their true purpose; once Senior Trend aeroplanes began to enter service, the A-7Ds were used as chase, or 'companion', aircraft.

Colonel James S. Allen took command of the 4450th Tactical Group on 17 May 1982 and accepted the first operational Senior Trend (80-0787) at Tonopah on 23 August 1982, after the aircraft had passed initial trials at Groom Lake. The group attained IOC (initial operating capability) on 28 October 1983 with delivery of its 14th aircraft.

Colonel Howell M. Estes III became commander of the 4450th TG on 15 June 1984 and led the group through its first ORI (operational readiness inspection). The group's third squadron, filling out its intended strength from the beginning, was the 4453rd Test and Evaluation Squadron 'Grim Reaper', or the Z-Unit, activated on 1 October 1985 under Lieutenant Colonel Roger Locher.

Colonel Michael W. Harris assumed command of the group on 6 December 1985. Colonel Michael Short became commander on 3 April 1987. Colonel Anthony J. (Tony) Tolin took command on 10 August 1988.

When the F-117 was made public, the USAF no longer needed a provisional group to operate the aircraft. Furthermore, the identity of a line fighter wing, the 37th TFW (which was then winding down F-4G Advanced 'Wild Weasel' operations at George AFB, California) was available for immediate transfer. On 5 October 1989, the USAF inactivated the 4450th TG and put the group's commander (Colonel Tolin), people and equipment under the 37th TFW banner. In practical terms, this was a change of name only, as everything stayed in place and Tonopah remained the home of the 37th Tactical Fighter Wing.

4450th Test Squadron (I-Unit) 'Nightstalkers'

The 4450th TS was one of two squadrons (with the 4451st TS) activated under the 4450th TG on 11 June 1981, some 14 months before the first operational Senior Trend aircraft was delivered. The 'Nightstalkers' were first commanded by Major William C. Helper, who did not become a Senior Trend pilot but performed interim organisational chores until replaced by pilot Lieutenant Colonel Ervin C. ('Sandy') Sharpe.

The 'Nightstalkers' flew the Senior Trend aircraft from late 1982 onwards. The squadron came under command of Lieutenant Colonel John F. Miller (replacing Sharpe) in June 1985, and then of Lieutenant Colonel David T. Holmes on 16 January 1987 (according to one source) or in June 1987 (according to another). Lieutenant Colonel William J. Lake was the final commander of the 4450th TS and remained in place when the squadron was inactivated 5 October 1989. On that date, the squadron's people and equipment remained at Tonopah and the 'Nightstalkers' were redesignated 415th TFS.

4451st Test Squadron (P-Unit) 'Ghostriders' ('LV'), Nellis AFB, Nevada (later Tonopah)

The 4451st was activated on 11 June 1981 (together with the 4450th TS) under Lieutenant Colonel Jerry Fleming. The 'Ghostriders' operated Vought A-7D aircraft at Nellis. The A-7Ds were used as cover for the real purpose of the stealth fighter group and later as chase or 'companion' aircraft for the Senior Trend. Lieutenant Colonel Medford C. ('Med') Bowman became commander in about 1985. Lieutenant Colonel Robert E. Bruce, Jr, who was not qualified in the Senior Trend aircraft, took command in August 1986. There is no indication the 4451st was ever equipped with F-117s through the date of its inactivation, 5 October 1989. It did, however, become an F-117 squadron when, on that date, it assumed its new identity as the 416th TFS.

4452nd Test Squadron (Q-Unit) 'Goat Suckers'

4452nd Test Squadron 'Goat Suckers' (Q-Unit) began as Detachment 1 of the 4450th and was assigned to Tonopah during the brief period when group headquarters remained at Nellis; the 'Goat Suckers' took on the popular term for the American night hawk, even though Lockheed never succeeded in persuading the USAF to adopt Nighthawk as the nickname for the Senior Trend aircraft, and were formed under Major Alton C. 'Al' Whitley in September 1982.

Major Dennis R. Larson commanded the squadron briefly after Whitley's 1985 departure and was followed by Major Robert D. Williams on 25 July 1985. Lieutenant Colonel Medford ('Med') Bowman, who had formerly commanded the P-Unit, moved to assume command of the Q-Unit in August 1986 and served briefly before being replaced on 7 January 1987 by Lieutenant Colonel Arthur P. ('Art') Weyermuller. Weyermuller was in turn replaced by Lieutenant Colonel James G. Ferguson on 14 August 1987. The squadron was inactivated on 30 May 1989, becoming the only stealth unit not to acquire a new identity as part of the 37th TFW later in the year.

4453rd Test and Evaluation Squadron (Z-Unit) 'Grim Reapers'

The 4453rd Test and Evaluation Squadron 'Grim Reaper' (Z-Unit) was activated on 1 October 1985 under Lieutenant Colonel Roger Locher to become the third Senior Trend flying squadron in the 4450th Tactical Group. In January 1989, this F-117 squadron began preparations to take charge of chase, or 'companion', aircraft with delivery of the first Northrop T-38 Talons that month; this new role became official on 30 May 1989, when the Vought A-7D unit at Nellis was inactivated.

Continuing to fly F-117s and T-38s, the 4453rd also took over the local area familiarisation function which had been an extra duty for the group's R-Unit, its small flight-test organisation, also inactivated on 30 May 1989. The final commander of the 4453rd TES was Lieutenant Colonel Richard C. Groesch. The squadron was inactivated on 5 October 1989, when its people and equipment, remaining in place at Tonopah, became the 417th Tactical Fighter Training Squadron.

A 4450th Tactical Group F-117 poses at Tonopah. In the early years the only unit marking was the unit badge on the intake trunk. Tail markings consisted of the last three digits of the serial and a Tactical Air Command badge.

37th Tactical Fighter Wing

('TR'), Tonopah Test Range, Nevada

The 37th Tactical Fighter Wing, which had operated F-4G Advanced 'Wild Weasels' at George AFB, California, took over the identity of the inactivated 4450th Tactical Group. The 37th raised its flag at Tonopah on 5 October 1989, taking over the three F-117 group's squadrons which were redesignated 415th TFS (former 4450th TS), 416th TFS (former 4451st TS) and 417th TFTS (former 4453rd TES). Colonel Anthony J. Tolin remained as commander when the change took place.

In December 1989, the wing launched six F-117s on a combat mission from Tonopah during Operation Just Cause in Panama. Two aircraft were spares, two were called off from a special operations mission aimed at Panamanian leader Manuel Noriega, and two bombed a field near the Rio Hato barracks as scheduled. Colonel Tolin continued to command the wing until 16 August 1990, at which time Operation Desert Shield was beginning.

Colonel Alton C. ('Al') Whitley, Jr, who had been the first operational pilot to fly the Senior Trend aircraft, returned to the stealth world as 37th TFW commander on 16 August 1990, and guided the wing through its deployment in Operation Desert Shield and combat in Desert Storm. The wing deployed its 415th TFS to the Middle East in August 1990 and its 416th TFS in December 1990; its third flying squadron, the 417th TFTS, remained at home at Tonopah but provided personnel and aircraft for the build-up against Iraq. As noted below, the deployed 37th TFW was designated a 'provisional' wing on 20 December 1990 to bring its nomenclature in line with other wings preparing at that time for a possible war with Iraq.

The war began on 17 January 1991 and ended just more than a month later. The US Air Force later said that the 37th TFW's F-117s comprised only 2.5 per cent of the shooters in-theatre on the first day of the war against Iraq, yet credited them with hitting over 31 per cent of the targets.

The unit's 'provisional' designation was dropped after the war and most of the 37th TFW returned to Tonopah, but the wing left some aircraft at Khamis Mushait as a contingency and to retain a striking potential in support of Operation Southern Watch, the coalition's enforcement of a 'No-Fly Zone' in Kurdish areas of northern Iraq. This Middle East presence has involved periodic rotation of squadrons and personnel.

The 37th TFW lost the modifier 'tactical' in its name and became the 37th Fighter Wing on 1 October 1991.

37th Tactical Fighter Wing (Provisional), King Khalid Air Base, Khamis Mushait, Saudi Arabia

The 37th TFW (P) designation, applicable to the bulk of the F-117 wing when it was deployed to Saudi Arabia, became effective on 20 December 1990. Colonel Alton C. Whitley served as commander of the wing before, during and after the war, when the 'provisional' modifier was dropped.

37th Fighter Wing ('TR'), Tonopah Test Range, Nevada

The 37th Fighter Wing accepted its designation on 1 October 1991, replacing the 37th TFW with no change in commander, personnel or equipment. When the USAF decided to move the F-117 force to Holloman AFB, New Mexico, partly to reduce operating costs now that the secrecy of Tonopah was no longer needed, a decision was taken to preserve the identity of the 49th Fighter Wing, which was then at Holloman (but giving up its F-15 Eagle fleet) and to retire the 37th designation. With the shift to Holloman, the F-117 establishment became the 49th Fighter Wing on 5 July 1992.

415th Tactical Fighter Squadron 'Nightstalkers'

The 415th Tactical Fighter Squadron came into existence on 5 October 1989 with the people and equipment of the former 4450th TS, including commander Lieutenant Colonel William J. Lake. The 415th TFS provided the six F-117s and pilots who flew the 19 December 1989 combat mission to Panama during Operation Just Cause (see main text and 37th TFW entry). Under contingency plans of the late 1980s, the squadron was considered to be the Atlantic component of the stealth fighter community, expected to 'chop' to US European Command in time of war. In fact, when war came in the Middle East, the squadron chopped to US Central Command during Operation Desert Shield.

The 'Nightstalkers' were the first of the wing's squadrons to be deployed to Khamis Mushait, Saudi Arabia, in Desert Shield, beginning 26 August 1990. The squadron bore the brunt of the difficult build-up in the Middle East, bolstered by a few personnel and aircraft from the 416th TFS (which deployed in December 1990) and 417th TFTS (which remained stateside but provided aircraft and personnel). Commanded in 1990-91 by Lieutenant Colonel Ralph Getchell, the 'Nightstalkers' fought in Operation Desert Storm from the first night, 17 January 1991, until the end on 26 February 1991. The 415th TFS had the first F-117 contingent to return from the Gulf War, eight aircraft which landed at Nellis AFB on 1 April 1991.

Final commander of the 415th TFS was Lieutenant Colonel Bruce E. Kreidler, who remained on board when the squadron's designation was changed. In keeping with USAF reorganisation, the 415th TFS became the 415th FS on 1 October 1991.

415th Fighter Squadron 'Nightstalkers,' later 'Nighthawks'

The 415th FS was the new name for the former 415th TFS, effective 1 October 1991. Lieutenant Colonel Bruce E. Kreidler was commander at the time of the name change. Another change in USAF nomenclature put an end to emblems and nicknames with satanic connotations, no matter obscure: with this change in late 1992 the 'Nightstalkers' lost their proud nickname and became, instead, the 'Nighthawks.'

When the F-117 force moved from Tonopah to Holloman AFB, New Mexico on 5 July 1992, the 37th FW became the 49th FW, but the squadron designation was not, at first changed. For a time, 416th TFS could not take on the name of the 9th Fighter Squadron because that designator was employed (from May 1992) by the F-4E Phantom unit which trains German Luftwaffe pilots; on 30 July 1993 the Phantom unit reverted to its earlier designator as the 20th FS, a move which enabled the 416th TFS, in turn, to be redesignated 9th Fighter Squadron on that date.

416th Tactical Fighter Squadron 'Ghostriders'

The 416th Tactical Fighter Squadron came into existence on 5 October 1989 with the people and equipment of the former 4451st Test Squadron, but with a new commander. On that date, Lieutenant Colonel Gerald C. Carpenter moved from the inactivated 4453rd Test Squadron to take charge of the 416th TFS. 'Ghostriders.'

The Pacific component of the 37th TFW earmarked for US Pacific Command (meaning Korea) in the event of war, the 'Ghostriders' were not at first chosen for deployment when Operation Desert Storm began in August 1990. As the build-up in the Middle East grew, the decision was made to deploy the squadron, and the long trip to Khamis Mushait, Saudi Arabia (with a stopover at Langley AFB, Virginia) began on 2 December 1990. Commanded in 1990-91 by Lieutenant Colonel Gregory ('Greg') Gonyea, the 'Ghostriders' fought in Operation Desert Storm from the first night, 17 January 1991, until the end on 26 February 1991.

In the immediate post-Desert Storm era, the 416th TFS made a deployment to Korea where it was part of contingency plans for a conflict there.

Lieutenant Colonel Gonyea was still in command when the squadron underwent its next name change, along with the other F-117 flying units. In keeping with USAF reorganisation, the 416th TFS lost its 'tactical' nomenclature and was redesignated 416th FS on 1 October 1991.

416th Fighter Squadron 'Ghostriders,' later 'Knight Riders'

The 416th Fighter Squadron was the new name for the former 416th TFS, effective 1 October 1991. Lieutenant Colonel Gregory ('Greg') Gonyea was commander at the time of the name change. When the USAF issued its ban on devilish nicknames, the 'Ghostriders' were forced to give up the nickname in which they felt considerable pride, and were renamed the 'Knight Riders'. The change is a curious one, because the taboo on satanic names followed an earlier ban on names deemed not to be 'gender neutral'; apparently no one noticed that knights, in theory at least, are male.

When the F-117 force moved from Tonopah to Holloman AFB, New Mexico, on

This pair of 37th TFW aircraft displays special markings for the wing commander (foreground), and the standard tail markings with large 'TR' code.

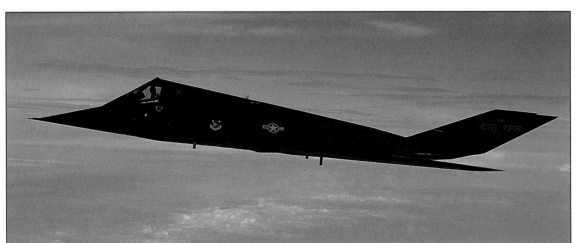

417th Fighter Squadron 'Bandits'

Various special markings have been applied to the F-117, this aircraft seen in 1991 wearing a revised tail marking for the 416th squadron commander.

5 July 1992, the parent 37th FW relinquished its designation in order to adopt the colours and lineage of the 49th FW. Squadron designations, however, were not changed at first. Serving as an F-117 squadron under the 49th Fighter Wing at Holloman, the 'Knight Riders' were redesignated 8th Fighter Squadron on 30 July 1993.

417th Tactical Fighter Training Squadron 'Bandits'

The 417th TFTS was formed on 5 October 1989 from the assets of the 4453rd Test and Evaluation Squadron, the 'Bandits'. The squadron served as the RTU (replacement training unit) for the F-117 and took over operation of the stealth community's Northrop T-38 Talon chase aircraft.

The 417th TFTS did not deploy during Operations Desert Shield/Storm but provided eight aircraft to stand by at Langley AFB, Virginia, as attrition replacements for

the F-117 force in the Middle East. In the event, there was no attrition and the aircraft were not needed. The 'Bandits' were commanded in 1990-91 Lieutenant Colonel Robert J. ('Bob') Maher.

In keeping with USAF reorganisation, the 417th TFTS lost the 'tactical' and 'training' adjectives in its title (although keeping its training duties) and was redesignated the 416th Fighter Squadron on 1 October 1991. Commander at the time was Lieutenant Colonel Barry Horne.

The 417th FS took on its new name on 1 October 1991 at Tonopah, retaining Lieutenant Colonel Barry Horne as commander and its mission as the RTU (replacement training unit) for the F-117.

When the F-117 force moved from Tonopah to Holloman AFB, New Mexico, on 5 July 1992, the 37th FW took over the colours and lineage of the 49th FW. Squadron designations, however, were not changed at first. In fact, the 417th FS was the last of the three F-117 squadrons to assume a new identity traditionally associated with its parent wing. Equipped with 10 F-117s and 11 AT-38B Talons, the squadron was redesignated 7th FS in December 1993.

49th Fighter Wing

('HO'), Holloman AFB, New Mexico

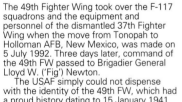

The 49th Fighter Wing took over the F-117 squadrons and the equipment and personnel of the dismantled 37th Fighter Wing when the move from Tonopah to Holloman AFB, New Mexico, was made on 5 July 1992. Three days later, command of the 49th FW passed to Brigadier General Lloyd W. ('Fig') Newton.

The USAF simply could not dispense with the identity of the 49th FW, which had a proud history dating to 15 January 1941 when the 49th Pursuit Group (Interceptor) trained in Seversky P-35s before moving to New Guinea. Among its 43 air aces were Lieutenant Colonel Boyd D. 'Buzz' Wagner, the first American ace in the Pacific theatre, and Major Richard I. Bong, who racked up 40 aerial victories. The 49th fought in Korea with F-80s and F-84s, flew F-4 Phantoms during the Cold War, and operated F-15 Eagles immediately prior to the change.

When it received its F-117s, the 49th FW took on the three flying squadrons, namely the 415th Fighter Squadron 'Nighthawks' (formerly 'Nightstalkers'), which was redesignated as 9th Fighter Squadron on 30 July 1993; the 416th Fighter Squadron

The 49th FW commander's aircraft displays the new 'HO' tailcodes, intake unit insignia and Air Combat Command badge.

'Knight Riders' (formerly 'Ghostriders'), redesignated 8th Fighter Squadron on 30 July 1993; and the 417th Fighter Squadron 'Bandits', redesignated 7th Fighter Squadron in December 1993. The last-named squadron change had to await the transfer of the wing's IFF (introduction to fighter fundamentals) training, performed in the AT-38B Talon, to Air Education and Training Command.

The move to Holloman brought the 'Cockroach', or 'Black Jet', out into the open, both literally and figuratively. While many aspects of F-117 operations remained classified, the warplane was no longer part of a 'black' programme; in contrast to the plush indoor facilities to which the F-117 community had become accustomed, much of the work at Holloman, today, is performed out of doors.

In addition to its three F-117 squadrons, the 49th FW operates the 20th Fighter Squadron which trains Luftwaffe pilots in German-owned F-4E Phantoms (and which

was briefly designated 9th FS from May 1992, until that designation went to an F-117 unit on 30 July 1993), the 48th Rescue Squadron with five HH-60G helicopters, and the 435th Fighter Squadron which trains Taiwanese pilots in the AT-38B Talon (to prepare them for the F-16 Fighting Falcon). In June 1993, Brigadier General Newton turned over command of the 49th FW to Brigadier General John F. Miller, Jr, who, as a lieutenant colonel, had commanded the old 4450th TS, the original 'Nightstalkers', and who also commanded the 8th TFW ('Wolf Pack') in Korea with F-16 Fighting Falcons.

7th Fighter Squadron 'Bunyaps'

The 7th Fighter Squadron 'Bunyaps' took over the F-117 operations of the former 417th FS 'Bandits' in December 1993. The 'Bunyaps' get their nickname from a mythical fanged creature in the lore of Australian Aborigines and owes their origins to the 7th Pursuit Squadron (Interceptor) formed on 20 November 1940 with Seversky P-35s. Curiously, the devil-like creature in the 'Bunyaps'' emblem

(approved in 1944) has survived the USAF's ban on satanic images even though the 'Nightstalkers' and 'Ghostriders' of the recent past did not.

The squadron's history includes combat in New Guinea and the Philippines in P-40s,

P-47s and P-38s; in Korea in F-80s and F-84s; and Cold War flying in the F-100, F-105, F-4 and F-15. Just before becoming an F-117 operator, the squadron performed IFF (introduction to fighter fundamentals) training for future F-15 Eagle pilots using the AT-38B Talon. The time consumed in winding down and transferring this function meant that the 8th and 9th FS became F-117 operators fully nine months before the 7th FS did. The 7th FS is now the RTU (replacement training unit) for the F-117 type.

8th Fighter Squadron 'Black Sheep'

The 8th Fighter Squadron 'Black Sheep' took over the F-117 operations of the former 416th FS ('Knight Riders', previously 'Ghostriders') on 30 July 1993. The squadron emblem is a silhouette of a black sheep inside a golden yellow circle bordered in black. The squadron began as the 8th

Pursuit Squadron (Interceptor) on 20 November 1940 with Seversky P-35s. The squadron's history includes combat in New Guinea and the Philippines in P-40s, P-47s and P-38s; in Korea in F-80s and F-84s; and

Cold War operations with the F-100, F-105, F-4 and F-15.

The 8th FS retains the Pacific contingency for the F-117 force and would be the first squadron deployed to Korea in event of a crisis there.

9th Fighter Squadron 'Iron Knights'

The 9th Fighter Squadron 'Iron Knights' took over the F-117 operations of the former 415th Fighter Squadron 'Nighthawks' (formerly 'Nightstalkers') 30 July 1993. The squadron emblem is a white, winged knight's helmet on a blue disk bordered in black. The squadron began as the 9th Pursuit Squadron (Interceptor) on 20 November 1940 with Seversky P-35s. The squadron's history includes combat in New Guinea and the Philippines in P-40s, P-47s and P-38s; in Korea in F-80s and F-84s; and Cold War operations with the F-100, F-105, F-4 and F-15.

The 9th FS retains the Atlantic contingency for the F-117 force and would be the first squadron deployed to Europe in event of a crisis there.

57th Fighter Weapons Wing

('WA'), Nellis AFB, Nevada

The 57th Fighter Weapons Wing at Nellis AFB, Nevada, conducted weapons, armament and tactics tests and training for the USAF's Tactical Air Command (TAC). In addition to maintaining squadrons at Nellis for various aircraft types (F-16, F-111, A-10), the 57th FWW has traditionally operated detachments at air bases in connection with less numerous types. Weaponeering with the Senior Trend aircraft was performed in the 'black' world by the 4450th Tactical Group until 5 October 1989, when (on the same day the 4450th TG became the 37th TFW) TAC activated Detachment 1, 57th FWW, at the group's base, Tonopah Test Range, Nevada. Typically, the detachment flew F-117 aircraft based at Tonopah, but carried out everyday operations, no longer constrained by 'blackness,' in better-known sectors of the Nellis reservation.

The 57th FWW detachment remained in operation on 1 October 1991 when its parent unit was redesignated 57th Fighter Wing.

57th Fighter Wing

The 57th Fighter Wing acquired its designation on 1 October 1991 and continued to operate its Detachment 1 at Tonopah.

On 12 November 1991, Brigadier General Anthony J. (Tony) Tolin, who earlier commanded the F-117 operation (10 August 1988 - 16 August 1990) took command of the 57th Fighter Wing. Tolin was in charge

of the 57th FW during the period when the F-117 force relocated from Tonopah to Holloman. His wing's Detachment 1, now known as the 'Dragon Test Team', was activated at Holloman on 1 June 1992, the date TAC became Air Combat Command (ACC), and roughly coinciding with the beginning of F-117 operations on 5 July 1992.

Typically, the 'Dragon Test Team' operates two or three F-117s at Holloman with 'WA' tailcodes but flies to Nellis for most weapon tests and training. Colonel Tolin was still in command of the 57th FW when a new change in designation took place, making it the 57th Wing, on 1 February 1993.

57th Wing

The 57th Wing at Nellis AFB, Nevada, conducts weapons, armament and tactics tests and training for the USAF's Air Combat Command, and acquired its current designation on 1 February 1993. The change was made because the wing absorbed the USAF Weapons School, which includes bombers as well as fighters. Colonel Tolin was replaced on 10 September 1993 by the current commander, Brigadier General John L. Welde, who does not come from the F-117 community.

The 57th Wing's Detachment 1, alias the 'Dragon Test Team,' continues to operate two or three F-117s at Holloman with 'WA'

Above: At least one F-117 is permanently assigned to Det 1, 57th Wing, and wears the parent unit's checkerboard fin-stripe, albeit in a toned-down version.

tailcodes and takes the aircraft to Nellis for most weapon tests and training.

The 57th Wing has an OL (operating location) at Kirtland AFB, New Mexico, where various aircraft types including the F-117 'Cockroach' have been evaluated for their vulnerability to EMP (electromagnetic pulse).

The 57th Wing is scheduled for a further major reorganisation on 1 October 1994, which is not expected to affect its F-117 element.

The 57th Wing badge highlights the weapon-testing role of the unit.

410th Flight Test Squadron

('ED'), Palmdale, California

The 410th Test Squadron acquired its designation on 1 May 1993 at the Palmdale 'Skunk Works' flight test centre. The 410th TS traces its roots, if not its formal lineage, to the 4450th Tactical Group's Detachment 2, or R-Unit, activated with the group on 15 October 1979 as a small flight test detachment which apparently kept a handful of test pilots at Burbank (later Palmdale) and Groom Lake. From the earliest days of the 'black' Senior Trend programme, the USAF maintained a detachment of test pilots at Lockheed's Burbank 'Skunk Works', where operational pilots went through an initial ground training course. An acceptance and test squadron with no name, the unit also operated at Groom Lake in early days, where the Baja scorpion was adopted as the symbol of the Lockheed-USAF development effort; the unit then moved to Tonopah with the rest of the F-117 community. R-Unit's last commander was Lieutenant Colonel Keat Griggers (who later commanded the 417th TFTS), and it was inactivated on 30 May 1989.

According to members of the Palmdale flight test unit, which is subordinate to the 412th Test Wing (previously 6510th Test

Wing) at Edwards AFB, California, the small flying unit operated without any designation from 1989 onward, and moved from Tonopah to Palmdale (rather than to Holloman, with the rest of the F-117 force) in March 1992. It was designated 410th Test Squadron on 1 May 1993 and today operates four F-117s (79-10782, 79-10783, 79-10784, and 85-0831, the first three being

the surviving full-scale development aircraft). Squadron commander is Lieutenant Colonel Steven Green, who recently became the first pilot to log 1,000 hours in the 'Cockroach.'

831 is the only production machine assigned to the 410th TS. There are also three FSD aircraft.

Above: A pair of Angolan 'Fitter-Ks' undergoes open-air maintenance. High attrition (mainly as a result of UNITA action) resulted in a rapid turnover of fighters and fighter-bombers, and Su-22M-4Ks soon replaced the original 'Fitter-Fs'. Study of serial numbers seems to suggest that reallocation of the same number is the normal practice, since C-510 once adorned one of the original Su-20s.

Below: South Africans examine a MiG-21bis which force-landed in South Africa during a defection attempt. The aircraft was subsequently flown and evaluated by the SAAF, before finding a home in the SAAF museum. The MiG-21bis has a useful secondary ground attack capability, and in Angolan service has often been flown by Cuban and East German pilots. MiG-21s have been engaged by SAAF Mirage F1s on a number of occasions.

Above: Dragging its white and orange cruciform braking parachute, an Angolan 'Flogger-C' taxis in, the backseater peering anxiously through the periscope which gives him his only view forward. The I-prefixed serial worn by this MiG-23UB is believed to indicate that it has an instructional (or training) function, single-seaters using a C (casa, or fighter) prefix. Most conversion training is undertaken overseas, in Cuba or Russia, but a handful of two-seaters are in use for standardisation, instrument flying training, and other roles.

Right: The MiG-23 has largely replaced the older MiG-21 in the fighter role. Surprisingly, these aircraft are MiG-23ML 'Flogger-Gs', a variant still in front-line Russian service and considerably more advanced than the MiG-23MF 'Flogger-Bs' in use in some European countries. The types of missiles that may have been exported to Angola remains unclear, but is unlikely to include the R-73 (AA-11 'Archer').

Força Aérea Populaire de Angola
Angolan People's Air Force

Above: South Africans take the opportunity to examine a MiG-21bis and a Mirage F1 side-by-side. The more astute among them may realise that the type of upgrades now being offered by companies like IAI and Elbit can transform the MiG-21 into a highly effective modern warplane, with the aircraft's excellent performance, acceleration and initial turn rate being complemented by modern avionics and a truly fire-and-forget BVR missile in the form of the Novator AAM-AE. Such an aircraft should "give an F-15 or Tornado ADV pilot anxious moments," commented one expert.

Above: Helicopter gunships have played a crucial role in the long civil war in Angola, although the serviceability of the Mi-24D 'Hind-D' in the background appears to be dubious. Early Mi-24 variants have almost certainly been retired, giving way to Mi-24V or Mi-35 'Hind-Es' like the aircraft in the foreground. This has the full fit of defensive aids, including RHAWS, a dorsal IR jammer, and chaff/flare dispensers on the cabin sides. Interestingly, the large IR exhaust diffuser boxes are not carried.

Right: Three Mi-24V or Mi-35 'Hind-Es' sit in front of a row of Mi-8 and Mi-17 transport helicopters. Although there is provision for AT-6 'Spiral' ATGM launch tubes on the wingtips, podded 57-mm rocket projectiles seem to be a more commonly used weapon. The nearest aircraft carries a single UV-32-57 rocket pod under its inboard underwing station, probably eschewing a heavier warload because of the high temperatures. The Mi-24V also has a built-in 12.7-mm four-barrelled cannon.

Above: Aérospatiale Alouette IIIs are in use with both Angola and South Africa. Some of the Angolan Alouettes are the survivors of 20 such helicopters left behind by the Portuguese air force, and remarkably, 19 years later, a handful are still believed to be operational. Others are Romanian-built aircraft delivered from early 1984. Other Western-supplied helicopters have included six armed Gazelles and 12 Aérospatiale Panthers, six of which are also armed.

Right: The starboard side tail rotor identifies this unusually camouflaged aircraft as a Mil Mi-8T 'Hip-C', despite the presence of PZU intake filters. There are persistant reports that Angola also has gun-armed Mi-8TBK 'Hip-Fs', but this cannot be confirmed. Mil Mi-8s have formed the backbone of Angola's support and assault helicopter force, and large numbers have been lost to ground fire and in operational accidents. Despite these losses, the type remains in service in large numbers.

Força Aérea Populaire de Angola

Left: Cuban 'volunteers' and Angolan pilots brief in front of a MiG-17 while it is refuelled. A handful of these ageing fighter aircraft remain in use for advanced training and fighter-bomber duties.

Below left: Aircrew from one of the 'Hip' assault helicopter squadrons pose in front of one of their aircraft. The number of foreign advisers is often exaggerated, while the Angolan pilots themselves are of higher quality than is sometimes supposed, highly experienced professionals who have been hardened in a real shooting war.

Below: A Pilatus PC-7 trainer is towed out prior to a mission. Some 16 of these versatile turboprop trainers have been delivered and are believed to serve at Luanda. Other non-Soviet aircraft types have also been delivered in recent years, including CASA and Fokker transports and maritime patrol aircraft.

Below: One of Angola's 12 CASA C.212 Aviocars taxis past a UN Mi-8 and a TAAG Yak-40, the latter apparently withdrawn from use. The exact order of battle of the Angolan air force remains unknown, and any further information (and photographs) relating to this and other African air arms should be addressed to the editors.

Right: An Angolan Alouette III and a South African Aérospatiale/Atlas Gemsbok (upgraded Puma) share a makeshift airstrip. Despite its age and relatively poor performance characteristics, the Alouette III remains popular with many military operators worldwide, prized for its ruggedness, reliability and simplicity.

Above: One of Angola's fleet of about 12 Antonov An-26 'Curls' roars into the air, landing gear already tucking away. Attrition has reduced the An-26 fleet from its original total of 16 aircraft, but the type continues to be the most important military transport aircraft in Angolan service, and further deliveries of this or of the dedicated hot-and-high An-32 variant are likely, or, according to some sources, have already taken place. Similar rumours suggest that Su-25s are also in service.

Right: Soldiers wait to emplane as an Angolan An-26 taxis in, kicking up dust and debris with its massive propellers. Three Douglas C-47s, a single Fairchild Hiller FH-227B and a handful of An-2s are probably also still in service in the transport role, together with the four newly delivered CASA C.212s. Two Fokker F27 Friendship 200MPAs are used exclusively in the long-range maritime patrol role.

Below: Angola's four CASA C.212 Aviocars wear a smart but subdued overall grey colour scheme, and are used for a variety of roles. Further orders for this dependable and versatile twin-turboprop are thought to be likely.

Grumman F-14 Tomcat Variant Briefing

Although overshadowed in the close-in manoeuvring arena by purpose-built air superiority fighters, it is worth remembering that the F-14 was never intended to destroy its targets in the aeronautical equivalent of a hands-on, down-and-dirty knife-fight. The Tomcat is an assassin, armed with weapons which enable it to pick off its victims at such extreme range that they often do not even know they are in danger. In that long-range intercept role it remains unbeatable, and a steady progression of improvements has led to successive new variants, each further adding to the aircraft's formidable long-range kill capability and adding new ones, including ground attack and all-weather reconnaissance.

A lot of aircraft design is simply fashion. A quarter of a century ago, pivoted 'swing wings' were in fashion. No fighter designed today is likely to have them, despite their obvious advantages. They are especially essential for a multi-mission aircraft, as will be explained, and yet the 'swing-wing' F-14 was designed as a single-mission aircraft.

Captain L. S. 'Scotty' Lamoreaux, project co-ordinator on the F-14 programme, said in 1969: "The time has come to provide our air wings with a fighter designed from scratch for air superiority... The F-14 is all fighter. Multi-mission capability has not been permitted to dilute the original concept, or degrade the performance required to out-fly and out-fight any aircraft encountered. Comparable in size to the F-4, it is a twin-tailed, swing-wing, twin-engined airplane carrying a mix of weapons and a two-man crew: pilot and missile control officer."

Configuration

The Navy VFX Specification of July 1968 required a crew of two seated in tandem, an internal M61A gun, an advanced radar/missile system and twin engines. It was expected that the engines and radar/missile system would be those used in the unsuccessful F-111B, for which Grumman had been principal sub-

Left: The long, clear blown canopy of the F-14 gives its crew a superb all-round view, as seen in this 'over-the-shoulder' view of an F-14 RIO and his wingman.

Above: The F-14 was the last in a long line of US Navy carrier-based fighters to be produced by the famous 'Ironworks', as the Bethpage-based company became informally known. Most bore cat names, from the piston-engined Wildcat, Hellcat, Tigercat and Bearcat through the jet-powered Panther, Cougar, Jaguar and Tiger to the Tomcat. Here an F-14 from VF-14 (appropriately known as the 'Tomcatters') is led by a Grumman F8F Bearcat.

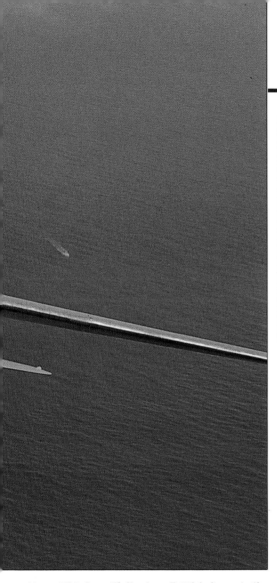

Above: This beautifully clean F-14A belongs to the Pacific Missile Test Center based at Point Mugu (now the Weapons Division of the Naval Air Warfare Center) with fuel tanks under the engine nacelles and an AIM-54C Phoenix and an AIM-9 Sidewinder on the port underwing pylon.

contractor. By 1965 impending failure of the F-111B had spurred Grumman to try out 6,000 shapes under Project 303, and via many convolutions these led to the YF-14, flown on 21 December 1970.

The shape of the basic production F-14A described below embodies both traditional and revolutionary features, although the overall configuration was based to an extent on the North American A-5 Vigilante, which established the use of two engines wide apart, leaving room between the inlets for a forward fuselage growing out of a broad flat area further aft. Later F-14 variants are closely based on the initial variant's aerodynamic configuration and structure, with avionics, engines and systems changes differentiating them from the baseline Tomcat.

In the F-14A, the main central and rear area of the fuselage comprises two propulsion systems (separate engines with independent ancillaries) joined by a shallow flat area which the designers called the 'pancake'. This leaves a deep tunnel between the engines, imposing a drag penalty, but adds to overall lift, gives an extra attachment area for weapons pylons and provides some fuselage volume for fuel and equipment. Precisely the same arrangement is seen in the MiG-29 and Su-27, which were

designed later. The main drag penalty of the configuration is that it puts the thrust line of each engine 54 in (138 cm) from the centreline of the aircraft. This, in turn, means that engine failure, and especially sudden asymmetric thrust in afterburner, causes a nose slice (rotation in yaw) so violent that spin departure and loss of the aircraft is the almost inevitable result.

Variable geometry

Outboard of the engines the two Russian fighters have rather stumpy fixed wings, but those of the F-14 are pivoted and this profoundly affects the wings' geometry. Wings of supersonic fighters have to be very thin, the ratio of thickness to chord (distance from leading to trailing edges) typically being about three per cent. Thin wings obviously have to be extremely heavy if they are not to break, and

Below: An early F-14A (still without the nose-mounted pitot probe) of VF-32 'Swordsmen' launches from the USS John F. Kennedy, laden with Phoenix, Sparrow and Sidewinder AAMs.

Grumman F-14 Tomcat Variant Briefing

Left: The most expensive warload in the world. An F-14A of VF-32 carries the type's theoretical maximum of six AIM-54 Phoenix missiles. The drag of such a load is tremendous, and the missiles put the aircraft above its maximum carrier landing weight, even with zero fuel; to land, several of the multi-million dollar missiles would actually have to be jettisoned or fired, whether or not 'trade' had been found.

Opposite page: This F-14B is from VF-101 (the 'Grim Reapers'), the Atlantic Coast Tomcat Fleet Replenishment Squadron. The aircraft carries four Mk 83 1,000-lb bombs, with high-drag Blute tailfins. The 'Bombcat' modifications have not been enough to save the F-14 community from several squadron disestablishments, as some F-14 units give way to Hornet squadrons on the decks of the US Navy's supercarriers.

even with complex high-lift devices they are inefficient at low speeds. In contrast, the F-14's wings more nearly resemble those of traditional aircraft, with a thickness/chord ratio at the pivot of no less than 10.2 per cent. This means the wing can have thinner skins and thus weigh less, and be fitted with efficient high-lift movable surfaces. Moreover, the aspect ratio (slenderness in plan) can be much higher, again increasing aerodynamic efficiency.

The movables on the outer wings comprise leading-edge slats and trailing-edge flaps. The slats are conventional constant-profile surfaces in two sections extending over the whole span of the movable wing, power-driven together to 7° for air combat manoeuvres and to 17° for landing. The flaps are simple-hinged, single-slotted surfaces, again in two sections extending to the tip. Auxiliary flaps are located even further inboard, on the trailing edge of that part of the wing which retracts into the fuselage, and these can thus only be used when the wing is swept fully forward. The normal two-section flaps can be extended to 35° for landing, or to 10° when used as fast-acting manoeuvre devices, controlled via the air data computer, and can be used at wing sweep angles of up to 55°. The provision of full-span flaps is possible because, instead of ailerons, control in roll is provided by tailerons (differential tailplanes) and spoilers. The final arrangement was the best compromise between many variables. A fixed wing would have had to be larger (745 sq ft/70 m²), and

Below: The AIM-7 Sparrow is a beyond-visual-range air-to-air missile which uses semi-active radar homing, which is to say that it homes in on radar reflections from the target, which were originally transmitted by the launch aircraft. This means that the launch aircraft has to continue illuminating the target throughout the missile's flight time.

Below: An F-14A of VF-114 'Aardvarks' lets fly with an AIM-54 Phoenix. Tomcat aircrew call the AIM-54 the Buffalo, because this is apparently what it looks like as it stampedes away from the launch aircraft.

Grumman F-14 Tomcat Variant Briefing

An F-14A of VF-124 'Gunslingers', the West Coast training unit, streams vapour as its reefs round in a fast hard turn. The F-14 is an extremely agile aircraft, particularly with its wings swept fully forward, and especially by comparison with the fighters which it replaced, although it is not as agile as the latest lightweight superfighters.

would have weighed 4,920 lb (2231 kg) more. Even the swing wings were made large (565 sq ft/53 m²) which, together with powerful lift from the huge pancake, reduces the maximum lift coefficient needed on landing.

For take-off, landing and low-speed loiter the wings are set to a minimum sweep of 20°. This gives the remarkable span (for a fighter) of 64 ft 1.5 in (19.5 m), far more than would have been possible with a fixed-sweep wing that would have been unable to meet the carrier wave-off requirement. For supersonic dash the wings fold back to 68°, and to reduce deck spotting area they can be 'overswept' to 72° when weight is on the landing gears. This is possible because, unlike the F-111B, the wings are higher than the horizontal tails. At the normal inflight sweep limit of 68°, the wing trailing edges are aligned with the leading edges of the horizontal tails.

Sweep angle in flight is normally controlled automatically by a Mach sweep programmer, as a function of Mach number and altitude. This moves the wings from 20° to 22° as speed builds to Mach 0.75 and then pivots them all the way to 68° as Mach number increases to 1.2. As the angle goes through 50°, the spoilers are cut out. Thereafter roll control is effected solely by the tailerons, which are more than powerful enough at high airspeeds and with the much-reduced roll inertia that results from the wings being folded back. At low speeds, for example on the approach to the carrier deck, the pilot can flick a switch to open all spoilers together to a neutral setting of 7°; a thumbwheel on the stick then gives direct lift control, increasing or decreasing the rate of descent without change of attitude or power. As the wheels hit the deck, all the spoilers and flaperons flick fully up to 55° to kill lift.

Manual control

The pilot can assume control of wing sweep, and should a ground-attack run (strafing or bombs) be tasked he can switch in a special mode which locks the wings at 55° sweep. This is the optimum for low-level manoeuvres with heavy ordnance loads, and makes the weapon-aiming calculations much simpler. Should the wing lock fully aft, the F-14 can still land safely, at 200 mph (323 km/h) with 4,000 lb (1814 kg) of fuel, or 166 mph (267 km/h) with 2,000 lb (907 kg) of fuel, despite the flaps being inoperative when the wing is swept.

As Mach number increases from subsonic to supersonic, the centre of lift moves aft, making the aircraft very nose-down. With a swing-wing aircraft the effect is obviously even more pronounced. The pilot could just haul back on the stick to maintain level flight, but this would make combat manoeuvres difficult. A better solution is extra lift at the front, and in the F-14A this is provided by glove vanes pivoted to the front of the fixed inboard part of the wing (called the wing glove). The vanes are triangular, and at Mach 1.4 they are automatically swung out hydraulically through an angle of 15° to push up the nose and unload the tailplanes, leaving the latter with enough authority to pull 7.5 g at Mach 2. The vanes can be manually extended between Mach 1 and Mach 1.4, but will not operate at wing sweep settings of below 35° at subsonic speeds because they would destabilise the aircraft in pitch to an unacceptable degree. If the pilot selects the ground-attack mode (constant wing sweep), the glove vanes lock fully out even down to Mach 0.35. On today's new or rebuilt aircraft – the B and D versions – the pivoted vanes are eliminated, longitudinal control being adequate without them even at supersonic speed with centre of lift fully aft. Even on surviving F-14As the vanes are locked shut, and their actuators are removed. The gloves themselves (i.e., the whole outer parts of the pancake) have sharp dihedral, to reduce cross-section and also to minimise supersonic wave drag. At rest, the outer wings are horizontal. Under vertical accelerative loads they naturally bend upwards, especially at minimum sweep. The wing-sweep mechanism is designed to function reliably even under the limit design load factor of 7.5 g, although rate of change of sweep is reduced from 7.5° to 4.0° per second.

Speed brakes

The rear part of the broad pancake is reflexed (gently curved upwards), which reduces both supersonic trim drag and the negative zero-lift supersonic pitching moment. Above and below this region are door-type speed brakes, the lower one split by the hook. Opening quickly above and below to 60°, they were deliberately made oversize to be valuable in combat (and also to stabilise speed in dive-bombing attacks, should an F-14 ever be called upon to do this), and their operation causes little trim change. On landing, the lower brake is prevented from going beyond 18°.

The flying controls are actuated using three systems, hydraulic and electro-hydraulic, with a back-up electro-hydraulic system available for pitch and yaw control. The four-section spoilers are usable at wing sweep angles below 57°. The

Above: The modifications which have earned fleet F-14s (like these VF-24 F-14As) the 'Bombcat' nickname allow the aircraft to drop only a narrow range of 'dumb' air-to-ground weapons, including Mk 80 series freefall bombs (slick and retarded) weighing up to 2,000 lb, and various CBUs. The aircraft is not compatible with any air-to-surface missiles, laser- or electro-optical-guided bombs.

inboard segments are actuated via the main hydraulic system and the outboard segments using the electro-hydraulic system, like the rudders and tailerons.

The final winning F-14 design had a single fin with two large ventral fins that hinged sideways to clear the deck on landing. The Navy (perhaps shortsightedly) objected to the ventrals on the grounds of weight, complexity and engine access, so the F-14 had to have two large fins, canted outwards by 5°. This at least minimises response to the violent vortices which stream back from the body, inlets and gloves at the (previously impossible) angles of attack which the F-14 can reach, in the region beyond 50°. Duplication in the event of battle damage is also a factor. To enhance directional stability the Navy did allow shallow fixed ventrals to be retained. These are canted outwards and exert lateral forces greater than their area might suggest. They not only enhance yaw stability but also oppose the twisting effect of the main fins on the rear fuselage, and thus enable structural weight to be reduced.

Utterly unlike the F-111B, the engine air inlets are two-dimensional sharp-lipped rectangles with the sides very acutely swept back. Due to the glove dihedral the inlets are tilted, and even at the top the inner wall is at least 8 in (20 cm) from the side of the fuselage upstream. Thus, the sluggish boundary layer from the forward fuselage can be ignored, no complex diverter system being needed. The upper wall of the duct is made up of front and rear hinged panels, driven by three hydraulic jacks controlled by a system that senses flight Mach number, duct-exit Mach number and angle of attack to feed the engine with the correct airflow. The hinged panels, or ramps, vary the diffusion in the inlet and at supersonic speeds close down the throat area while diverting a large excess airflow out through a door in the top of the pancake. At Mach 0.5 there is no flow through this aft-facing door, while at low speeds (especially on take-off) the flow is in the reverse direction, extra air being sucked in. The nacelle installation gives quick access for preflight inspection and engine oil replacement. Grumman claims that 80 per cent of on-aircraft engine accessory corrective maintenance can be performed with the aircraft in an operational mode and its clamshell access doors open.

Construction

In a fighter designed today most of the airframe would be of advanced composites, but 96 per cent of each F-14 is plain metal. In a very few places the metal is used unconventionally, notably the tailerons whose skins are panels of boron-filament composite bonded with epoxy adhesive. On the other hand, only 36 per cent is aluminium alloy, whereas 20 years earlier the

Left: The skull and crossbones insignia on the fin of this F-14A identifies it as belonging to VF-84 'Jolly Rogers'. Taking off from a carrier deck in daylight is difficult, landing back aboard is even more challenging, and trying to land at night is harder yet. Only the pick of the US Navy's elite fighter pilots get to fly the F-14, where such operations have to be routine.

percentage would have exceeded 95. The brutal strength requirements of catapult shots, arrested landings and hitting the deck at a vertical velocity of 24.7 ft (7.5 m) per second results in no less than 15 per cent of the F-14 being steel (opposed to 5.5 per cent in the F-15). A total of 25 per cent is titanium, a remarkable figure for the 1960s. The extensive use of titanium instead of steel results in a weight saving of 40 per cent (900 lb/1984 kg in the case of the wing box alone). The use of titanium was also significant in that its corrosion resistance makes it particularly suited to maritime aircraft applications, but it is a very difficult material to work with, requiring expensive hot- and creep-forming processes which make manufacture expensive and time-consuming. Grumman broke much new ground in titanium working, developing new hot-forming processes, refining chemical etching methods and perfecting the moulding of components from heated titanium powder. These processes have since been exploited in many newer aircraft.

The aircraft's structural heart is the 22-ft (6.7-M) wing carry-through box, which joins the pivots for the wings. It is entirely made of 6Al/4V titanium alloy, and was the largest electron beam-welded titanium structure fabricated up to that time. The use of bolts was studiously avoided in the vital and highly-stressed wing box in order to avoid any of the fatigue problems which such fasteners can produce. The box

Above: A flight of four 'Diamondback' F-14s breaks for the camera. As the long-range defender of the carrier battle group, the F-14 usually mounts a lonely combat air patrol (often in conjunction with one more F-14, to allow constant radar coverage of the most likely threat axes) miles out from the ship, often with tanker support from a KA-6D Intruder, and perhaps under the control of an E-2C Hawkeye.

forms a fuel-tight integral tank. At its ends are the pivots which, instead of being massive steel rings enclosing a giant cylinder as in other 'swing-wing' aircraft, are titanium annular rings with a part-spherical surface coated

Right: Steam streams from the catapult shuttle and the deck crew rush forward to prepare to launch another aircraft as an F-14D of VF-2 (the 'Bounty Hunters') blasts off from one of the two bow catapults of the USS Constellation. The new engines of the F-14D (and F-14B) allow it to make zero-wind take-offs or to take off at higher weights, or merely give a greater safety margin. The Tomcat's full-span flaps are clearly visible in this view.

Grumman F-14 Tomcat Variant Briefing

On final approach to the carrier, this F-14A has hook, flaps and gear down and airbrakes deployed. The orange meatball and line of green horizontal lights which the pilot use to maintain the correct approach path can just be seen on the port side of the deck, beyond the parked A-6s.

with Teflon and rhenium/silver. Either the upper or lower bearing can fail without danger to the aircraft. Each wing is swept by a ball-screw actuator behind the carry-through box, the left and right drives being synchronised to ensure that sweep is always the same on both sides. The tight sliding joint between the glove and the front of the wingroot is designed to 'breathe' as the sweep changes, while the rear seal is maintained by a curved row of flexible plates. The rotary flap and slat drives are telescopic to allow for wing sweep changes. The wing box is so strong that the component from the crashed first prototype was actually recovered intact from the wreckage and used for ground testing.

Fuselage structure is mainly conventional, although many frames are machined forgings. Almost the whole centre-fuselage structure is titanium alloy, although the flush-riveted skins are aluminium alloy. The nose is an enormous

Below: For close-in engagements, for extra combat persistence or for destroying low-value targets, the F-14 uses the IR-homing AIM-9 Sidewinder AAM.

radome of epoxy/glass-fibre that can be hinged upwards for access to the radar. Equally impressive for its size, the canopy is moulded from a single sheet of Plexiglas, bulged for minimal optical distortion yet giving both crew a superb all-round view. The propulsion pods, including the ducts, are composed primarily of bonded aluminium-alloy honeycomb. The fins and rudders are likewise of bonded aluminium honeycomb structure, whereas the tailerons are boron/epoxy composite laid on a titanium multi-spar sub-structure, but with honeycomb leading and trailing edges. The taileron skins were the first major structural production components on any aircraft, civil or military, to be of composites.

Among the most highly stressed parts are the landing gears, which in consequence use shock-absorbing legs made largely of high-tensile vacuum-melted steel. The main legs are single tubes, nearly vertical when extended, and are hydraulically retracted forwards as the single wheel rotates through 90° to lie flat above the leg in the wing glove. The tyre has high pressure (there is little chance of deployment to a soft airstrip) and the brakes are multidisc carbon. The nose gear has twin steerable wheels and retracts forward under the front cockpit. Once aligned over the carrier catapult the nose gear is compressed, shortening it by about 14 in (36 cm). The steel towbar, or strop link, is then

released to fall downwards and be positioned over the catapult shuttle. The brutal pull of the shuttle would fling the F-14 off the bows at flying speed even with engines off and the park brake on. Shortening the leg reduces the severe bending strain and, by making the fighter 'kneel', prevents the wings from trying to lift until rotation as the aircraft leaves the ship. On return, as the hook is lowered the nosewheels are automatically centred. This avoids problems on hitting the deck, and especially prevents the gear from castoring as the fighter rolls back under wire tension after coming to rest.

The crew boards via a retractable ladder on the left side, from the top of which outward-folding steps give access to the front and rear cockpit. The seats are Martin-Baker GRU.7A or, in the F-14D, the NACES (Mk 14). The arrester hook is a single 'sting' of high-tensile steel, normally housed in a small fairing under the extreme tail on the centreline. No braking parachute is provided.

Powerplant

The obvious engine to choose for the F-14A was the Pratt & Whitney TF30, as qualified for the F-111B. This bypass jet engine, or low-bypass-ratio turbofan, was marginally adequate in thrust but had a bad history of compressor stalls in its only previous application, the F-111. It was expected that the much better inlet and longer duct of the F-14 would avoid this problem, and in any case a much later and more powerful engine, the F401, was planned for

Right: An F-14D taxis on the deck of the Constellation. The aircraft is externally distinguishable from the similarly-powered F-14B by the small RHAWS antennas on the wing glove leading edge, and by the dual sensor pods below the nose.

most F-14s. The actual F-14A engine, today the TF30-P-414A, at least features an excellent variable nozzle with movable petals which, instead of merely being hinged, slide on curved tracks to preserve the optimum profile, closed down to minimum area in subsonic flight (except for afterburner take-off) and fully opened to a convergent and then divergent profile at supersonic speed in afterburner.

Engine problems

The planned F401 was cancelled, however, and for 20 years the TF30 was the worst feature of the F-14. Only over many years was the problem of compressor stall, and the usually associated one of blade containment, progressively solved. Even then the power has never been more than marginal, the combined thrust at sea level in full afterburner being 41,800 lb (186 kN), compared with the maximum weight of 74,349 lb (33725 kg), which makes it harder to dogfight with later aircraft whose thrust/weight ratios are well above unity. A further drawback is that in any dogfight situation the pilot has always had to handle the engine carefully to avoid a stall. With or without a stall, afterburner ignition failure posed a further problem and is still a hazard with the F-14A. Severe asymmetric thrust can all too easily lead to con-

trol loss and entry to a spin, from which the answer is to eject. This is a problem in all flight regimes, but particularly at take-off when, because of basic lack of thrust, use of afterburner is mandatory. Pratt & Whitney has striven over the years to improve matters, but it has been an uphill struggle.

A total of 557 F-14s was built, the majority of them F-14As. Their engine is the TF30-P-414A, still rated at 20,900 lb (93 kN) but producing much less visible smoke than earlier TF30 engines. Compressor stalls and even blade shedding remain a problem, although a much reduced one, and containment of shed blades is now considered to be certain.

The final answer to the engine problem was, of course, to use a different engine, and the first F-14 with General Electric engines made its initial flight on 14 July 1981. Dubbed 'Super Tomcat', it was fitted with engines called F101DFE (Derivative Fighter Engine). From these were developed the F110-GE-400 fitted to all the latest Tomcats, and which will almost certainly be fitted to any future variants.

Below: Although the US Navy F-14 fleet has seen some unit disestablishments recently, the type's future is not in doubt, and it continues to play a vital role in defending the US Navy's carrier battle groups, still the tip of America's foreign policy spear.

Grumman F-14 Tomcat Variants

Design 303 variants

The F-14 was born because of the failure of the Naval TFX, the F-111B, for which Grumman had been the principal sub-contractor. The F-111B was too complex, too heavy, too slow, never right for the carrier mission and unlikely to be rendered so despite herculean efforts. Not even a costly Colossal Weight Improvement Program (CWIP) could transform this aircraft into a shipboard interceptor. The Pentagon scrapped the TFX, the notion of commonality and the F-111B programme, although the US Air Force version of the 'one eleven' has since matured into a potent low-level, long-range bomber.

In October 1967, at the height of the war in Vietnam, Grumman proposed that a new airframe be developed to accommodate the avionics, missile, engines and weapon system of the discredited F-111B. Between the F-111B and the new proposal, the AN/AWG-9 had picked up new fighter-attack modes, gained in flexibility and lost a staggering 600 lb (272 kg) in weight, and took to the air in a modified TA-3B Skywarrior during April 1970. The new airframe promised to be vastly superior to the F-111B in all regimes. The Grumman proposal came just as the Navy was restating its requirement for a fleet interceptor, and the VFX-1 requirement was

Vought's unsuccessful VFX proposal is seen in mock-up form, complete with rather unconvincing dummy AIM-54 missiles.

formulated around the new design, with the contemporary VFX-2 requirement describing the same aircraft with advanced technology engines. VFX-2 eventually resulted in the F401-engined F-14B. Design 303 was primarily designed around an armament of four AIM-7 missiles, although the AIM-54 Phoenix grew in importance, especially after the development of low-drag pallet carriage of the big missiles, which minimised the impact on the basic fighter role.

Grumman's long record of development with the XF10F-1 Jaguar, F11F-1 Tiger and F-111B gave the Bethpage, New York, manufacturer – long the US Navy's key supplier of carrier-based warplanes – a significant advantage over any other manufacturer which might have wanted to produce a new-generation fighter/interceptor, especially one using a VG wing. Competition had to be encouraged, however, and other companies were eager for a production order. When a Request for Proposals (RFP) went out to the aerospace industry in July 1968, calling for a two-seat, twin-engined, Phoenix-armed carrier interceptor, North American, LTV, McDonnell and General Dynamics all submitted designs.

Grumman's design was refined from the single-finned 303-60 through the 303A, 303B, 303C (submerged engines and high-set wing), 303D (submerged engines and low-set wing), 303E (single fin), 303F (submerged engine), and 303G (without Phoenix) before arriving at the final configuration with twin fins, widely

separated podded engines and high-set wing. Single-seat configurations were even examined, although the design numbers of these are unknown. On 14 January 1969, with the award of a development contract covering six prototypes and 463 production aircraft, Grumman's design 303E became the VFX winner and was designated F-14.

In this artist's impression of the 303E in US Navy markings, some differences between this aircraft and the F-14 can be detected.

Below: The unsuccessful North American VFX proposal.

YF-14A

There were at least two full-scale mock-ups before the first actual YF-14 prototype was built. The original mock-up had a single tail, and a later version introduced the now-familiar twin fins shortly before the design was frozen, in March 1969. Development was expedited through the use of a detailed mock-up, known as EMMA (Engineering Mock-up Manufacturing Aid), that was built like a real aircraft, albeit without external skinning but, since it would never fly, using cheaper manufacturing methods. Thus,

Below: The 12th YF-14A had the numeral 1 painted on its fin and was known as aircraft 1X, taking over the flight test responsibilities of the ill-fated first prototype.

Right: Streaming hydraulic fluid, the first YF-14A returns to Calverton during its doomed second sortie on 30 December 1970, which ended in complete hydraulic failure on final approach. The aircraft was totally destroyed, but both crew members ejected safely.

Below right: The second YF-14A refuels from one of Grumman's fleet of converted A-6 Intruder tankers, which were used to extract the maximum benefit from each test sortie. The candy-striped nose boom carries test instrumentation air data sensors.

bulkheads were sand cast instead of milled, but they were aluminium and they were real bulkheads. This allowed Grumman engineers to locate hydraulic lines, electrical wires and systems, and to use EMMA to produce patterns and even to fit-check the TF30 engines. The first prototype itself was rolled out at the Grumman plant in December 1972.

Twelve prototypes were procured (individual flight test responsibilities are detailed in the main text) with Bureau Numbers from 157980-157991. These wore large sequential numerical codes from 1-11 on their tailfins, with the last being painted as 1 and known as 1X. The first prototype began taxi trials at Calverton on 14 December 1970, with high-speed taxi trials six days later. On 21 December, company chief test pilot Robert Smythe and (in the backseat) project test pilot William ('Bob') Miller made the first flight, two wide circuits of the airfield with the wings in the forward position, and laden with four dummy Sparrow missiles. A more definitive 'first' flight was begun by Miller and Smythe on 30 December 1970 but was to prove disastrous, the Tomcat experiencing a primary hydraulic system failure. Miller manoeuvred back towards a landing, using the nitrogen bottle to blow down the landing gear when the secondary hydraulic system failed, too. The two men ejected a mere 25 ft (8 m) above the trees, suffering only minor injuries – but the first Grumman Tomcat was destroyed.

A 'fix' to the Tomcat's hydraulic systems proved relatively easy to accomplish, the cause having been a fatigue failure of a hydraulic pipe caused by resonance and a loose connector. The loss of the first aircraft caused a delay in envelope-expansion tests and high-speed developmental flying, but the programme moved forward with almost its original momentum. On 24 May 1971, Smythe took the second Tomcat aloft.

The first five and the last (No.12, 157991, which took over the responsibilities of the first aircraft after its crash) were funded in FY69, and 157985-157990 in FY70. The individual aircraft had different model or 'Block' numbers, being F-14A-01-GR (Block 1), F-14A-05-GR (Block 5), F-14A-10-GR (Block 10), F-14A-15-GR (Block 15), F-14A-20-GR (Block 20), F-14A-25-GR (Block 25), F-14A-30-GR (Block 30), F-14A-35-GR (Block 35), F-14A-40-GR (Block 40), F-14A-45-GR (Block 45), F-14A-50-GR (Block 50), and F-14A-55-GR (Block 55). The seventh aircraft, 157986 (F-14A-30-GR), was later converted to serve as the F401-engined F-14B prototype. Aircraft from the first

production lot of F-14As were also assigned to the flight test programme, in order to hasten the transition to service.

The 12 prototypes had different flight test responsibilities. The No. 2 aircraft was assigned the low-speed regime and the critical stall/spin trials. For the latter, the aircraft was fitted with retractable canard foreplanes on the upper sides of the nose, ahead of the windscreen, and initially the wings were locked at 20°, the intakes were locked open, and an anti-spin parachute was fitted to the boat tail fairing. Wind tunnel tests (actually carried out in NASA Langley's spin tunnel), trials of models dropped from helicopters and computer analysis had shown a tendency towards flat spins, with very high rates of rotation, so Grumman was not prepared to take chances. No. 2 later tested the F-14's gun. No. 3 flew envelope-expanding trials with steadily increasing loads and speeds, and acted as the structural test vehicle. Nos 4, 5 and 6 went to NAS Point Mugu, the fourth for integration of the AWG-9/AIM-54 system, the fifth for systems, instrumentation and compatibility tests, and the sixth for weapons system and missile separation work. Of these, No. 5 was lost during a Sparrow separation on 20 June 1973. No. 7 became the test ship for the F-14B with F401 engines, while No. 8 was used to test the production configuration and to provide contractual guarantee data.

The 11th YF-14A sits on the deck of the USS Independence *during initial carrier suitability trials.*

Nos 9 and 11 went to Point Mugu for radar evaluation and auxiliary system trials (including ACLS), respectively. No. 11 also flew air-to-ground gunnery trials.

No. 10 was delivered to the Naval Air Test Center at Patuxent River, and from there it was flown on structural work and then carrier-compatibility work. During preparation for an air display, the aircraft crashed into the sea, killing the pilot, Bob Miller, who was flying the aircraft solo.

No. 17 replaced this aircraft on carrier-compatibility tests just, as No. 12 (redesignated No. 1X) had replaced the first prototype on high-speed flight trials. This aircraft was the most comprehensively instrumented of the test Tomcats, able to transmit up to 647 measurements back to the ground, and fitted with hydraulic 'Shakers' for flutter testing. 1X had exceeded Mach 2.25 by December 1972. 1X was actually the third F-14 to fly.

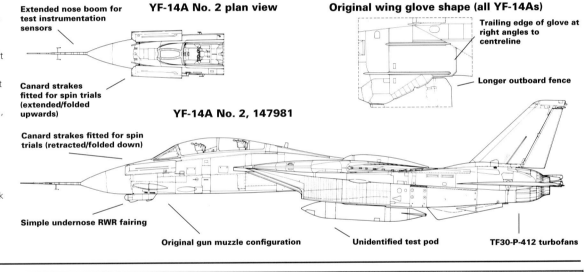

Extended nose boom for test instrumentation sensors

YF-14A No. 2 plan view

Original wing glove shape (all YF-14As)

Trailing edge of glove at right angles to centreline

Canard strakes fitted for spin trials (extended/folded upwards)

Longer outboard fence

YF-14A No. 2, 147981

Canard strakes fitted for spin trials (retracted/folded down)

Simple undernose RWR fairing

Original gun muzzle configuration

Unidentified test pod

TF30-P-412 turbofans

F–14A

Production of the baseline F-14A for the US Navy was spread over 18 Production Blocks and 15 Fiscal Years (FY71-FY85) and totalled 545 aircraft.

Minor changes were incorporated throughout the production run and, although such changes were introduced 'on-the-line', they were often retrofitted to earlier aircraft. Such changes included beaver tail and airbrake configuration, undernose sensor fit, and even gun bay purging vents. Early Tomcats were also equipped with a gimbal-mounted AN-ALR-23 infra-red detection set which could be slaved to the radar or used independently to scrutinise areas not being scanned by radar. The IRST was particularly useful for detecting rocket-engined stand-off missiles, and afterburning targets at higher altitude, or for situations when use of radar was tactically unsound or impeded by heavy ECM. Angular tracking was more accurate than with radar, providing better target elevation and azimuth data than radar. It was sufficiently accurate to allow it to be used for missile launch.

This sensor was replaced by the Northrop AAX-1 Television Camera Set, or TCS, which can be likened to a high-resolution closed-circuit TV with telephoto lens, following a 1977 evaluation of F-14s equipped with the broadly similar TISEO, then in use on USAF F-4E Phantoms. The success of this led to trials by VF-14, VF-32, VF-24 and VF-211 aboard *Kennedy* and *Constellation* with Northrop's TVSU, which was in turn developed to become the TCS. TCS is a passive electro-optical sensor

An early F-14 in Canadian markings reflects CAF interest in the aircraft as an F-101 Voodoo replacement in the long-range air defence role.

which gives the pilot an ultra-long-range telescope able to spot an enemy visually and identify him early. TCS is operated via a stabilised, gimbal-mounted closed-circuit television system. Two separate cameras are used for the two modes: wide angle for target acquisition, and close-up for target identification. The TCS is normally slaved to

the radar, and automatically locks on to the first target acquired. The NFO can also manually control the unit in the target identification mode, steering the lens with a joystick. The picture can be projected onto the radar display. Under a $12.5-million contract, Northrop began deliveries of the first 36 TCS systems in late 1983, the first

examples being operated by VX-4 at NAS Point Mugu, California. Subsequent orders rose to 133.

Some credit the TCS with enough definition to allow the F-14 crew to identify the weapons being carried by an enemy aircraft, which would be of great tactical value. On a hazy day, however, natural

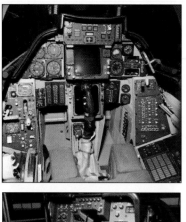

Top and above: The pilot's and NFO's cockpits of the F-14A look rather dated by modern standards, with their analog instruments and old-fashioned displays.

conditions apply. From Block 65, the TF30-PW-412A engine was fitted. The production-standard wing glove fairing with shortened outboard wing fence was introduced with 158978 (first Block 70 aircraft), while the beaver tail and airbrake were modified from

159421 (first Block 75). Earlier aircraft had their beaver tails cut down (with dielectric fairings removed) to a similar shape. The last Block 85 aircraft (159588) introduced the new AN/ARC-159 UHF radio in place of the AN/ARC-51A, while from 159825 (the first Block 90) a small angle of attack probe was added to the tip of the nose radome, while high AoA performance was also improved by the provision of automated manoeuvre flaps. These aircraft introduced changes to the vertical display indicator group, and the provision of improved fire extinguishers and fire suppressors. During Block 95, the TF30-PW-414 engine was installed, actually

starting with 160396 instead of the first aircraft of the batch, as was initially planned. This engine was retrofitted to early aircraft and improved maintainability and reliability, with redesigned fan blades and a 'containment shell' around the whole turbine section. From Block 100, a slip clutch and coupler installation was added in the flap/slat system, as well as fuel system changes, AWG-9 reliability improvement measures, and a raft of anti-corrosion improvements, including seals, baffles and drain holes. The AN/ALQ-126 antennas were added to the beaver tail and below the wing gloves from the last aircraft of Block 110

The F-14A's primary task is to intercept bombers and missile carriers far away from the carrier battle group. Here an M-4 'Bison' becomes trade for a 'Diamondback' F-14A.

(161168). The first production installation of TCS was incorporated in 161597 (the first Block 125 aircraft).

Twenty early Block 60/65 F-14As were refurbished and modified to Block 130 standard for service with VF-201 and VF-202 at NAS Dallas. These were 158613 - 618,

Inside the F-14A

Radar antenna
The AN/AWG-9 uses a simple slotted planar array antenna, on which can be seen four horizontal IFF antenna dipoles.

Intakes
The F-14A's TF30-414 turbofan engines draw air through fully-variable intakes. These sharp-lipped, highly-swept intakes are set well out from the fuselage (to minimise the chance of ingesting sluggish boundary layer airflow) and incorporate three automatically-actuated ramps that vary the volume (and thus the speed) of air entering the intake duct. Massive spills are located in the roof of each intake.

Powerplant
The F-14A was originally powered by the Pratt & Whitney TF30-P-412 turbofan. This has since been replaced by the TF30-P-414 with steel containment cases around the fan stages, and by the further improved TF30-P-414A which was less prone to compressor stalls but which has proved more smoky than early engines.

Radome
The radar antenna is protected by a radar-transparent radome, tipped by a small pitot probe.

Missile
The primary air-to-air armament of the F-14A is the Hughes AIM-54 Phoenix missile. This incorporates its own radar for active terminal homing.

Cannon
The Tomcat's internal gun is a six-barrelled General Electric M61A1 Vulcan cannon, installed in the port side of the lower forward fuselage, with feed from a 675-round drum below the rear cockpit.

158620, 158624, 158626 - 637.

In 1988, the US Navy embarked on an ambitious programme to equip all F-14, F/A-18C/D and T-45 aircraft with the Martin-Baker SJU-17A/V NACES (Naval Aircrew Common Ejection Seat), partly to achieve a greater degree of commonality and partly because the newer seat (also with 'zero-zero' capability) offers higher velocity escape, at speeds of 700 kt (803 mph; 500 km/h) in level flight and 600 kt (688 mph;

428 km/h) in any attitude. The new seat dispenses with the optional face blind handle employed on its predecessor. Because production of the Tomcat was abruptly halted in February 1991, the Navy halted installation of the new ejecton seat in the F-14, except in the new-build and converted F-14Ds.

A single early F-14A was converted to JF-14A configuration for test duties. Four F-14As were converted to serve as F-14D

prototypes, 18 F-14As have been converted to F-14D(R) standards by Grumman and NADEP Norfolk, and 32 others were converted to F-14A+/F-14B configuration. Five to seven more F-14B conversions have been funded in FY92 ($143 million), with Grumman and NADEP Norfolk competing for the contract to install Grumman-built conversion kits. A further $175 million allocated in FY93 should fund 12 more conversions. Originally, plans called for the

conversion of 400 F-14As to F-14D standard. Installation of Tape 115B or 116 software to all surviving in-service F-14As from May 1991 gave full conventional ground attack capability and led to the 'Bombcat' nickname.

The F-14MMCAP (previously F-14A++) upgrade is a $392-million 1992 proposal for a Multi-Mission Capability Avionics Programme to be applied to surviving

F-14A approach configuration

Production standard wing glove fairing, with extended outboard fence, from Block 70

AN/ARC-159

Early aircraft (pre-Block 90) initially lacked nose pitot

The nozzle of the TF30 engine is covered by 'turkey feathers' that are rather more complex than those which make up the nozzle of the F110-PW-400.

TF30-P-412A from Block 65

Arrester hook deployed

Undercarriage extended, no load

Early undernose fairing with ALQ-100 and IRST

F-14A underside plan

Glove vanes (shown extended) locked shut since the mid-1980s

Nose probe added from Block 90

AN/ALE-40

Original shape

Interim change with dielectric panels deleted

Formation lights
The F-14 carries conventional red (port) and green (starboard) wingtip navigation lights, together with low-intensity electro-luminescent formation lights (also known as 'slime' lights).

Wing sweep
The outer wing panels can be swept between 20° and 68° in flight, with the automatic wing sweep programme matching sweep angle to speed and attitude.

Wing fully swept - 68°

AN/ALR-45 receiver

Boat tail variations

Post Block 75

Definitive production standard

F-14A rear view

Flaps extended

Leading-edge slats extended, flaps shown dotted

Arrester hook
The F-14 is provided with a highly-stressed, steel arrester hook to allow it to operate from carrier decks. The hook pivots left and right, as well as hinging up and down, which is helpful in crosswinds or off-centre arrivals.

F-14A (Block 125) launch configuration

TACAN and ARC-182 UHF antenna

GRU-7 ejection seats

AN/APR-50 antenna

Later muzzle with simplified gun bay purge system vents

AN/APX-72 IFF & UHF datalink

Late undernose fairing with TCS

Undercarriage fully compressed

Catapult holdback

AN/ALQ-126 under wing gloves from Block 110

Later 270-US gal fuel tank

An F-14A on the catapult. The aircraft lacks a probe at the radome tip and has the early production gun bay purging vents.

This F-14A of VF-301 'Devil's Disciples' from NAS Miramar has been retrofitted with a radome-tip probe, but still retains the early gun bay vents. It has only a simple RHAWS antenna below the nose.

F-14As. This will add an AN/ALR-67 RWR system, provision for a Bol chaff dispenser, addition of a programmable tactical information display in the rear cockpit, and modification of the existing analog 5400 mission computer with digital capabilities from the F-14D AN/AYK-14. Twin Mil Std 1553B databuses will also be added. The validation aircraft is due to be redelivered in June 1994, with the first 'production' upgrade emerging from NADEP Norfolk in January 1995. The programme will last until 2002, when the Navy plans a so-called 'Block One' upgrade, which would add an attack FLIR (that will also add laser designation capability), the F-14D's HUD, an NVG cockpit, the AN/ALE-50 towed decoy, and an integrated GPS.

Further conversions/upgrades to F-14D, F-14B or to one of the advanced strike configurations remain at least theoretically possible.

One of the stars of the film 'Top Gun', wearing fictitious and already rather eroded squadron markings, has the later single-strip upper and lower gun bay vents.

Block Number	BuNos	Fiscal Year	Total
60 (F-14A-60-GR)	158612 - 158619	FY71	8
65 (F-14A-65-GR)	158620 - 158637	FY71	18
70 (F-14A-70-GR)	158978 - 159006	FY72	29
75 (F-14A-75-GR)	159007 - 159025	FY72	19
	159421 - 159429	FY73	9
80 (F-14A-80-GR)	159430 - 159468	FY73	39
85 (F-14A-85-GR)	159588 - 159637	FY74	50
90 (F-14A-90-GR)	159825 - 159874	FY75	50
(F-14A-05-GR)	160299 - 160328	For Iran	30
(F-14A-10-GR)	160329 - 160360	For Iran	32
(F-14A-15-GR)	160361 - 160378	For Iran	18
95 (F-14A-95-GR)	160379 - 160414	FY76	36
100 (F-14A-100-GR)	160652 - 160696	FY77	45
105 (F-14A-105-GR)	160887 - 160930	FY78	44
110 (F-14A-110-GR)	161133 - 161168	FY79	36
115 (F-14A-115-GR)	161270 - 161299	FY80	30
120 (F-14A-120-GR)	161416 - 161445	FY81	30
125 (F-14A-125-GR)	161597 - 161626	FY82	30
130 (F-14A-130-GR)	161850 - 161873	FY83	30
135 (F-14A-135-GR)	162588 - 162611	FY84	24
140 (F-14A-140-GR)	162688 - 162711	FY85	24

*Some later aircraft, like this **TCS**-equipped, crudely-camouflaged F-14A from VF-213 'Black Lions', have later F-14D-style NACA-type gun bay venting system inlets.*

Above: A Naval Fighter Weapons scheme features 'Flanker' camouflage for adversary training.

Below: Wearing smart two-tone grey, this CBU-toting F-14A serves with the Strike Test Directorate.

F-14A (TARPS)

Forty-five aircraft were built with the Tactical Air Reconnaissance Pod System Capability Retrofit Installation (AFC712PT), which enabled them to carry the TARPS reconnaissance pod. The Navy had previously relied upon aircraft designed specifically for the reconnaissance role, primarily the RF-8G Crusader. TARPS, however, could be fitted to the rear left Phoenix station of any Tomcat 'wired' for it, the current total being about 50 aircraft, with one of the two F-14A squadrons on each carrier usually having three reconnaissance-configured ships. All F-14Ds can carry TARPS.

Designed for a low-to-medium altitude reconnaissance role, the pod contains a KS-87 frame camera (vertical or forward oblique), a KA-99 panoramic camera giving horizon-to-horizon coverage, and an AAD-5 infra-red line scanner. The TARPS pod also includes an AN/ASQ-172 data display system for putting event marks on the sensor's film output to aid later interpretation. TARPS Tomcats accommodate pod controls in the rear cockpit and the aircraft provides power and air conditioning to the pod. TARPS became operational in 1981. Original trials TARPS pods were converted from external fuel tanks, which are a commonly carried Tomcat store.

The TARPS aircraft were 160696, 160910, 160911, 160914, 160915, 160920, 160925, 160926, 160930, 161134, 161135, 161137, 161140, 161141, 161146, 161147,

A TARPS pod undergoes maintenance, slung under the belly of a Patuxent River F-14A.

161150, 161152, 161155, 161156, 161158, 161159, 161161, 161162, 161164, 161168, 161270, 161271, 161272, 161273, 161275, 161276, 161277, 161280, 161281, 161282, 161285, 161604, 161605, 161611, 161620, 161621, 161622, 161624 and 161626. Seven more (158614, 158620, 158637, 159591, 159606, 159612 and 160696) were modified retrospectively. Three TARPS aircraft are usually assigned to each recce-capable F-14 squadron. Several more F-14As have sometimes been described as being TARPS capable, including 158978, 160916, 160921, 161138, 161143, 161144, 161149, 161153, 161165, 161167, 161278, 161283, 161286, 161430, 161601, 161625, 161864, 161866 and 161868.

A VF-102 'Diamondbacks' F-14A banks away to show the belly-mounted TARPS pod.

F-14A-GR (Iran)

From the beginning, Grumman had searched for other customers for the Tomcat and first proposed a long-range interceptor version to the US Air Force. In the 1970s, when the Shah of Iran (himself a pilot and infatuated with high-tech hardware) was striving to become the dominant force in the Persian Gulf, Teheran exhibited considerable interest in the Tomcat and other Western fighters. Iran also looked seriously at the F-15 Eagle and, soon afterwards, placed firm orders for the F-16 Fighting Falcon and the Northrop F-18L, land-based version of the F/A-18 Hornet. A few voices were warning that the Shah's fascination for top-of-the-line weaponry was growing excessive and that rumbles of discontent from the country's population threatened turmoil ahead. Iran, however, was a long-term ally that directly bordered on what was later called 'the evil Empire', and was a major supplier of oil to the USA; in any event, arms sales were decided in personal conversations between the Shah and President Nixon, and Imperial Iran's ambitious armament programme forged ahead.

In the competition for the Shah's favour, the Tomcat gained an edge when a strong showing was made at the 1973 Paris air show, and by a personal demonstration for the Shah at Andrews AFB, in late 1973. Iran's case was not hindered when, in August 1974, the Iranian Melli bank stepped in with a loan when Congress voted to cut off the loan which was then keeping Grumman afloat. Motivated in part by incursions by Soviet MiG-25 'Foxbats' flying from bases on its northern border, the Imperial Iranian Air Force (IIAF) became the first and only foreign purchaser of the Tomcat, ordering 40 aircraft in June 1974 and 40 more in January 1975. The Iranian Tomcats were virtually identical to US Navy F-14As (with different harness locks and a diluter demand oxygen system), as were their Phoenix missiles, except for deletion of the ECCM (electronic counter-countermeasures) suite.

At the time, the General Accounting Office and other watchdog agencies were accusing Grumman of cost overruns in the Tomcat programme – a charge which seems to arrive with every major aircraft

An Iranian F-14A in flight. Iran is thought to remain the only foreign operator of the Tomcat, although rumours suggest that two F-14s were evaluated by Israel and may have been retained.

procurement – and the Iranian order helped to level the Tomcat's price and silence the critics. The first Iranian Tomcats were delivered to Mehrabad air base on 27 January 1976, and eventually equipped a peak of four squadrons at Khatami and Shiraz. After 79 of the 80 Tomcats had been delivered, aircraft No. 80 being retained for trials, the Persian state was swept by revolution, culminating in the fall of the Shah. This killed off all prospects for the repeat order for 70 more F-14s which had been discussed, and led to dramatic changes for the Imperial Iranian Air Force, which became the Islamic Republic of Iran Air Force (IRIAF). Many pilots and groundcrew were purged, and the force was suddenly cut off from its prime source of equipment, spares, support and training. It managed to keep most of its F-4D and F-4E Phantoms operational even during the 1980-88 war with Iraq, but this was largely due to clandestine assistance from Israel, which also operated Phantoms.

The Tomcat force never proved very effective, since only a small number could be kept airworthy, many aircraft being grounded through shortages of brakes and tyres. They did see some action, however,

The star-and-bar and H35 on the fin, applied for the long ferry flight, did little to disguise the intended destination of this desert-camouflaged F-14A at Calverton during 1977. One of the Iranian Tomcats was retained for trials.

often in a mini-AWACS role. Several were lost. Two are known to have been downed by Iraqi Mirage F1s, and another fell to a MiG-21. One was claimed on 4 October 1983, another on 21 November, and more single examples on 24 February and 1 July 1984, while on 11 August 1984 Iraq claimed to have shot down three F-14As. Iranian

F-14s are known to have claimed at least three Iraqi fighters in return, including a MiG-21 and two Mirage F1s. A rumour persists, despite the revolution's anti-Communist bent, that one F-14 was secretly whisked from Iran to the Soviet Union for study. Other stories suggest that this aircraft was flown to the USSR by a

disaffected pilot. Perhaps more damagingly, Iran received 284 of 714 AIM-54 Phoenix missiles it had ordered, some of which were passed on to the USSR, where they proved of inestimable value to development of the AA-9 'Amos' missile.

Iranian Tomcats were officially F-14A-GRs, and were produced between Block 90 and Block 95 (F-14A-90-GR and F-14A-95-GR). They did not differ greatly from their Block 95 US Navy counterparts, and were delivered with virtually full carrier equipment, although some more sensitive systems, including the radar, ECM and AIM-54 missiles, were downgraded. The tactical software tape was unique to foreign sales aircraft. The AN/ARA-63 ILS was removed, as were the KIT-1A, KIR-1A and KY-28 cryptographic systems and the catapult abort mechanism. Crew equipment was also revised, with USAF-style harness attachments, including a centrally opening lap belt and new survival kit, and a chest-mounted oxygen regulator (normally panel-mounted) The covers over the inflight-refuelling probe were removed, giving the

A pair of Iranian F-14As refuels from one of that country's Boeing 707-3J9 tankers, the latter equipped with wingtip-mounted Beech 1800C wing pods.

only major external difference between Iranian and contemporary US Navy F-14s, although the arrester hook on Iranian aircraft was also given a sharper point, with much-reduced edge radius. The last Iranian F-14 was not delivered and was taken over by the US Navy as 160378. Allocated US Navy Bureau Numbers (160299 - 160378), the aircraft were assigned Iranian serial numbers 3-863 to 3-892 and 3-6001 to 3-6050.

It is easy to underestimate the number of F-14s remaining active with the IRIAF. Even as early as 1985, 25 were available for a mass flypast over Teheran, and serviceability and spares supply has probably improved since then, with the aircraft being accorded a high priority due to their capability and operational utility.

Left: Most Iranian F-14s have uncovered inflight-refuelling probes, as shown in this impressive line-up of Iranian F-14Bs.

Right: The US Naval Fighter Weapons School operates at least one standard USN F-14 in Iranian markings. This is not the aircraft built for Iran, whose delivery was halted by an embargo and which eventually reached the Pacific Missile Test Center.

F-14A IMI

The F-14 was proposed in 1971 as a contender for the USAF's Improved Manned Interceptor requirement for an F-106 replacement. A mock-up was constructed using the Model 303E mock-up as a basis, but with the addition of enormous conformal fuel tanks. USAF interest in the Tomcat was spurred by its very long range, which exceeded that of the F-15, and the capabilities of its AN/AWG-9 fire control system and the performance of the associated AIM-54 Phoenix missile. The F-14A IMI was eventually defeated by its very high price.

This F-14A IMI mock-up features four external fuel tanks, a single semi-conformal belly tank, and a combination of two underwing AIM-7 Sparrows and four belly-mounted AIM-54 Phoenix AAMs. Such a configuration gave range and combat persistence.

JF-14A

A single early F-14A, 158613, was assigned to test duties under the designation JF-14A.

F-14B

From the very start it was realised that the TF30-powered Tomcat would be somewhat underpowered, and would thus be best suited to being an interim aircraft, on which the Navy could gain experience while a more powerful variant was developed. Accordingly, a VFX-2 requirement (which became the F-14B) was written, describing an up-engined version of the TF-30-powered VFX-1 (which became the F-14A). It was estimated that development of an up-engined version would give 40 per cent better turn radius, 21 per cent better sustained *g* capability and 80 per cent greater radius of action. The engine chosen was the Pratt & Whitney F401-PW-P400, a derivative of the JTF-22 Advanced Technology Engine that also spawned the F100 used by the F-15 and F-16. The naval F401 used the same core, with a larger fan and afterburner, and a single-stage aft of the three-stage fan designed to supercharge the

The seventh YF-14 served as the prototype for the proposed F-14B. The F-14A was initially conceived to be an interim type, and the 67 aircraft originally ordered were to have been brought up to F-14B standard, with F401 engines. The latter engine was also to have powered the more advanced multi-role F-14C, some of which were to have gone to four US Marine Corps fighter squadrons.

core. As well as providing a degree of commonality with the USAF's standard fighter engine, the F401 offered lower weight and better specific fuel consumption than the TF30, and delivered 16,400 lb st (72.95 kN) dry thrust, and a staggering 28,090 lb st (125 kN) in reheat. This marked an increase of 16,000 lb st (71.17 kN) reheat thrust over the basic F-14, and raised the thrust to weight ratio from a modest 0.75:1 to more than unity.

It had originally been intended that only the first 67 Tomcats (including prototypes) would be TF30 powered F-14As, and that all subsequent aircraft would be built to VFX-2 standards, powered by the new advanced technology engine and designated F-14B. Existing F-14As would then be re-engined with the new powerplant. The eventual projected total was for over 700 aircraft, including aircraft for four Marine fighter squadrons, but many of these, it was felt, would be of the advanced multi-mission F-14C variant. The 469 aircraft initially contracted for were to have been procured in eight lots, of six, six, 30, 96, 96, 96, 96 and 43 aircraft. On this basis, unit cost (in 1970) was set at $12.4 million.

The seventh YF-14 was converted to serve as the F-14B prototype, flying on 12 September 1973. Some reports suggest that the aircraft first flew with an F401 in one nacelle only, but Gruman has recently stated that the aircraft flew only with two F401s installed from the very beginning. The engine proved too ambitious, however, and ran into many problems (failing its initial flight rating tests in 1975).

The Tomcat was already running into criticisms based mainly on its cost escalation, so costly and public engine development problems were the last thing the US Navy needed. Accordingly, they decided to stick with the TF30 and cancel the F-14B, while the USAF pressed ahead and set about slowly solving the similar problems which beset their version of the engine. Given the benefit of a crystal ball, or 20-20 hindsight, many might have preferred to stick with the F401 (whose Air Force equivalent suffered similar problems but eventually came good) rather than stay with an engine which remains both troublesome and lacking in thrust, and which forced a later (and thus more costly) switch to another new engine, the F110-GE-400. The F-14B prototype was put into storage, later emerging as the F-14B Super Tomcat to test the F101-DFE and its production derivative, the F110-GE-400.

The F-14B prototype waits at Calverton, virtually complete, for the installation of its F401 engines. The aircraft was the seventh of the YF-14s, and was probably the most valuable of the prototype batch, laying the groundwork for the later F-14A+ and F-14D versions, which transformed the Tomcat into the aircraft it always promised to be.

F-14B Super Tomcat

Ongoing problems with the TF30 engine (and, coincidentally, with the F100 used in US Air Force F-15s and F-16s) had led to the examination of a number of possible replacements, including the General Electric F101-X, the Pratt & Whitney F401-PW-26C, and both afterburning and non-augmented versions of the Corsair's Allison TF41, the TF41-912-B32 and -B31, respectively. No money was available for a formal competition, however, and it was not until 1979 that a development contract was awarded for a common USAF/USN future fighter engine.

In an effort to build up General Electric (which was felt to be lagging behind Pratt & Whitney in advanced fighter turbofan development), the company was given a development contract to produce a common USAF/US Navy fighter engine that might replace the TF30 in the F-14, and the F100 in the F-16. The resulting F101-DFE (Derivative Fighter Engine) was based on the core of the basic F101 being developed for the B-1 bomber, with a fan scaled up from that fitted to the F/A-18's highly successful F404. The same Tomcat that had been the original F-14B prototype, the seventh of the YF-14s, BuNo. 157986, was picked to evaluate the F101-DFE. As the so-called 'Super Tomcat' the aircraft made its first flight in its new configuration at Calverton on 14 July 1981, with the new engines installed in both nacelles and painted up with 'Super Tomcat' tail logos. At the same time, an F-16 (the so-called F-16/101) was already flying with the new engine, the first FSD F-16A, 75-0745, having initially flown with the new powerplant on 19 December 1980. This paved the way for the eventual F110 engine installation in the F-16C. Tests with the F101-DFE in the Super Tomcat were finally completed in the autumn of 1981.

The test programme showed impressive performance gains, including a highly significant 62 per cent increase in intercept radius, and useful gains in take-off performance that promised to allow unreheated carrier launches. A second aircraft allocated to the development programme, F-14A 158630, was deemed to be unnecessary. It was probably never fully converted, and was returned to standard F-14A configuration for further US Navy service. The engine's promise was such that a derived design, the F110-GE-100, was put into production for the F-16C, and a related version, the F110-GE-400, was selected to power the F-14D and the planned F-14A+. The Super Tomcat was

Laden with 1,000-lb Mk 83 bombs, fuel tanks and AIM-7 Sparrow and AIM-9 Sidewinder missiles, the Super Tomcat is seen here during the F-14D development programme.

Originally YF-14A No. 7, 157986 successively served as the F-14B prototype with F401-P-400s, as the F-14B Super Tomcat with F101-DFEs, and as the *de facto* A+/D prototype with F110-GE-400s. External configuration, sensor pods etc. changed to reflect this, although the colour scheme remained constant.

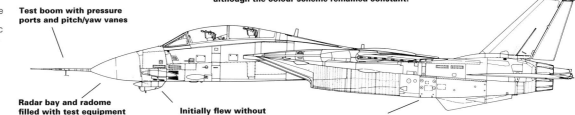

Test boom with pressure ports and pitch/yaw vanes

Radar bay and radome filled with test equipment

Initially flew without undernose sensor pod

General Electric F101-DFE turbofans eventually replaced by lengthened, productionised F110-GE-400s

F-14B Super Tomcat

re-engined again, flying with the F110-GE-400 as the F-14D engine prototype, gaining a representative undernose sensor package. With the F110-GE-400 the aircraft made another 'maiden' flight on 29 September 1986. In this guise the hardworking aircraft was flown to 762 mph (1226 km/h) and 35,000 ft (10836 m) by test pilot Joe Burke.

Right: The F-14B (originally YF-14 No. 7) is seen here flying with F101-DFE engines in both nacelles as the Super Tomcat prototype.

F-14B (formerly F-14A+)

Designed as an interim improved Tomcat under the designation F-14A+, pending availability of the full-standard F-14D, it was originally envisaged that all F-14A+s would eventually become F-14Ds. Modifications to some secondary structure permit the installation of the General Electric F110-GE-400 turbofan in the new variant. This engine was developed from the USAF's DFE F110 tested in the Super Tomcat, described above.

The F110 is almost completely installationally interchangeable with the TF30, needing just an extra 50-in (127-cm) section downstream of the turbine (because the newer engine is much shorter, basically 182 in/462 cm compared with 236 in/600 cm). Almost the only other change was rearrangement of the engine accessories and their drive gearbox, plus minor modification to the surrounding F-14 secondary structure. The costs involved were modest. Diameter of the GE engine is actually less, at 46.5 in (118 cm), yet airflow at take-off is increased from about 242 to 270 lb (109 to 122 kg) per second. This increases power in a similar ratio, nominally to 29,000 lb (129 kN), although the Navy -400 engine is matched to F-14 requirements at 27,000 lb (120 kN). This not only dramatically improves all-round combat performance, but it enables catapult take-offs to be made in MIL power (without afterburner).

This backs up the great increase in power by a significant reduction in fuel consumption, because fuel burn in afterburner is multiplied by about four. Thus, at a round figure, the mission radius is increased by the new engine by no less

Below: Wearing markings indicating a recent or forthcoming deployment aboard the USS Nimitz, an F-14B of VF-211 'Fighting Checkmates', laden with a full load of six AIM-54C Phoenix missiles, gets airborne. The Pacific Fleet F-14B squadrons transitioned back to F-14As when it was decided to rationalise the Tomcat fleet with As and Ds on the West Coast, and As and Bs on the East Coast.

than 62 per cent. Time to high altitude is reduced by about 61 per cent. Not least, the F110 allows the pilot to forget about the engines during air combat and slam the throttle shut or wide open no matter what the angle of attack or airspeed.

While the TF30 was an advanced engine for the 1960s, the F110 shows the progress made in the intervening 20 years. The TF30 has a total of 16 stages of compression, the three-stage fan rotating on the same shaft as the six-stage low-pressure compressor. The F110, in contrast, has only 12 stages in total, comprising a three-stage fan and a nine-stage high-pressure compressor, yet, with hundreds of blades fewer, the overall pressure ratio of 31 is much higher than that of the older engine, which equates with better fuel economy. A further index of

progress is overall length. The comparative figures given previously show how modern engines can burn fuel in a shorter distance, and this is particularly true of the afterburner. The distance from the augmentation fuel nozzle rings to the end of the exhaust nozzle of the F110 is not much over half that of the TF30, but it was cheaper to add an unnecessary extra section to the F110 than to shorten the F-14.

Other changes include removal of the wing glove vanes, cockpit changes, the installation of the new AN/ALR-67 RWR with antennas below the wing gloves, installation of a new Direct Lift Control/Approach Power Control system, and redesign of the gun bay, incorporating a gas purging system, with NACA-type inlets

replacing the original grilles. A fatigue/engine-monitoring system and AN/ARC-182 V/UHF radios are installed. The modernised and modified radar fire control system is redesignated AN/AWG-15F. Six aircraft were involved in F-14A+ development, including the hard-working test-ship, former F-14B Super Tomcat 157986, which made another landmark first flight on 29 September 1986 with the F110GE-400 engine. Piloted by Joe Burke at Grumman's Calverton facility, 157986 reached 762 mph

AIM-54s wait to be loaded onto a VF-211 F-14B. The NACA-type inlets for the gun bay gas purging system can clearly be seen aft of the muzzle.

This F-14B belongs to VF-103 'Sluggers', one of two F-14B units that participated in Operation Desert Storm, losing one aircraft.

Right: Apart from its F110-GE-400 engines (with different nozzles) and the lack of glove vanes, the F-14B is outwardly similar to the F-14A.

(1226 km/h) and 35,000 ft (10836 m) during this 54-minute trial run. Success with tests of the F110 powerplant led to a $235-million contract on 15 February 1987, the first of several for production of the GE powerplant. The Navy took delivery of its first production GE F110GE-400 engine for the F-14A+ on 30 June 1987.

The first FSD F-14A+ to fly was 162910,

on September 1986. The same aircraft later flew in full F-14A+ production configuration on 14 November 1987. The F-14A+ was redesignated F-14B on 1 May 1991, the original F-14B then serving as an F-14A+ development aircraft, leaving its designation 'free'. Thirty-eight F-14A+s were newly built, as detailed below. None of these aircraft were TARPS-capable.

Block Number	Bu Nos	Fiscal Year	Total
145 (F-14B-145-GR)	162910 - 162927	FY86	18
150 (F-14B-150-GR)	163217 - 163229	FY87	15
155 (F-14B-155-GR)	163407 - 163411	FY88	5

With a temporary desert camouflage applied in water-soluble paint, and with nose art proclaiming it to be the 'Thief of Baghdad', this Tomcat belonged to VF-24, one of two West Coast F-14B units.

Above: An F-14B of VF-101 'Grim Reapers' turns belly-on to the camera to show off its load of iron bombs.

Right: Before its disbandment, VF-74 pressed its F-14Bs into service in the adversary role, with a hastily applied camouflage scheme.

In addition to the newly-built F-14A+s, 32 aircraft were produced by conversion from F-14A airframes. The conversions were allocated the sequential KB- series identifications KB-1 to KB-32 (respectively F-14As 161424, 161426, 161429, 161418, 161287, 161428, 161433, 161417, 161419, 161440, 161444, 161427, 161416, 161442, 161437, 161441, 161421, 161422, 161425, 16159, 161601, 161430, 161608, 161432, 161434, 161435, 161438, 161851, 161871, 161610, 161870 and 161873). KB-1, -3, -6, -8, -13, -16, -18, -20, -22, -23 and -30 were equipped to carry TARPS. KB1-7 were funded in FY1986, KB8-25 in FY1987 and KB26-32 in FY1987 (purchase of kits) and FY1988 (installation of kits). About 17 more conversions have since been funded. Grumman has been funded to produce 11 conversion kits, with an option on eight more. Grumman and NADEP Norfolk are competing for the contract covering the installation of these kits.

Most F-14Bs may be upgraded under the same depot-level MMCAP update programme as some surviving F-14As, and are also potential targets for the Navy's proposed Block 1 upgrade.

F-14B (formerly F-14A+)

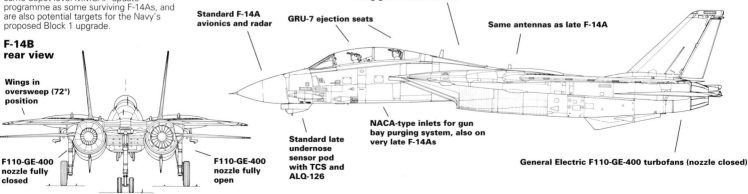

F-14B rear view

Wings in oversweep (72°) position

F110-GE-400 nozzle fully closed

F110-GE-400 nozzle fully open

Standard F-14A avionics and radar

GRU-7 ejection seats

Wing glove vanes deleted

Same antennas as late F-14A

Standard late undernose sensor pod with TCS and ALQ-126

NACA-type inlets for gun bay purging system, also on very late F-14As

General Electric F110-GE-400 turbofans (nozzle closed)

Undernose sensors
The F-14 has carried a variety of sensors in pods below the forward fuselage. These have included a simple ALQ-100 RWR antenna, an IRST, the IRST with RWR underslung, or the Northrop TCS with underslung RWR.

Radar
The F-14B is fitted with the AN/AWG-9 fire control system, which consists of a powerful pulse-Doppler radar capable of simultaneously tracking up to 24 targets and engaging up to six, with a two-way datalink, computers, cockpit displays and (originally) an IR detection system. The radar was based on the AN/ASG-18 developed for the F-108 and uses a slotted planar array antenna.

Grumman F-14B

This F-14B wears the markings of VF-74 'Bedevilers', an Atlantic Fleet Tomcat unit which was disestablished on 1 July 1994, having spent the last few days of its existence flying in the adversary role. The 101 'Modex' identifies this as the skipper's aircraft, the CAG being assigned Modex 100 and the XO getting 102. Like many Tomcat squadron commander's aircraft, this F-14B has more colourful unit insignia (applied in black, red and yellow) and has full-colour national insignia.

Wing
A massive one-piece carry-through structure of electron beam-welded titanium alloy spans the upper centre-section of the F-14. The use of an all-welded structure reduced weight and limited the chance of cracking around the (absent) bolts and bolt-holes. At each end are the spherical pivot bearings and actuators for the variable-geometry outer wing panels.

Datalink
The ASW-27B provides for the automatic display of targets detected by ships, an E-2C Hawkeye or other F-14s, while simultaneously transmitting data on its own contacts. This can give the F-14 crew the reassurance of a 360° view of the area around them, which is also useful in enhancing tactical awareness. ASW-27B is also compatible with the Boeing E-3 Sentry and the Basic Air Defense Ground Environment.

Flight controls
The wing has full-span leading-edge slats and trailing-edge flaps in three sections, the inboard sections usable only with the wing swept forward. Four-section spoilers are fitted immediately ahead of the two outer flap sections.

Tail surfaces
The F-14 has conventional rudders on the trailing edge of each fin, with all-moving tailplanes moving symmetrically for pitch and differentially for roll control.

Powerplant
The F-14B is powered by a pair of 23,100-lb st (102.75-kN) General Electric F110-GE-400 turbofans. As well as giving commonality with the engines used by later variants of the F-16, the new engine is less prone to compressor stalls than the TF-30, and is considerably more economic.

Computer network
The radar and the other elements of the fire control system are linked via the Computer Signal Data Converter. This controls the Central Air Data Computer (which programmes wing sweep), the HUD, the datalink, the INS and the computerised cockpit displays. Most of the computers are digital, but analog computers are used for the AFCS and for fuel management.

F-14C

The F-14C was a proposed advanced version of the F-14B, with the same engines but with more advanced avionics and weapons systems.

Underwing pylons
The pylons under the wing gloves can carry either a single Phoenix or AIM-7 Sparrow, in each case with the option of a single AIM-9 Sidewinder on the stub 'shoulder' pylon.

Above: This new-build F-14D of VF-31 'Tomcatters' is in landing configuration, but with the arrester hook raised for an airfield landing. The squadron uses Felix the cat (carrying a bomb) as its insignia, a traditional badge going back to before World War II.

F-14D

The F-14D designation was originally applied to an unbuilt, austere version of the Tomcat, proposed at a time when the spiralling cost of the baseline F-14A was causing great concern. The F-14D we know today was first announced in 1984, and was conceived as an advanced Tomcat derivative with improved digital avionics. The F-14A+ was simultaneously conceived as an interim lower-cost supplement, which would be produced primarily by conversion of existing airframes.

The success of the F-14B Super Tomcat/F101-DFE combination led to an early decision (in February 1984) that the new variant would be powered by the 27,600-lb st (122.8-kN) F110-PW-400, the productionised version of the DFE engine, to take advantage of the promised improvement in performance, and to free the new variant from reliance on the TF30 turbofan that had proved so troublesome. This gave a 30 per cent lower fuel consumption in reheat, a 50 per cent increase in intercept radius and a 33 per cent greater CAP endurance. The increased thrust allowed carrier take-offs in dry power, a useful safety feature and particularly significant at night, when the bright flames generated by a typical 'burner take-off defeats any measures taken to darken the ship. The F-14B Super Tomcat prototype was re-engined with this powerplant, which introduced a 50-in (127-cm) plug in the afterburner section to move the heavy fan and compressor sections of the lighter, shorter engine further forward to maintain

Above: With basic F-14A-style TF30 turbofans still fitted, the first prototype F-14D takes off on its first flight in US Navy hands, on 8 December 1987.

Below: The boat-tail of an F-14D features the high-band AN/ALQ-165 RHAWS antenna and the fuel dump pipe. Bays for tandem chaff/flare dispensers can just be seen.

The F110-PW-400, the powerplant used by the F-14D, has distinctive 'turkey feathers'. The nozzle is seen here in the fully open position, making an interesting comparison with the picture at the top of the page.

A VF-124 'Gunfighters' F-14D rests on the Miramar flight line, its cockpit shown here. The heavily framed and separate windscreen and quarterlights seem especially anachronistic in an era when most modern fighters (even including the latest variants of the Mikoyan MiG-31 'Foxhound') feature a frameless, wraparound windscreen. The cockpit of the F-14D has, however, been extensively redesigned internally, with a new head-up display and with two multi-function display screens replacing some of the analog instrumentation in the F-14A's cockpit.

centre of gravity tolerances, and to allow installation in existing F-14s without major structural changes. The heavy sections of the engine actually moved forward only 39 in (99 cm), since the afterburner nozzles were mounted 11 in (28 cm) further back than on the F-14A. The re-engined F-14B made its first flight with the new engines in 1986, and later received other elements of the F-14D upgrade including the General Electric/Martin-Marietta dual undernose TCS/IRST sensor pod.

The avionics changes of the F-14D are actually the most important elements of the upgrade, and dramatically improve the combat capability of the F-14 in its primary intercept role, where all-out performance is of secondary importance. The F-14D is equipped with AN/APG-71 radar, which is essentially based on the hardware of the original AN/AWG-9, but with digital processing and NVG-compatible displays. The aircraft also has a multibus systems architecture with dual AYK-14 computers, AN/ALR-67 radar warning receivers, and provision for JTIDS. An AN/ASN-139 digital INS, and a digital stores management system are provided. All F-14Ds have expanded ground attack capability, and all are fitted with Martin-Baker Mk 14 NACES ejection seats.

Four prototypes were converted from F-14As, while the re-engined F-14B Super Tomcat was also involved in engine development work, first flying with F110-GE-400 engines on 29 September 1986. The first (PA-1 161865) made its maiden flight on 23 November 1987 and had F-14D APG-71 radar, digitised avionics and cockpit, but retained TF30-PW-414 engines. It was used for COM/NAV display system integration, radar systems testing, and datalink integration. The second (PA-2

Below: Externally, the F-14D can be distinguished from other variants by the General Electric/Martin-Marietta twin side-by-side sensor pods undernose, which house the Northrop AN/AXX-1 TCS to starboard and the General Electric Aerospace Electronic Systems AN/AAS infra-red search and track sensor to port (seen here with a solid cover, perhaps indicating that the equipment is not fitted). These were ordered in 1993 for installation before 1996.

Right: The F-14D backseater has a single multi-function display screen in addition to his radar scope. Dual controls and emergency flight instruments are also fitted.

Making a rare visit to a carrier deck is one of VF-124's F-14Ds. The squadron is the West Coast Tomcat training unit, and is equipped with both F-14As and F-14Ds. No F-14D training is undertaken on the East Coast, and the Atlantic Fleet has no F-14D squadrons.

161867) was the only one of the four FSD aircraft actually fitted with F110-GE-400 engines, and had the same radar and avionics. It flew on 29 April 1988 and was used for radar and avionics integration, environmental systems integration, TARPS integration and radar fault isolation and verification trials. The TF30-PW-414-engined third and fourth prototypes (PA-3/ 162595 and PA-4/161623) made their maiden flights on 31 May and 21 September 1988, respectively, and were used for radar and stores management integration, ECM and RWR testing, and IRST and TCS integration, plus live weapons firing (PA-3) and JTIDS development and systems verification (PA-4). A TA-3B also took part in the flight test programme. The first prototype was delivered to VX-4 in May 1990.

Thirty-seven of the planned 127 F-14Ds were completed (as detailed below) before the programme was cancelled as an economy measure in 1989. The first of these was rolled out on 23 March 1990, and the last was delivered on 20 July 1992. Another 18 F-14Ds were produced by conversion of F-14As, and this total of only 55 aircraft was sufficient to equip three front-line squadrons and part of the Pacific Fleet training unit, VF-124. After a false start, in which VF-51 and VF-111 received Ds, VF-2 'Bounty Hunters' and the two units of Air Wing Six (VF-11 'Red Rippers' and VF-31 'Tomcatters') became the three F-14D units, each with a mix of new-build and remanufactured aircraft. A handful of prototype and early test F-14Ds have been redesignated as NF-14Ds and serve with a number of dedicated test units.

With the F-14Bs, the in-service F-14Ds are scheduled to receive some elements of

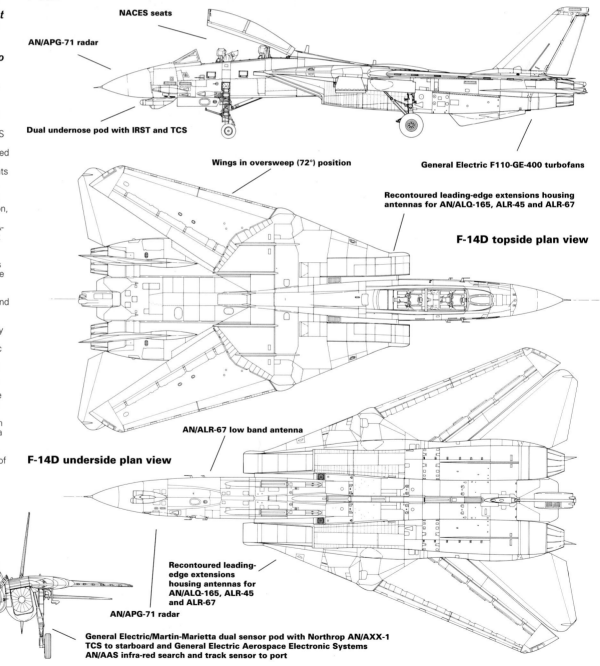

F-14D

- NACES seats
- AN/APG-71 radar
- Dual undernose pod with IRST and TCS

Wings in oversweep (72°) position

General Electric F110-GE-400 turbofans

Recontoured leading-edge extensions housing antennas for AN/ALQ-165, ALR-45 and ALR-67

F-14D topside plan view

F-14D underside plan view

AN/ALR-67 low band antenna

F-14D front view

Recontoured leading-edge extensions housing antennas for AN/ALQ-165, ALR-45 and ALR-67

AN/APG-71 radar

General Electric/Martin-Marietta dual sensor pod with Northrop AN/AXX-1 TCS to starboard and General Electric Aerospace Electronic Systems AN/AAS infra-red search and track sensor to port

the planned Block 1 upgrade (other elements are already present in the F-14D), including GPS from FY95, a digital flight control system, AN/ARC-210 radios from FY98, and probably an attack FLIR, plus the AN/ALE-50 towed decoy.

Block Number	Bu Nos	Fiscal Year	Total
160 (F-14D-160-GR)	163412 - 163418	FY88	7
165 (F-14D-165-GR)	163893 - 163904	FY89	12
170 (F-14D-170-GR)	164340 - 164357	FY90	18

Above: From directly head-on, the only way of distinguishing between the F-14D and earlier variants is by looking at the side-by-side dual undernose sensor pods. This VF-124 aircraft is seen taxiing at NAS Miramar, the West Coast home of the Pacific Fleet F-14 community.

Above: When it transitioned to the F-14D, VF-2 adopted new markings, consisting of a skull with stars in its eye sockets, superimposed on twin stripes.

Right: The distinctive heraldic shield of VF-11 'Red Rippers' is scarcely visible on the fin of this extremely toned-down aircraft. Most squadrons have a couple of aircraft with more colourful markings, sometimes even with full-colour national insignia. Unusually, this F-14D is parked with its inflight-refuelling probe extended.

F-14D inboard profile

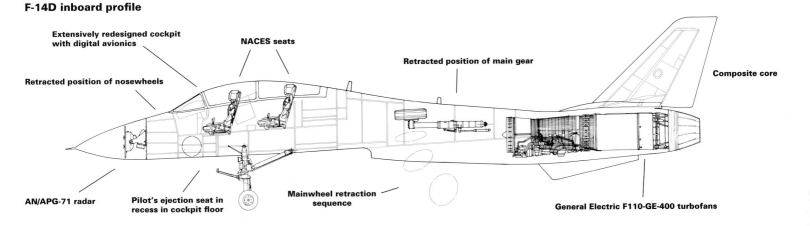

Extensively redesigned cockpit with digital avionics

NACES seats

Retracted position of main gear

Composite core

Retracted position of nosewheels

AN/APG-71 radar

Pilot's ejection seat in recess in cockpit floor

Mainwheel retraction sequence

General Electric F110-GE-400 turbofans

Grumman F-14 Tomcat Variants

F-14D(R)

The first of a planned 400+ F-14As for rebuild to F-14D standards under the designation F-14D(R) was delivered to Grumman in June 1990, the second following in September. The rebuild cycle was scheduled to take some 15 months, and eventually would have given the US Navy a Tomcat fleet consisting almost entirely of F-14Ds and F-14Bs. These ambitious plans were abandoned due to budgetary constraints. The six aircraft contracted for in FY90 were safe, but the 98 F-14D(R)s funded between FY91-FY95 (12, 18, 20, 24 and 24 aircraft) were cancelled, although the FY91 aircraft were later reprieved, to give a total of 18 conversions, all of which have now been redelivered from both Grumman and NADEP Norfolk.

The conversions were allocated the sequential DR- series identifications DR-1 to DR-18 (respectively 161159, 159610, 161158, 159613, 159600, 161166, 159629, 159628, 159619, 159592, 161133, 159595, 161154, 159603, 159635, 159633, 159618 and 159630). 159608 and 159631 were assigned as alternate aircraft for F-14D conversion. Like the F-14D, the F-14D(R) is scheduled to receive the relevant portions of the Block 1 upgrade.

The 18 F-14Ds produced by conversion of existing F-14As have been split between all three current front-line F-14D squadrons, comprising VF-2 'Bounty Hunters', VF-11 'Red Rippers' and VF-31 'Tomcatters'. All Pacific Fleet units home-based at NAS

Miramar, VF-51 and VF-111 each received a handful of F-14Ds but reverted to F-14As when the two squadrons of Air Wing Six (VF-11 and VF-31) swapped from East Coast to West Coast to become the first two operational F-14D units.

Above: A pair of remanufactured F-14D(R)s of VF-2 sits aboard the Constellation. The only way of telling remanufactured from new-build F-14Ds is by looking at the BuNo., and most squadrons have a mix of both types. Only by looking at minor differences in antenna configuration is it possible to differentiate these aircraft from the F-14B.

Conversion Nos	Conversion by:	Fiscal Year	Total
DR-1 to DR-4	Grumman	FY90 (Lot I)	4
DR-5 to DR-6	NADEP Norfolk	FY90 (Lot I)	2
DR-7, 9, 10, 11, 13, 16, 18	Grumman	FY91 (Lot II)	8
DR-8, 12, 14, 17	NADEP Norfolk	FY91 (Lot II)	4

Below: An F-14D(R) of VF-11, the 'Red Rippers', manoeuvres on the deck of the USS Abraham Lincoln. Only three front-line squadrons use the F-14D, which is a considerably more advanced version of the Tomcat featuring advanced avionics as well as more powerful engines.

F/A-14D

The latest Tomcat upgrade proposal is designated F/A-14D and is designed to produce an upgraded strike derivative of the F-14D, by conversion of existing airframes, to replace A-6 Intruders, with no effect on planned F/A-18E/F procurement. If funding is made available in FY94, the programme could be launched in 1995, with deliveries for operational evaluation within two years of the programme start. Approximately $1.5 billion would be required for the upgrade of 54 F-14Ds to the new configuration, or $9.2 billion for 250 aircraft converted from F-14D, F-14B and even F-14A airframes.

Grumman proposes the F/A-14D upgrade as an alternative to the Block 1 upgrade to existing F-14As and F-14Bs, and envisages a four-stage programme, with the last three stages being incorporated as field modifications. Grumman's plan would bring all the aircraft involved up to a virtual F-14D standard, with F110 engines, AYK-14 computer, digital avionics and a new wiring harness. This would eliminate the high-maintenance analog systems that would be retained under the Navy's proposed Block 1 upgrade.

Grumman's seven-month first stage

would also add an attack FLIR, Mil Std 1760 wiring for compatibility with advanced weapons like JSOW, a programmable tactical information display, a 'night vision' one-piece windscreen, stealth measures to reduce frontal RCS, and a dry bay foam system for fuel tank protection. Finally, the AYK-14 computer will be upgraded with a new XN8 memory module.

The second stage of the programme will add the AN/ALE-50 towed decoy, a navigation FLIR, and a full night vision cockpit, with many elements from the F/A-18D and night attack AV-8B, including a

colour digital moving map. The HUD would be converted to use a Raster scan, allowing it to present FLIR data, and an inert gas generator would fill fuel tanks with nitrogen as fuel is consumed.

The third stage would add software modes from the F-15E's AN/APG-71, including Doppler beam sharpening, synthetic aperture, sea surface search, moving target indication, and a terrain-following mode.

The fourth stage would add the advanced weapons like JDAM and JSOW.

NF-14D

The former second and fourth prototype F-14Ds (161867 and 161623) and early

F-14Ds 163415/16 have been permanently assigned to test duties under the designation NF-14D. They were respectively operated by the Naval Air Warfare Center/ Weapons Division (formerly PMTC), the

Naval Air Warfare Center/Aircraft Division (formerly NATC) and by VX-4 (163415 and 163416). The N prefix infers a level of modification which makes it impossible to return the aircraft to operational status.

161867 was never a true F-14D, in that it retained TF-30 engines, while 161623 never received the dual undernose sensor pod. The two later NF-14Ds are much closer to the definitive production F-14D.

One of the four NF-14Ds, 161623, was originally F-14D PA-4. It is now in service with the Strike Aircraft Test Directorate, having initially been allocated to the NATC (which became the NAWC/AD) after conversion to NF-14D standards.

The former F-14D PA-2, now an NF-14D, is seen during early service with the Pacific Missile Test Center. The aircraft has the full-standard F-14D powerplant but lacks the distinctive dual undernose sensor pod fitted to production F-14Ds.

F-14T

The F-14T was a very austere, very basic F-14 derivative designed as an alternative to the increasingly costly F-14A and F-14B. The type competed for an order with a navalised version of the less expensive USAF F-15 known as the F-15N, and also competed with the option of procurement

of upgraded F-4s. The aircraft would have offered only Sparrow and Sidewinder armament, and would have offered little advantage over the ageing F-4 Phantom. The lack of capability offered by the F-14T led to less radically downgraded F-14 variants.

F-14X

The F-14X designation covered a group of slightly less radically degraded Tomcats, some of which had no AIM-54 capability, and some of which had the simultaneous target-tracking capability halved from 24 to 12. DLC, glove vanes and APC (Approach Power Compensator) were removed. The

Westinghouse WX-200, WX-250 or Hughes APG-64 were the fire control system options.

High Israeli attrition rates in the 1973 war led to the type's cancellation, the US Navy preferring to equip its carriers with the best-available aircraft.

F-14 Optimod

The Optimod F-14 was a proposed austere F-14 using one of three different computers with the AWG-9, giving a reduced level of capability. It was intended to reduce the

unit price of the aircraft, which at one time threatened procurement for the US Navy. It may also have been proposed to some export customers.

RF-14

The RF-14 designation originally covered a proposed dedicated reconnaissance derivative of the F-14A, presumably equipped with internal sensors. It was

eventually abandoned in favour of equipping lightly modified (i.e., rewired) standard F-14s with external TARPS pods.

Quickstrike

Drawdowns in Naval Aviation funding and the cancellation of the A-12 as an A-6 replacement have led to a number of plans to offer the F-14 as a long-range strike fighter. Such plans have resulted in the 'Bombcat' modification to F-14As, and the incorporation of a high level of ground attack capability in the F-14D.

They have also resulted in Grumman offering a succession of proposed new strike fighter variants as competitors to the F/A-18E/F, which has been selected as the successor to the A-6. The first of these variants was the Quickstrike, which was a minimum-change FLIR-equipped aircraft with more radar modes for its APG-71 radar,

including synthetic aperture and Doppler Beam Sharpening for mapping, bringing it closer to the APG-70 used by the F-15E. Four fuselage hardpoints each had five sub-stations, while the two wing pylons had two. Navigation and targeting pods similar to LANTIRN would be installed, and cockpit changes would include FLIR, HUD, moving-

map display and large colour displays. Software changes would allow the carriage of laser-guided bombs, stand-off SLAM missiles and Maverick, in addition to HARM and Harpoon. The cockpit was NVG-compatible, and had colour displays, including a digital moving map.

Super Tomcat 21

The Super Tomcat 21 was proposed as a more radical update, a multi-role fighter alternative to the Naval ATF, offering 90 per cent of the capability at 60 per cent of the cost. It was to have incorporated all Quickstrike improvements, with further cockpit and sensor improvements, and a significantly reduced radar cross-section, plus it was to have been powered by improved F110-GE-129 engines which would allow 'supercruise' (i.e., sustained supersonic cruise without afterburner), and which would even incorporate thrust-vectoring. An APU was also planned. The type was to also to have been fitted with enlarged tailplanes (with extended trailing edges giving greater area), new extended wing gloves housing additional internal fuel, and increased-lift slotted flaps and extended-chord slats to allow nil-wind carrier take-offs or take-offs at higher weights. A single point

maintenance panel and other improvements were to have reduced MMH/FH figures by 40 per cent. An improvement in the weapons system package would have seen the adoption of helmet-mounted sights and a new radar with double the power of the APG-71. FLIR pods would have been installed for attack missions.

Above and right: Two views of the Super Tomcat 21 – an advanced F-14 derivative with podded sensors below the nose and forward fuselage, minor aerodynamic improvements and other changes – was intended as a low-cost alternative to the naval ATF and probably also intended as a conversion of existing F-14A, F-14B or F-14D airframes.

Attack Super Tomcat 21

A proposed dedicated Mach 2-capable strike aircraft, the Attack Super Tomcat 21 was based on the Super Tomcat 21, but with thicker outer wing panels housing extra fuel, provision for larger external fuel tanks, and further refinements to the high

lift system to give a 15-kt (18-mph; 27-km/h) reduction in approach speeds. These included redesigned, composite, single-slotted Fowler flaps and a blunter, composite, extended-chord slat. The aircraft was to have had the Norden radar

developed specifically for the GD/McDD A-12. The Attack Super Tomcat 21 has received great attention as a potential successor to the cancelled A-12, a highly advanced but much-troubled flying wing intended as a stealthy naval attack aircraft.

ASF-14

Due to the postponement of development of the Naval ATF, the ASF-14 was proposed as an evolutionary development of the F-14 but with ATF systems, armament and powerplants, and intended as a lower-cost, lower-risk alternative to the Naval ATF.

Bronco Farewell

Reservists VMO-4 retire the OV-10D from US Marine Corps service

Photographed by Greg L. Davis and Chris A. Neill

Rockwell's diminutive OV-10 Bronco has been an important part of USMC operations since 1968, when it was pressed into service as a forward air control and light attack platform in Vietnam. In its twilight years the type played an important part in Desert Storm with the two active-duty squadrons, VMO-1 and VMO-2. The single Reserve unit, VMO-4, was put on alert but did not deploy. On 16 April 1994 the OV-10's Marine career came to an end when VMO-4 flew its last mission after 22 years with the Bronco.

VMO-4 first acquired the OV-10A Bronco in 1972 while based at NAS Grosse Isle, Michigan. The unit soom moved to Selfridge ANGB, and then in 1976 to its final base at NAS Atlanta, Georgia. On 29 May 1991 the first of eight OV-10D (Plus) Broncos was handed over. A single Bell UH-1 was on charge for training and utility purposes. When the unit deactivated in April 1994, it had amassed over 60,000 accident-free flight hours, having only ever lost one aircraft, back in 1973.

*Left and above: **VMO-4 OV-10Ds** seen on the last deployment for the unit, a weapons exercise at MacDill **AFB**, Florida. The **OV-10D** was used primarily for the all-weather **FAC** mission, for which it was fitted with an **AAS**-37 chin turret containing a **FLIR** and laser designator.*

*Below: **For** much of its **USMC** career the **OV-10** wore a drab dark green camouflage, but in the later years a dark green/dark grey/light grey camouflage was adopted, while those which went to the **Gulf** wore two-tone sand schemes. Finally the low-visibility light grey prevailed.*

Bronco Farewell

Above: Purpose-designed for the FAC mission, the OV-10 features very low aspect ratio wings for maximum agility in the face of heavy groundfire and a large bulged canopy offering an outstanding all-round view.

Right: Loaded with LAU-68 pods, a pair of VMO-4 OV-10Ds overflies the Gulf of Mexico during its last armament deployment to MacDill. VMO-4's aircraft were ferried to St Louis, Missouri, for storage, the last arriving on 8 June 1994. The aircraft are reportedly destined for the US Forestry Service and the Drug Enforcement Agency.

Below: The principal weapon of the OV-10D was the rocket, used for target-marking. Other stores included AIM-9 Sidewinders for self-defence or the similar AGM-122 Sidearm for anti-radiation work carried underwing and various types of freefall stores on the four sponson pylons, including Mk 82 500-lb bombs, CBU-78 Gator cluster bombs, CBU-55 fuel-air explosive and Mk 77 fire bombs. The centreline hardpoint was stressed for the carriage of a Mk 83 1,000-lb bomb, a 150-US gal fuel tank or a GPU-2 gun pod.

Above: A plane captain checks a marker rocket pod, which for peacetime training has one tube left empty for safety reasons. Rocket options for the OV-10 included 2.75-in Mk 66 WAFAR rockets fired from LAU-68 seven-round or LAU-69 19-round pods, and the 5-in Zuni fired from a four-round LAU-10. For the most part the warhead was white phosphorus or smoke for marking targets. The standard gun armament of four 7.62-mm M60 machine-guns in the fuselage sponsons could be removed and an M197 20-mm three-barrelled cannon turret installed under the centreline.

Right: An unusual feature of the OV-10 was its rear fuselage compartment, which could accommodate cargo, two stretchers or four armed paratroops.

Greece

The Greek armed forces play a vital role in defending the vulnerable Southern flank of NATO, Europe's so-called 'soft underbelly'. Increasing instability around the 'Mediterranean rim' and the diminution of the Soviet/Warsaw Pact threat has led to a growing importance for Greek air power, and the country's air arms, once equipped largely with the cast-offs from Western European nations, have been radically modernised during recent years. The semi-obsolete aircraft perceived to be too out of date for the Central/Northern Front are largely gone, replaced by the latest superfighters and a new generation of secondhand warplanes – Phantoms and A-7 Corsairs 'cascaded' down from the USAF and USN after the Cold War, numerically surplus but still very potent weapons.

Elliniki Aeroporia (Hellenic Air Force)

Greece is almost unique among NATO nations in not experiencing any 'Peace Dividend' as a result of the end of the Cold War. In fact, the reductions in armed forces experienced by other NATO nations have provided an opportunity for Greece to modernise its air force by obtaining newly retired, but still viable, aircraft, and by taking advantage of aircraft manufacturers' need to find markets for their products. The 1994 Greek Defence Budget was for 900 billion drachma (about $3.7 billion) and the 1995 budget is expected to be at least as large, in real terms. The dramatic disappearance of the Warsaw Pact threat has not been accompanied by any diminution in the other threats perceived by Greece, which have always appeared to be more immediate. Despite the obvious danger posed by instability in North Africa and the Balkans, which has been the stated reason for continued high expenditure, Greek air power continues to be aligned primarily against neighbouring Turkey, continuing a longstanding rivalry dating back to Ottoman times and exacerbated in recent years by tension over Cyprus and over territorial rights in the Aegean. This situation was not anticipated in 1952, when the two nations joined NATO, which promised to be an ideological meeting point and a telling reason for collaboration, mutual aid and even friendship. Such promise was not fulfilled, with Greco-Turkish relations steadily becoming more sour as a result of the Greek-Cypriot independence movement in Cyprus. Turkey suspected that this would actually lead to independent Cyprus becoming a virtual Greek possession, at the expense of the significant Turkish minority on the island. The two sides had to be separated by UN forces in 1963, but there were further problems, culminating in Turkish air force strikes against Greek troops attacking Turkish villages in August 1964.

Cyprus – a focus for disagreement

Cyprus continued to provide a focus for disagreement between the two nations, the problems being exacerbated by the growing importance of oil and mineral rights in the disputed Aegean. This new arena for dispute became more important in 1974, when Greece militarised the tiny islands of Mytilene, Chios, Samos and Nikaria

(only about 3 miles/4.8 km from the Turkish coast) ostensibly as a defensive measure to counter the build-up of Turkish military forces on the adjacent coast. Greek attempts to extend its territorial waters from 6 to 12 miles (9.6 to 19.3 km), and extension of its airspace by 10 miles (16 km), caused further tension, Turkey fearing that the Aegean would become little more than a 'Greek Lake'.

The Turkish invasion of Northern Cyprus in 1974 (amid accusations of atrocities against the minority Turkish population) actually led to Greece pulling the plug on NATO communications landlines running through its territory, and refused to feed early warning information into the NATO network. Greece also withdrew its personnel from NATO headquarters in Turkey (the 6th Allied Tactical Air Force at Izmir and HQ Allied Land Forces South) before withdrawing from NATO altogether.

Greek forces rejoined the alliance in 1980, having originally proposed setting up a 7th ATAF to support NATO-assigned Greek forces and controlled from a headquarters at Larissa. Eventually Greece and Turkey were able to reach agreement over jurisdiction of the Aegean, and Greece rejoined NATO, initially under the same arrangements as before. Greece soon withdrew its forces from the 6th ATAF, however, and today the Hellenic air force still remains outside the NATO AFSOUTH/SIXATAF command structure. Successive socialist administrations have always publicly underplayed the Warsaw Pact threat, yet have been happy to play the nationalist card by continuing to emphasise the danger posed by Turkey.

Vacillating Greek attitudes to the NATO alliance mirror equally ambiguous relations with the United States, which continues to be the country's primary supplier of military aid and equipment. The USA has, on the whole, remained committed to its troublesome ally through thick and thin, seeing Greece, surrounded as it is by Albania, Yugoslavia and Bulgaria, as an invaluable bulwark against Communism in the eastern Mediterranean. During the early 1970s, however, when a military dictatorship assumed power, the US halted its FMS, MAP and IMET assistance, which was resumed at a lower level

when the colonels stood down in 1974. The temporary US embargo did not prevent the transfer of US-built aircraft from other NATO nations, although it did lead to Greek selection of the Mirage F1CG as a replacement for its ageing F-102 interceptors. Relations with the democratic Socialist government which followed remained strained, since the new administration continued to be hostile to Turkey (a full NATO member) even after Greece rejoined the alliance, and engaged in what was effectively an embarrassing arms race with its neighbour and supposed alliance partner. There were protracted wrangles over the continuing use of US bases on Greek territory, with simultaneous refusals to assign units to NATO command from January 1985.

US bases

Relations with the conservative government elected in April 1990 have been somewhat better, with an eight-year extension to the existing base agreement paving the way for further US aid. Before 1972, US aid to Greece and Turkey was given on a 3:5 basis, but the proportion going to Greece has now increased, the new ratio being 7:10. Furthermore, Greece has been able to extract from the USA a commitment to actively participate in defending the country against threats from any quarter. Hellenikon airfield (home to rotational deployments of VQ-2 EP-3Es and 55th SRW RC-135s) and the communications base at Nea Makri have been handed back by the USA, but American units continue to use Souda air base, port facilities at Malia and communications bases at Gournes, Hani Kokkini, Lefkas Island, Mount Ederi, Mount Pateras and Mount Parnes. Greece has continued to state its belief that a US military presence in Europe remains crucial, and has been one of the most vociferous opponents of US Congresional attempts to reduce funding for US forces in Europe. Since 1963 Greece has also received aid from Germany, but since 1979 this has been frozen at DM46,666,665 per annum, paid in 18 monthly installments, with no increase to take account of inflation.

Greek military aviation dates back to before the Balkan Wars of 1912-13, when a small air arm with four Farman biplanes was formed with

Above and right: Flying suit badges of 337 Mira.

The original batch of RF-4Es, like the aircraft seen here in service with 348 Mira, is now being augmented by ex-Luftwaffe aircraft.

A well-worn 337 Mira F-4E wears the blue-grey camouflage applied locally to aircraft used in the fighter intercept role. More recent deliveries retain their USAF grey colour scheme, while aircraft tasked with close support duties wear three-tone Vietnam-style camouflage.

This badge can be seen on flying suits worn by Phantom aircrew from 348 Mira.

349 Mira includes this single example of the NF-5B, the Canadair-built Royal Netherlands Air Force two-seat trainer variant.

349 Mira continues to operate the RF-5A, although some of its aircraft have been de-modded and none is used in the reconnaissance role.

The Nea Ankhialos gate is guarded by one of the North American F-86 Sabres once flown from the base, the others serving as decoys.

T-33s are still in use as hacks and for instrument training and liaison with three Greek bases. Those at Larissa serve with 370 Mira.

The flying suit badge of 349 Mira combines F-5 silhouettes with a camera iris.

A Greek F-16C, armed with a wingtip AIM-9 Sidewinder AAM, taxis out for a training sortie. LANTIRN navigation and targeting pods have been procured for these versatile tactical fighters, and a second batch has been ordered.

330 Mira, one of the two F-16 squadrons at Nea Ankhialos, sports this flying suit badge.

One of the Elliniki Aeroporia's F-16Ds stands ready for a sortie, massive clear-view canopy already open and cockpit ladder in place. 346 Mira serves as the F-16 training unit, and operates most of the two-seaters.

French assistance. Bombs were dropped by hand from October 1912, one of the earliest examples of the offensive use of air power. Neutral for the first few years of World War I, Greece joined the war effort on the Allied side, with the army air force being placed under the Supreme Allied Command's (French) Macedonian Front, and the naval air force being placed under British command as part of the Supreme Allied Command's Mediterranean Front. France and Britain, respectively, provided aircraft and training for the two air arms, with Greek aircraft and pilots initially serving in mixed squadrons with the French and British. The end of the war did not mean inactivity for the Greeks, whose infant air arms flew combat operations in Asia Minor until 1922, with 20 pilots killed. During the 1920s the Royal Hellenic Army and Naval Air Forces were expanded and modernised, with the air arms continuing to reflect their Great War experience in their procurement of new equipment, the army taking largely French types, and the navy, British. The two air arms were finally combined as the Royal Hellenic Air Force in June 1928, with a separate Air Ministry being established on 23 December 1929. The 1930s saw further modernisation and re-equipment, with the delivery of Fairey Battles, Bristol Blenheims, Potez 63s, Bloch and PZL fighters and Dornier flying-boats. Greece was

invaded in 1941, overwhelmed by Italian and German forces despite the help of a detachment of RAF fighter and bomber squadrons.

The Hellenic Air Force as we know it today was formed in 1946, the pre-war air force having effectively ceased to exist with the German invasion of 1941, although a skeleton Royal Hellenic Air Force re-established itself in Egypt and Palestine, with Hellenic units attached to equivalent, co-located RAF training and support formations. Some air and ground crew fought on under RAF auspices, some of them serving with three Greek squadrons (Nos 13, 335 and 336) in North Africa and the Mediterranean. These three units were disbanded and absorbed into the Greek air force in the summer of 1946. Immediately after the end of World War II, Greece was in the British sphere of influence, as agreed between Stalin, Roosevelt and Churchill at Yalta, and Britain was largely responsible for the immediate post-war re-equipment of the Greek air force, mainly with a mixed bag of ex-RAF Dakotas, Harvards, Spitfires, Tiger Moths and the like. Remarkably, some of the Dakotas, still wearing their RAF serial numbers, remain in use to this day.

In 1948, the British Mission in Greece was replaced by an American Military Aid Mission, which organised the delivery of the first of a flood of US-built aircraft, commencing with

Curtiss Helldiver dive-bombers, which proved well-suited to operations against Communist forces in the civil war which raged between 1946 and 1950. Deliveries of US-built aircraft have continued ever since (sometimes via third parties, most notably Germany), despite fluctuating relations between Greece and the USA.

Greek participation in the UN effort in Korea (the air force sent a flight of Dakotas) paved the way for NATO membership, which brought with it closer links with the USA, and regular deliveries of military equipment under the Military Assistance Program. Concurrent with entry into NATO, the air force was reorganised, with the establishment of three numbered commands. These were the 28th Tactical Air Force Command, the 31st Air Training Command and the 30th Air Material Command. The 28th Tactical Air Force was then placed under the operational control of NATO. A republic was proclaimed in 1973, after a referendum and, as a result of this, the prefix 'royal' was dropped from the air force's official title.

Today the Greek air force is still divided into three functional commands, for training, support and tactical operations. The largest of these commands is the Taktiki Aeroporikis Dynamis (Tactical Air Force) which controls all front-line fast jets.

Taktiki Aeroporikis Dynamis (Tactical Air Force)

For many years the Tactical Air Force was equipped with cast-off, virtually obsolete USAF aircraft: the first jets (Lockheed T-33 trainers) did not arrive until 1951, and the first front-line jets (straight-winged F-84Gs) not until 1952. More than 200 of these ageing aircraft were delivered for use in the fighter-bomber role, serving until 1960 and augmented by 104 F-86E Sabre interceptors. One hundred and fifty F-84F and RF-84F Thunderstreaks and Thunderflashes were delivered from 1956. Fifty radar-equipped F-86Ds served from 1960 to 1965, by which time the air force had commenced a major re-equipment programme. This involved the delivery of 43 F-104G, two RF-104G and six TF-104G Starfighters, and 52 F-5A, 16 RF-5A and nine F-5B Freedom Fighters. The Starfighters and Freedom Fighters, together with the F-84Fs and RF-84Fs, were to form the backbone of Greek tactical air power until well into the 1980s, with further deliveries of all types from NATO stocks. Such deliveries included 11 F-104Gs and a single TF-104G from Spain, 10 F-104Gs from the Netherlands and batches of German F-104Gs, RF-104Gs and TF-104Gs totalling 44, 24 and 23, respectively. The F-104G was finally withdrawn from service on 31 March 1993, and the last Starfighter units transitioned to ex-US Navy A-7 Corsairs. The last RF-84Fs also lingered on into the 1990s, being withdrawn from use individually as they reached 9,000 flying hours. The last example was withdrawn in February 1991.

Freedom Fighters remain operational with two squadrons to this day, the original MAP deliveries having been augmented by 10 F-5As and two RF-5As from Iran, 29 F-5As and six F-5Bs from Jordan and nine F-5As from Norway. Eleven NF-5As and a single NF-5B were transferred from the Netherlands in April 1991. Many F-5s are now held in storage, or have been reduced to

spares, while most surviving airworthy aircraft have been fitted with Martin-Baker Mk 10LF ejection seats. Five RF-5As have been converted back to standard F-5A configuration, and only eight survivors remain in their original configuration with a flight of 349 'Kronos' Mira Anakethisis Imeras (day fighter squadron) at Larissa, albeit with cameras removed and no longer flying in the recce role. F-5A fighters serve with the same unit, and also with 343 'Asteri' Mira Anakethisis Imeras at Thessaloniki. 343 Mira initially flew the survivors of the original MAP-supplied F-5s, while 349 Mira includes some more recently delivered ex-KLu aircraft. The recent disbandment of 341 'Assos' Mira Anakethisis Imeras at Nea Ankhialos, which had ex-Jordanian, ex-Iranian and ex-Norwegian aircraft, may have led to a change-around of F-5s, in order to keep only the lowest-houred aircraft in front-line service. Apart from the two squadrons of F-5s, all Greek front-line fast jet squadrons are equipped with aircraft delivered since 1974.

Air defence

Fulfilling the air defence role is a mixed fleet of Dassault Mirage 2000s and General Dynamics F-16s. These were procured to fulfil a single requirement, but a split purchase of European and American aircraft was felt to offer political advantages which outweighed military considerations such as commonality (and, according to some sources, operational utility). Contracts were placed for 40 of each type, with options for 20 more of each, although it was made clear that only one 20-aircraft option would actually be exercised.

The $940 million contract for F-16s (with 100 per cent offsets) was finally signed in January 1987, after protracted disagreements over the price of the aircraft, and by the US requirement

to prevent any transfer of sensitive technology or information to the Warsaw Pact. The contract covered the supply of 34 single-seat F-16CGs and six F-16DGs, all powered by the General Electric F110-GE-100 engine. In April 1993, General Dynamics received a further contract for a follow-on batch of 40 more aircraft, which will be delivered from early 1997. These will be Block 50 F-16Cs and F-16Ds. Some 24 LANTIRN navigation pods and 16 targeting pods have also been ordered for the F-16Cs, and more may follow. The F-16 order may be increased further, since the Greek government's stated priorities are for the upgrading and modernisation of existing weapons, and the procurement of new combat aircraft. The initial batch of F-16s was delivered between November 1988 and October 1989, and equipped 330 'Keraunos' Mira Pantos Kerou (all-weather fighter squadron) and 346 'Jason' Mira Skoli Meteklaidefseos (operational conversion school) at Nea Ankhialos, replacing F-5s. 346 Mira functions as the F-16 conversion unit, and includes all the F-16Ds delivered. F-16 conversion is spread over 100 sorties.

Dassault's $1,380 million contract, signed in September 1985, included offsets worth 60 per cent of the programme cost, spread over 15 years, and covered the supply of 36 Mirage 2000EGs and four two-seat 2000BGs, all with RDM3 radar, all armed with Magic 2 and Super 530D missiles and all powered by M53-P2 engines. They further differ from French aircraft in having extra RWR antennas on the fin leading and trailing edges and wingtips. The low level of offsets achieved initially cast a shadow over the programme, and unhappiness with radar performance led to deliveries being halted temporarily after the 28th aircraft. Deliveries were eventually resumed, and today the Mirage 2000 equips 331 'Aegeas' Mira Pantos Kerou and 332 'Geraki'

343 Mira at Thessaloniki includes both F-5As (including some of the original batch delivered under MAP provisions), F-5Bs and ex-Dutch NF-5As and NF-5Bs.

The Mirage F1CG has proved both popular and successful in Greek service, and remains in use with 342 Mira at Tanagra (and Thiria) and 334 Mira at Iraklion.

Still bearing the RAF serial KK156, this Douglas Dakota is one of those originally donated to Greece by Britain after World War II. The aircraft serves with 355/1 STM at Thessaloniki in the transport role.

After some teething troubles, the Mirage 2000 has become a vital pillar in Greek air defence, and is today operated by two squadrons at Tanagra.

A-7H and TA-7H Corsairs serve with 340 and 345 Mira at Souda.

A Dayglo orange and grey colour scheme is applied to some of the Souda-based T-33s of 222 Mira to make them more conspicuous when used in the target-towing role.

The Greek air force's 'Tiger' squadron, 335 Mira, has this insignia .

Araxos was the last home of the F-104G in Greek service, one of the unit's aircraft being specially decorated before the type's retirement.

A-7Hs from 115 Pteriga Mahis were used as interim equipment, but the F-104's replacements are refurbished ex-USN A-7Es as shown above, with US markings for ferrying.

The flying suit badge of 338 Mira reflects the Andravida-based Phantom unit's ground attack commitment.

338 Mira F-4Es wear a mix of camouflage schemes. The outer pair wears Vietnam-style camouflage, while the centre aircraft has the blue-grey scheme applied locally for air defence duties.

This 339 Mira F-4E shows clear signs of its previous owners, with US star and bar crudely overpainted on the rear fuselage, and US serial retained, with Greek national markings added to intakes and fin.

Mira Pantos Kerou at Tanagra. No. 332 acts as the conversion unit and has all of the two-seaters on charge, although conversion is a brief process (consisting of only 10 hours flying, plus simulator time), since only pilots experienced on other front-line types transition to the Mirage 2000. The two units are charged with the air defence of Athens.

Delivery of the Mirage 2000 allowed the 32 surviving Mirage F1CGs of 334 Mira and 342 Mira, originally responsible for air defence of the capital, to be allocated to other duties. 334 Mira moved to Iraklion, on the island of Crete, where it forms the air component of 126a Sminarkia Nakia (Autonomous Group). 342 Mira, responsible for air defence of the Greek islands and originally expected to move to the island of Skiros, or to Agrinion in Western Greece, actually remains at Tanagra with about 16 aircraft. Air defence of the Aegean is a vital role, and Mirage F1s have engaged in mock dogfights with Turkish Phantoms (in 1987) and F-16s. During an engagement with two Turkish F-16s on 18 June 1992, a Mirage F1CG was actually lost, crashing into the sea. Each of the squadron's aircraft wears the name of a Greek island on its nose.

The 40 Mirages (all F1CG single-seaters) were delivered from August 1975, the first 16 diverted from production for the Armée de l'Air. They were purchased because the arms embargo imposed by Washington after the colonel's *coup* threatened to prevent delivery of the air force's preferred option, the McDonnell Douglas F-4 Phantom. The lack of two-seat trainers makes F1 conversion a difficult process, involving a great deal of simulator time and a background of at least 150 hours on the T-33.

In fact, the first batch of 38 F-4Es was delivered before the Mirage F1s, during March 1974, under Operation Peace Icarus. These deliveries allowed the re-equipment of 337 'Fantasma' Mira Pantos Kerou (all-weather fighter squadron) at Larissa, and of 339 'Ajax' Mira at Andravida. Two attrition replacements were delivered in June 1976. Eighteen further F-4Es, together with eight RF-4Es, were delivered during 1978, these allowing the conversion of the RF-84-equipped 348 Mira Taktikis Anagnorisis (tactical reconnaissance squadron) at Larissa and of 338 'Ares' Mira at Andravida.

Of these units, 337 Mira is a dedicated interceptor squadron, while 348 Mira is tasked with tactical reconnaissance. At Andravida 339 Mira (originally an interceptor squadron) and 338 Mira (originally a ground attack squadron) have been redesignated as multi-role units. 339 Mira also acts as the F-4 conversion unit, although Phantom conversion is made complex by the Greek air force requirement that every F-4 pilot must first amass 300 hours as an F-4 WSO.

Following the 1990 signature of an eight-year extension to the US basing agreement, 28 additional secondhand F-4Es, drawn from the 113th TFS, Indiana ANG and 163rd TFS, Indiana ANG were delivered during late 1991. Most of these aircraft went to the multi-role squadrons at Andravida, retaining their USAF 'Egyptian One' grey camouflage. Earlier F-4Es either retain their Vietnam-style camouflage (those assigned to reconnaissance or ground attack) or, since November 1983, have been repainted in a new two-tone blue-grey camouflage. At the time, the latest delivery was referred to as the first stage of a

process which might see the transfer of 50 F-4Es and 19 F-4Gs, but further transfers from the USA have not yet occurred. Twenty ex-Luftwaffe RF-4Es were passed to Greece, with another seven aircraft provided unrefurbished for spares recovery and ground crew training. Whereas other Phantom operators have embarked upon, or expressed interest in ambitious upgrade plans, Greece has yet to announce any modernisation or upgrade effort for its large Phantom force. Without such an upgrade, the Phantom's ageing radar and AIM-7 Sparrow missile make it increasingly less credible in the air defence role, although it remains effective enough as a fighter bomber.

Between September 1975 and April 1977, Greece took delivery of 60 A-7H Corsair IIs, with five two-seat TA-7Hs following in July 1980. These were used primarily in the maritime strike role, replacing F-84Fs, with a secondary air defence commitment with AIM-9 Sidewinder missiles. The Corsairs equipped 340 'Lailaps' Mira Taktikis Vomvardismou (tactical bomber squadron) and 345 'Perseus' Mira Taktikis Vomvardismou at Soudha, and 347 Mira Taktikis Vomvardismou at Larissa (which moved to Soudha in July 1993, and then to Araxos). 338 Mira reportedly operated A-7s briefly before converting to the F-4. The A-7 conversion unit is 345 Mira. The Corsair has proved popular in Greek service, and a further 36 aircraft (refurbished US Navy A-7Es and TA-7Cs) were transferred to Greece to augment the 47 survivors of the original batch, following the 1990 signature of an extension to the US base agreement. These equip two squadrons at Araxos, which were previously flying the F-104G Starfighter. Greece has periodically expressed an interest in upgrading and modernising its A-7s, although no progress has been made, and the end of the USAF YA-7F programme has probably sounded the death knell for such ambitions. Even without an upgrade, though, the A-7s rugged airframe and turbofan engine make it an outstandingly effective tactical aircraft, as the last two US Navy squadrons demonstrated during Operation Desert Storm.

The only other aircraft types on charge with the Tactical Air Force in recent years have been the Lockheed/Canadair T-33 and the Douglas C-47. These long-serving old stagers remained in use in significant numbers, about 75 of each having been delivered over the years. In Tactical Air Force service, the T-33 equips 222 Sminos Ekpetheuisis at Soudha, 370 Sminos Ekpetheuisis at Larissa and 366 Sminos Ekpetheuisis at Tanagra, Thessaloniki's 221 Sminos Ekpetheuisis having recently disbanded. The ageing jet trainers are used mainly for instrument flying training, and for liaison flying (and as target tugs at Soudha). About 15 remain on charge with each unit, the Soudha aircraft wearing an eye-catching Dayglo red colour scheme. There remains a possibility that Greece may receive surplus Alpha Jets from Germany as T-33 replacements, if conditions can be agreed, although the T-33's simplicity and single-engined configuration make it a particularly inexpensive aircraft to operate.

A handful of Dakotas remain active with the command's own VIP flight at Larissa, and perhaps with 355 Mira's 1 STM detachment at Thessaloniki. These veterans are becoming increasingly expensive to operate, and in recent years large numbers of C-47s have been withdrawn from use to languish in open storage at various airfields.

The aircraft and units described above are divided between seven wings (*Pterix*) and two autonomous combat groups (*Sminarkia Nakis*). These wings are geographical rather than functional, although one, 110 Pteriga Mahis at Larissa in north-eastern Greece, embraces several roles with its mix of F-4 Phantom variants. Thessaloniki is the most northerly major base, and is closest to Yugoslavia and to Bulgaria. Despite this important strategic position, the wing (113 Pteriga Mahis) has only one combat squadron and that is equipped with elderly F-5s. This must make the base the most likely recipient of a third F-16 squadron, when the new batch of Fighting Falcons is delivered. 116 Pteriga Mahis at Araxos and 117 Pteriga Mahis at Andravida are located close together on the west coast and combined represent a powerful and versatile force, with A-7 fighter-bombers and multi-role Phantoms. The F-16s of 111 Pteriga Mahis at Nea Ankhialos, and the Mirage 2000s and F1s of 114 Pteriga Mahis at Tanagra, guard the east coast of the mainland, while Thiria's Mirage F1s and those at Iraklion stand guard over the Aegean, augmenting Souda's A-7 Corsair-equipped 115th Pteriga.

Air defence fighters are backed up by a single battalion of 36 Nike-Hercules SAMs and 40 Contraves Skyguard systems using 280 Raytheon AIM-7M Sparrow missiles. Two Marconi Martello radars were ordered in early 1990 for fighter control.

Taktiki Aeroporikis Dynamis (Tactical Air Force)

UNIT	TYPE
110 *Pteriga Mahis*, Larissa	F-4E
337 'Fantasma' Mira Pantos Kerou	RF-4E
348 'Matia' Mira Taktikis Anagnorisis	RF-/F-5A/B
349 'Kronos' Mira Anakhethisis Imeras	T-33A
370 Sminos Ekpetheusis	C-47
Taktikis Aeroporiki Dynamis	
111 *Pteriga Mahis*, Nea Ankhialos	F-16C/D
330 'Keraunos' Mira Pantos Kerou	F-16C/D
346 'Jason' Mira Skoli Meteklaidefseos	
113 *Pteriga Mahis*, Thessaloniki	NF-/F-5A/B
343 'Asterix' Mira Anakhethisis Imeras	C-47A/B
355/1 STM	
114 *Pteriga Mahis*, Tanagra	Mirage 2000
331 'Aegeas' Mira Pantos Kerou	Mirage 2000
332 'Geraki' Mira Pantos Kerou	Mirage F1
342 'Sparta' Mira Pantos Kerou	T-33A
366 Sminos Ekpetheusis	
115 *Pteriga Mahis*, Souda	T-33A
222 'Alepou' Mira Epercherisiakis Ekpetheusis	A-/TA-7H
340 'Lailaps' Mira Taktikis Vomvardismou	A-/TA-7H
345 'Perseus' Mira Taktikis Vomvardismou	
116 *Pteriga Mahis*, Araxos	A-7E
335 'Tigreis' Mira Taktikis Vomvardismou	A-7E
336 'Olympus' Mira Taktikis Vomvardismou	A-/TA-7H
347 Mira Taktikis Vomvardismou	
117 *Pteriga Mahis*, Andravida	
338 'Ares' Mira Pantos Kerou	F-4E
339 'Ajax' Mira Pantos Kerou	F-4E
126 *Sminarkia Nakis*, Iraklion	
334 'Thalos' Mira Pantos Kerou	Mirage F1
134 *Sminarkia Nakis*, Thiria	
342 'Sparta' Mira Pantos Kerou detachment	Mirage F1

This **HU-16 Albatros** of 353 Mira is reportedly used for **ECM** training duties, and lacks underwing searchlight. The main role of the unit is sea surveillance and long-range **SAR**.

A handful of **Do 28Ds** serve with 355 Mira in the light utility transport role. The aircraft is prized for its rugged dependability and **STOL** performance.

This is the colourful unit insignia of 355 Mira, which parents three aircraft types.

Above: One of 356 Mira's C-130Hs sits on the Elefsis ramp as paratroops emplane.

Right: 355 Mira operates the CL-215 amphibian in the fire-fighting role.

Greece is the only military operator of the **YS-11** outside the type's native Japan. The aircraft were taken over from Olympic Airlines and are used primarily for transport duties.

A single **NAMC YS-11** is used for calibration duties, and wears a more conspicuous colour scheme than the other YS-11s serving with 356 Mira.

Although its external configuration differs only slightly from other Greek Hercules, this **C-130H** is one of those used for 'Ibex' Elint duties. Other 355 Mira Hercules have provision for the installation of the **MAFFS** fire-fighting system.

This lone **Gulfstream I** wears a similar colour scheme to the calibration YS-11 pictured above and is used by 356 Mira at Elefsis, primarily for **VIP** transport and liaison duties.

The flying suit badge of 357 Mira, which operates the **Bell 47** on behalf of the Ministry of Agriculture.

357 Mira operates about eight **Bell 47Gs**, all equipped for crop-spraying and tasked by the Ministry of Agriculture. The squadron is a lodger unit at Dekelia, but its aircraft are based all over Greece, wherever their services are required.

Diikissi Aeroporikis Ipostirixis (Support Command)

All support units come under the control of Support Command, which has a single wing at Elefsis, albeit with numerous detachments at other airfields around Greece. Support Command's main task is transport, for which it controls 11 new-build C-130Hs of 12 delivered from 1975, and six ex-USAF/ANG/AFRes C-130Bs delivered between August and November 1992. The latter aircraft retain their 'European One' colour scheme. At least one Hercules has been modified to carry out 'Ibex' Elint/Sigint duties, and at least two more are compatible with MAFFS (Mobile Airborne Fire-Fighting System). The Hercules force is augmented by six ex-Olympic Airways NAMC YS-11As transferred to the air force in 1981. One of these aircraft, painted in a gaudy Dayglo and white colour scheme, doubles as a navaid calibration aircraft. A single Gulfstream I is in use for VIP flights. All of these aircraft serve with 356 'Iraklis' Mira Taktikis Metaforon (tactical transport squadron). These longer-range transports are augmented by the three surviving Dornier Do 28D-2s (of 15 ex-Luftwaffe aircraft delivered in 1985) of 355 'Ifaistos' Mira Taktikis Metaforon, which also operates a handful of Dakotas, and 13 surviving CL-215s.

The squadron's aircraft are generally operated away from Elefsis, the Dorniers frequently acting as liaison aircraft for individual bases, while the big Canadairs move to wherever their fire-fighting duties dictate. The Canadairs have a secondary transport capability, but this is not practised. The 357 Mira Everna Diasosi/Mira Exipiretisis Diomosion Ypresion (SAR/crop-spraying squadron) and 359 Mira Everna Diasosi/Mira Exipiretisis Diomosion Ypresion are actually based at Dekelia, and work directly for the Ministry of Agriculture, from detached locations all over the country. They respectively operate about 10 Bell 47s and a mix of 10 Grumman G-164 Agcats and 27 PZL M-18 Dromaders. These aircraft are responsible for spraying mosquitos as well as for conventional crop-dusting. Until the West German Luftwaffe absorbed large numbers of ex-East German aircraft (most notably the MiG-29s, which remain in use to this day), the Greek PZL M-18 Dromaders were the only aircraft of Warsaw Pact origin in service with a NATO air arm.

Support Command is also responsible for maritime patrol, ASW, SAR, and fisheries protection roles. These duties are the responsibility of 353 Mira Nautikus Aeroporiki Synergasias (maritime surveillance squadron). This unit operates about three very old Grumman HU-16B Albatross amphibians, the survivors of 12 delivered in 1969 (after they had completed lengthy service with the Norwegian air force). Ten survivors were refurbished and upgraded by Grumman and HAI from 1986, each receiving a nose-mounted search radar. The aircraft can carry an underwing searchlight, and can be armed with depth charges, torpedoes, or rockets for ASW and ASV attacks. One of the HU-16s was modified for ECM training, and this may be one of the survivors in service with 335 Mira. These aircraft are augmented by the helicopters of 358 'Faethon' Mira Everna Diasosi, which include 14 Agusta-Bell AB 205As (operating from detached locations all over Greece) and three VIP transport Bell 212s.

Diikissi Aeroporikis Ipostirixis

UNIT	TYPE
112 Pteriga Mahis, Elefsis	
353 'Albatros' Mira Nautikis Aeroporiki Synergasias	HU-16B
355 'Ifaistos' Mira Taktikis Metaforon	CL-215, Do 28D
356 'Ifaistos' Mira Taktikis Metaforon	C-130H,YS-11A, Gulfstream I
357 Mira Everna Diasosi/Mira Exipiretisis Diomosion Ypresion	Bell 47G/OH-13
358 'Faithon' Mira Everna Diasosi	AB 205, Bell 212
359 Mira Everna Diasosi/Mira Exipiretisis Diomosion Ypresion	G.164/M-18A

Diokisi Aeroporiki Ekpitheyseos (Training Command)

Unlike some NATO nations, Greece does not participate in the NATO pilot training scheme, but instead selects, screens and trains its own aircrew, including instructors. This is the vital role of Training Command, which controls both the air force academy at Dekelia (also known as Tatoi) and the 120 Pteriga Ekpetheusis Aeros, with its constituent training squadrons, at Kalamata. The Ethniki Aeroporiki Acadiymia, sometimes known as the Skoli Ikaron (School of Ikarus) was formed in 1931, when the army and navy flying schools were amalgamated. Students spend four years at the Academy, which doubles as an officer training college and a primary flying training/flying selection school. They gain their first air experience in one of four Grob G-103 Twin Astir gliders on charge. Screening and primary training is undertaken during a three-month, 45 flying-hour course on the Cessna T-41D Mescaleros of 360 Mira. This squadron operates 19 T-41Ds, of 21 delivered in 1970.

Basic training

Successful graduates from Dekelia then move to Kalamata to continue their flying training, which is modelled on the US flying training syllabus. Basic flying training is undertaken on the Cessna T-37 Tweety Bird, which serves with 361 Mira Vassiksis Ekpetheusis (basic training squadron). The squadron has some T-37s, including 24 T-37Cs delivered under MDAP provisions, and augmented by eight surplus USAF T-37Bs transferred from 1978, and eight more ex-Royal Jordanian Air Force T-37Bs received in 1988. The T-37B was the main production version of the Tweety Bird for the US Air Force, with 1,025-lb st (4.6-kN) J69-T-25 engines and revised avionics, while the T-37C was a further version of the aircraft produced specifically for export through the Mutual Aid Program, with provision for wingtip fuel tanks and underwing armament. Trainee pilots undergo a six-month, 80 flying-hour course on the 'Tweet'. It was originally intended to replace the T-37 with an indigenous turboprop trainer, but this ambitious idea was quickly dropped and plans now call for local production of a foreign design. Greek air force priorities are such that selection of any trainer will now not take place until after a USAF/USN JPATS winner is selected. If this aircraft is a turboprop (the Pilatus/Beech PC-9 Mk II, for example), it may well attract a Greek order.

Hellenic Buckeyes

Pilots transition from the T-37 to the Rockwell T-2E Buckeye. Greece is the only European operator of the T-2, and one of only two users of the aircraft outside the US Navy, for whom this carrier-compatible jet was developed, the other operator being the Venezuelan air force. Forty T-2Es were delivered from 1976-77 and the survivors equip 362 Mira Prochoremenes Ekpetheusis (advanced training squadron) and 363 Mira Prochoremenes Ekpetheusis. Officially, 362 Mira is responsible for advanced training, and 363 Mira for weapons training. In fact, the large through-put of students means that 363 Mira undertakes both roles when required. Students spend a year on the Buckeye at Kalamata, Greece's busiest military airfield, and amass some 130 T-2 hours before conversion to a front-line type. The T-2 does have a secondary emergency war role as a ground attack role, in which it would be flown by the 120 Pteriga Ekpetheusis Aeros' instructors.

Training command is also responsible for ground-based training. Basic training is provided by 124 Basic Training Wing at Tripolis: Airframe, armament and engine technicians undergo trade training with 123 Technical Training Wing at Dekelia, which has a large number of grounded instructional airframes. Other training units include 125 Administrative Training Group at Thessaloniki-Sedea, 128 Telecommunications and Electronic Warfare Training Group, an English language training school and a women's training unit.

The academy at Dekelia also hosts lodger units from 112 Pteriga Mahis at Elefsis, including the crop-spraying Ag Cats and Dromaders of 359 Mira and the Bell 47s of 357 Mira. Dekelia also serves as home for the small fleet of aircraft used by the Limeniki Astinomia (Coast Guard), which comprise a pair of Cessna 172Q Cutlasses and a pair of Socata TB.20 Trinidads. Two Nardi/Hughes 300 helicopters reportedly delivered to Dekelia in late 1985 may have gone to the latter squadron, or may have been destined for army use.

Diokisi Aeroporiki Ekpitheyseos

UNIT	TYPE
120 Pteriga Ekpetheusis Aeros Mahis, Kalamata	
361 'Mystras' Mira Vassikis Ekpetheusis	T-37B/C
362 'Nestor' Mira Prochoremenes Epercherisiakis	T-2E
363 'Danaos' Mira Epercherisiakis Ekpetheusis	T-2E
Ethniki Aeroporia Academya, Tatoi-Dekelia	
360 Mira Ekpetheusis	T-41D, G.103

The Limeniki Astinomia (Coast Guard) is a lodger unit at Dekelia, with its Cessna 172Q Cutlasses and Socata TB.20 Trinidads, as are the Ag Cats and Dromaders of 359 Mira and the Bell 47s of 357 Mira.

*Cessna Ag Cats (above) and **PZL Dromaders** (not shown) equip 359 Mira, based at Dekelia, which operates alongside 357 Mira in the crop-spraying role.*

The Agusta-Bell AB 205As of 358 Mira operate from Elefsis and from a number of detached locations, including Kalamata, where this aircraft is used in the SAR role.

This 358 Mira AB 205A is equipped with emergency flotation gear and a rescue winch, and is operated from Araxos in the SAR role. The AB 205As augment the ageing HU-16s of 353 Mira, and have a secondary coastal surveillance role.

Greece is the only NATO operator of the T-2 Buckeye, designed as a carrier training aircraft for the US Navy and otherwise exported only to Venezuela.

The flying suit patch of 361 Mira features a heroic figure astride a T-37.

361 Mira has gathered its T-37s from a number of sources, this well-worn example being an ex-Royal Jordanian Air Force T-37B.

The badge of 362 Mira, which uses the T-2 in the advanced training role.

A rocket-armed Rockwell T-2 Buckeye of 363 Mira, which uses the type for advanced and tactical training. All Greek T-2s wear camouflage, with high-visibility tail stripes.

Twin rocket launch tubes nestle under the wing of a 363 Mira Buckeye. The squadron's T-2s are also used for advanced training when student numbers are large.

Many unit badges feature characters drawn from Greek mythology, like this 363 Mira flying suit patch.

This line-up of redundant Convair F-102 interceptors (including four TF-102 two-seat trainers) is now used for technical trade training at Elefsis. These were replaced by the Dassault Mirage F1.

Another ground instructional airframe at Elefsis is this Nord Noratlas, whose tailboom frames one of the YS-11s that replaced the ageing French transports.

Elliniki Polimiko Naftikon (Hellenic Navy Aviation)

After a 48-year gap, the Greek navy regained an independent air arm in March 1976. Until the late 1920s, when army and naval air arms were combined to form the Royal Hellenic Air Force, Greece had two air arms, both responsible for a wide range of roles. The emergence of a single independent air arm disguised the need for specialised air wings for the direct support of the army and navy, as well as absorbing all of the defence budget allocated to military aviation. Developments in naval warfare during the postwar years gradually pointed to the need for shipborne helicopters, and it became clear that these would best be controlled and operated by an air arm which would report directly to, and come under the operational control of, the naval staff.

The first helicopters delivered to the service were four Aérospatiale SA 319B Alouette IIIs delivered to Hellenikon (Athens airport) in July 1975 and relocated to Amfiali Heliport, near Pireus, in May 1977. The SA 319B is a dedicated navalised derivative of the SA 316C, with an 870-shp (649-kW) Turboméca Astazou engine derated to 600 shp (447 kW). This delivers 30 shp (22 kW) more than the SA 316 engine, allowing the aircraft to operate at heavier weights. The SA 319B has a nose-mounted Omera ORB 31 search radar, and can carry a MAD on one of the fuselage pylons. These can otherwise each accommodate a Mk 46 homing torpedo. The aircraft fulfils the dual primary roles of both ASW and surface surveillance. Since 1992 the Alouette III has been used for training all Greek navy helicopter pilots (who were previously trained by the army). Secondary roles

include SAR and medevac duties, and the aircraft can carry an underslung load weighing up to 1,653 lb (750 kg). The four original Alouette IIIs were augmented by three secondhand Aéronavale aircraft from June 1993. The Alouettes are operated by a flight at Kotroni Heliport on top of Mount Pentelli near Marathon, which replaced Amfiali Heliport as the primary naval air arm base in 1985. This unit is known simply as the Sminos Alouette (Alouette Flight). Alouette pilots undertake an 87 flying-hour course, with two months of ground school.

Numerically the most important aircraft on Elliniki Polimiki Naftikon charge is the Agusta-Bell AB 212ASW. Twelve of these aircraft were delivered between 17 July 1979 and 21 June 1984, together with two similar AB 212EWs, additionally equipped for ECM duties. The AB 212ASW differs from the baseline Bell 212 in having a strengthened airframe, anti-corrosion features and ASW/ASV role equipment. This comprises a Ferranti Seaspray surveillance radar, Bendix AN/ASQ-13B dunking sonar and a Canadian Marconi AN/APN-208(V)2 Doppler navigation system. One of the AB 212ASWs was written off in 1982. For its secondary roles of SAR, medevac and general utility support, the AB 212ASW can carry an underslung load of 5,000 lb (2268 kg).

During Operations Desert Shield and Desert Storm, AB 212ASWs made four-month deployments to the Red Sea aboard the 'Kortenaer'-class frigates HS *Elli* and HS *Limnos*, supporting the multinational UN forces. All Greek navy helicopters can be deployed aboard these frigates,

and a 'Meko'-class frigate, three LCVs and a naval cadet training vessel. Pilots for the AB 212ASW (all of whom are already qualified on the Alouette) undertake three months of ground-school and a 157 flying-hour course.

In January 1992, Greece signed a $161 million contract for the supply of five S-70B-6 Seahawks. These new-generation ASW helicopters have been ordered to equip the Blohm und Voss Meko 200 frigates being built by Hellenic SY, and will be equipped with the French-developed Samahe harpoon system. They will be Harpoon-capable SH-60B/F hybrids, with Bendix AN/ASQ-18(V)3 active dipping sonar, Eaton AN/APS-143(V)3 pulse compression surveillance radar, and AN/ALR-606(V)2 RHAWS. Deliveries are scheduled to begin in 1995. The Seahawks will fulfil the same primary roles as the Alouette IIIs and AB 212ASW/EWs, with an additional electronic warfare capability. The aircraft will equip an additional (third) Sminos, bringing the naval aviation wing up to full strength.

The Coast Guard operates a small fleet of fixed-wing aircraft (two Cessna C.172Q Cutlass and two Socata TB.20 Trinidad) from Dekelia.

Elliniki Polimiki Naftikon

UNIT	TYPE
Sminos Alouette	Aérospatiale SA 319B Alouette III
Sminos AB 212	Agusta-Bell AB 212ASW/EW

All based at Kotroni, with frequent shipborne deployments and detachments to Amafiali.

Elliniki Aeroporia Stratou (Hellenic Army Aviation)

Hellenic Army Aviation was formed in 1956 following the US Army aviation model. Initially a small force with only fixed-wing equipment, and later with some light observation helicopters, the Elliniki Aeroporia Stratou received its first assault helicopters during 1975. The primary role of this air arm remains one of troop and utility transport, giving the Greek army a flexibility which is intended to allow it to represent a credible deterrent to the much larger armies of the nations which are perceived to offer the major threat. Recent developments promise to add a genuine anti-tank and anti-helicopter capability.

From token force to tiger

Until 1971, army aviation remained little more than a token force, undertaking observation and light utility duties only, and with a small number of aircraft (mainly fixed wing) on charge. On 15 September 1971, however, a full-strength aviation battalion was formed at Stefanoviklio near Larissa.

Initial equipment included the Cessna U-17A and U-17B, and even a single example of the de Havilland Canada L-20A Beaver. The U-17A is a militarised version of the Cessna 185. The

U-17A is equivalent to the Model 185C and is powered by a 260-hp (194 kW) Lycoming IO-470-F, while Greek U-17Bs use a 300-hp (224-kW) Continental IO-520-D and are fitted with new ailerons and an enlarged spinner. About 20 U-17s remain in use to this day, of about 50 delivered during the early 1960s. Bell 47Gs and OH-13As, and Agusta-Bell AB 204Bs, which were delivered from 1966 and which once formed the rotary-wing backbone of the service, have since been retired.

Expansion and modernisation

Expansion in the mid-1970s resulted in the delivery of the first of more than 100 Bell Iroquois assault helicopters. The initial batch comprised 15 Agusta-Bell AB 205As, which were later augmented by batches of 22 Bell UH-1Hs, 35 additional AB 205A (and AB 205Bs), and batches of 26, 14 and 32 Bell UH-1Hs, for an estimated total of 93 US-built and 50 Italian-built Iroquois. Originally painted in a brown and green camouflage, the UH-1s and AB 205s have now mainly been repainted in current US Army-style overall olive drab. The aircraft are now divided evenly between the three front-line bat-

talions at Stefanoviklio in the eastern part of the mainland, at Megara near Athens, and at Alexandropouli in northern Greece.

Between 1981 and 1983, the army received five Italian-built Elicotteri Meridionali/Boeing Vertol CH-47C Chinooks, with another five being delivered to the air force during the same period. They were intended primarily for paradropping, and for the supply of army units on islands in the eastern Aegean. The air force aircraft were transferred to the army in 1988. Nine Chinooks are currently going through an upgrade programme in the USA, which will bring them up to CH-47DG standards, with T55-L-712 turboshaft engines, uprated transmission, composite rotor blades, a new NVG-compatible cockpit, triple external load hooks, and various new systems and avionics items. The 1992-95 programme yielded a first redelivery in October 1993, resplendent in infra-red-absorbent dark green paint, like that applied to RAF Chinook HC.Mk 2s.

Observation and reconnaissance

The delivery date remains uncertain of the 16 Agusta-Bell AB 206B JetRangers operated pri-

Above: The Agusta-Bell AB 212 ASW forms the backbone of Greek naval aviation.

Below: The AB 212s have Ferranti Seaspray radar above the cockpit.

One of two rarely photographed AB 212ECMs. These retain Seaspray radar above the cabin but have a number of new fairings on the nose and tailplanes, most of which serve as antenna mountings for what appears to be a 360° RHAWS.

The flying suit patch of the Sminos AB 212 features a seahorse.

Sminos Alouette III, operator of the Greek navy Alouettes, has this badge.

Greek navy Alouette IIIs usually fly with a nose-mounted search radar, and are fitted with emergency flotation gear.

marily in the observation role, although they were first noted in service during 1983. A handful of the JetRangers are used for training, but most augment U-17s with the single observation company attached to each battalion.

Other types in front-line service include the Aero Commander 680FL, two of which serve with an operational company attached to the army aviation school in the agricultural photo-survey role, also fulfilling secondary liaison duties. The solitary Aero Commander 500, used purely in the liaison and light transport role, has been retired recently.

Today Greek army aviation is divided into three front-line Tagma Elliniki Aeroporia Stratou (Greek army aviation battalions) and a busy flying training school. Expansion remains likely, with a perceived need for a fourth battalion that could conceivably be based in the Aegean, or perhaps on Crete. As new equipment is received, the existing battalions are likely to gain new roles.

Each *Tagma* includes two *Lokos* (companies) equipped with a mix of Bell UH-1Hs and Agusta-Bell AB 205As, plus one artillery-spotting and observation *Lokos* with Agusta-Bell AB 206Bs, and Cessna U-17As and U-17Bs. The 2nd *Tagma* also parents a *Lokos* equipped with the Elicotteri Meridionali/Boeing Vertol CH-47C and CH-47DG Chinook, and a liaison *Lokos* with an Agusta-Bell AB 212 and a Beech C-12C.

The Greek army trains its own pilots at the Skoli Aeroporias Stratou (army aviation school) which is co-located beside the 1st Tagma at Stefanoviklio. The course lasts 10 months, during which pupil pilots move from the first to the second company, with potential fixed-wing pilots going from the first to the third, or sometimes directly to the third. The army was responsible for training naval helicopter pilots for many years, and still trains the handful of rotary-wing pilots required by the air force.

Rotary training

The first company operates the survivors of 30 Nardi-Hughes NH-300Cs delivered in 1969 to replace the Bell 47Gs and OH-13Hs previously in use. About 15 NH-300s remain in use providing basic rotary-wing training in a 150 flying-hour course. Student pilots then undergo Huey simulator training before moving to the second company, where type conversion and basic role training is undertaken on the Huey and on the JetRanger. Fixed-wing pilots learn to fly the U-17 in a 150 flying-hour course.

In 1994 Greek army aviation remained very much a support arm, with no offensive aircraft, although M60 machine-guns can be carried by the UH-1Hs and AB 205As, and M24 and M41 machine-guns by the Chinooks. These are useful for providing suppressive fire, and improve aircrew morale, but cannot transform UH-1s or CH-47s into offensive helicopters by any stretch of the imagination.

The lack of a dedicated armed, anti-tank helicopter type has become a major perceived weakness, underlined by the re-equipment of several Turkish army aviation units with TOW-armed AH-1 Cobras. The latter represent a potent anti-armour tool, but also have a useful anti-helicopter capability. Plans have already been formulated which will take the Elliniki Aeroporia Stratou into a new era, giving the small air arm a genuine offensive capability. Twelve McDonnell Douglas AH-64A Apaches are apparently on order, and Greece is said to hold options on 12 more. Greece may also be expected to benefit from drawdowns in US Army aviation, and may yet find itself operating the AH-1 Cobras it once turned down.

Apache deliveries

The first of these are expected to arrive in Greece in 1995, although *Flight International* has reported that McDonnell Douglas revealed that they had delivered AH-64s to Greece during 1992. Such deliveries cannot be substantiated, however, and there have been no confirmed sightings of Greek Apaches. When they do arrive, the Apaches will operate in the anti-armour role, using TOW and Hellfire ATGMs. Their delivery will end what has been a long and tortuous search for an attack helicopter. This began in 1980 when the USA offered Greece eight AH-1 Cobras (an offer repeated in 1983, with a higher price tag, and again turned down). A single Agusta A 109 was reportedly evaluated during 1985, with a view to ordering 25 more to meet the attack helicopter requirement formally revealed in 1989. In late 1993, there was intense speculation that Greece was a prospective customer for the Russian Kamov Ka-50 'Hokum'. In fact, discussions following the rejection of the A 109 eventually resulted in the order for the considerably more capable AH-64. The delivery of 12 Apaches would allow the equipping of a single *Lokos*, and it can be seen that at least one *Lokos* (or half a mixed *Lokos* with scout helicopters) will be required for each of the geographic battalions.

Elliniki Aeroporia Stratou

UNIT	TYPE
Scholi Aeroporias Stratou, Stefanoviklio	
1 Lokos	NH-300C
2 Lokos	AB 206B, UH-1H
3 Lokos	U-17A/B
4 Lokos	Aero Commander 680 FL
1 Tagma EAS, Stefanoviklio	
1 Lokos	AB 205A, UH-1H
2 Lokos	AB 205A, UH-1H
3 Lokos	AB 206B, U-17A/B
2 Tagma EAS, Megara	
1 Lokos	AB 205A, UH-1H
2 Lokos	AB 205A, UH-1H
3 Lokos	CH-47C/D
4 Lokos	AB 206B, U-17A/B
5 Lokos	C-12C, AB 212
3 Tagma EAS, Alexandroupoli	
1 Lokos	AB 205A, UH-1H
2 Lokos	AB 205A, UH-1H
3 Lokos	AB 206B, U-17A/B

The map reproduced here gives an idea of some of the security problems facing Greece. Surrounded by unstable or potentially unstable neighbours to the north, across the relatively narrow Aegean, Greece is also faced by Turkey, which has one of the world's largest and best-equipped standing armies. Some Greek islands are within swimming distance of the Turkish coast. The spelling of Greek placenames differs dramatically, since transliteration from Greek characters can vary. The range and reaction time of modern aircraft allow all permanent air bases to be located on the mainland or on the very largest islands.

The Cessna U-17 is used for both training and observation duties, and serves with the third Lokos (company) of each Tagma (battalion) and with the army aviation school.

Like the Cessna U-17, the AB 206 is used for both training and observation, and serves with the same units as the fixed-wing aircraft.

Hueys form the backbone of Greek army aviation, with each Tagma operating a mix of US-built UH-1Hs and Italian-produced Agusta-Bell AB 205s. This aircraft is a UH-1H of the 2nd Tagma at Megara.

This Agusta-Bell AB 205 carries emergency flotation gear on the undercarriage skids, but is otherwise externally identical to the UH-1H pictured top right.

The flying suit patch of the Elliniki Aeroporia Stratou has English text.

The flying suit badge of the 1st Tagma at Stefanoviklio features a lynx's head.

The insignia of the 2nd Tagma incorporates a map of Greece and a roundel.

The Greek army includes Boeing Vertol CH-47C Chinooks in its inventory. These aircraft are currently being cycled through a major upgrade cycle.

Greek Army Aviation operates this Beech C-12A Huron (Super King Air), which wears the colour scheme of its previous operator, the US Army.

Another one-off type in Greek army service is this extremely smart Agusta-Bell AB 212, which is similarly used by the 2nd Tagma's 5th Lokos primarily for VIP and liaison duties. AB 212s are used by all three of the Greek armed services.

INDEX

INDEX

Picture acknowledgments

Front cover: Randy Jolly. **4:** British Aerospace, Antoine J. Givaudon. **5:** SIRPA via Paul Jackson, François Rude. **6:** Gerry Turner, Robin Polderman, Herman Buttigieg. **7:** Paul Jackson. **8:** British Aerospace, T. Gibbons. **9:** Marshalls, A.B. Ward. **10:** Gert Kromhout. **11:** Aldo Ciarini, Paul Jackson. **12-13:** Mario Roberto Vaz Carneiro. **14:** Régent Dansereau, Stuart Lewis, Marcus Fülber. **15:** Chris Schmidt, Carey Mavor. **16:** Chris Schmidt, Gilles Auliard. **17:** Doug Youngblood (two). **18:** Bob Archer, Tim Ripley. **19:** Tim Ripley (two). **20:** Tim Ripley, Antoine J. Givaudon. **21:** Bob Archer, Tim Ripley (two). **22:** Bob Archer, Tim Ripley. **23-25:** Tim Ripley. **26:** Brane Lučovnik (three), Lockheed. **27:** US Customs Service (two). **28:** US Customs Service (three), Ted Carlson/Fotodynamics. **31:** René van Woezik (all). **32:** Peter Steinemann. **33:** René van Woezik (eight), Peter Steinemann. **34:** AviaData, Carey Schofield. **35:** Carey Schofield, Gerard Keysper. **36:** AviaData. **37:** Kamov, Carey Schofield. **38:** AviaData, Kamov. **39:** AviaData. **40:** Carey Schofield, Photolink, Kamov. **41:** Kamov, Photolink. **42:** Photolink (four). **43:** Austin J. Brown/APL. **44:** Austin Yakutin/AviaData, Sophearith Moeng, Austin J. Brown/APL. **45:** AviaData. **48-49:** Randy Jolly. **50-51:** Randy Jolly, US DoD via Randy Jolly. **52:** US DoD via Randy Jolly. **53:** Randy Jolly, Lockheed. **54-55:** Lockheed. **57-59:** Lockheed. **60:** Randy Jolly, US DoD, Bill Turner, David Donald, Ted Carlson/Fotodynamics, US DoD via Randy Jolly. **61:** Lockheed, Randy Jolly, David Donald. **62:** Lockheed, Frederick Sutter. **70:** Lockheed (two). **71:** David Donald, Lockheed. **74:** Jim Dunn via René J. Francillon. **75:** Lockheed, Ted Carlson/Fotodynamics. **76:** Lockheed, US DoD via Randy Jolly. **77:** Lockheed. **78:** Lockheed (two). **79:** Lockheed, David Donald. **80:** Lockheed (two). **81:** Lockheed (two). **82:** Flightline/Chuck Lloyd, James Benson. **83:** Randy Jolly, John Gourley. **84:** Randy Jolly (two). **85:** Randy Jolly. **86:** Randy Jolly, Ted Carlson/Fotodynamics. **87:** Lockheed, Frederick Sutter, P. Martin. **89:** Flightline/Chuck Lloyd. **90-92:** US DoD via Randy Jolly. **93:** US DoD via Randy Jolly (two), US DoD. **94:** David Donald. **95:** 49FW/PA, Randy Jolly. **96:** R.A. Cooper (two). **97:** Lockheed (two). **98-99:** Randy Jolly (two), James Benson. **100-103:** Randy Jolly. **104:** Steven D. Eisner (three), René J. Francillon, Lockheed. **105:** René J. Francillon (three), Randy Jolly. **106:** Randy Jolly (two), René J. Francillon, John Gourley. **107:** Randy Jolly (two), Chris Lofting. **108:** T. Ashford-Smith (two). **109:** FAPLA via Vasco Enrique (two). **110:** via Hopper, T. Ashford-Smith. **111:** FAPLA via Vasco Enrique (two), T. Ashford-Smith. **112:** FAPLA via Vasco Enrique, T. Ashford-Smith. **113:** FAPLA via Vasco Enrique (three), T. Ashford-Smith (two). **114:** Vance Vasquez via Robert L. Lawson, Robert L. Lawson. **115:** Robert L. Lawson (two). **116:** Grumman (two), Robert L. Lawson. **117:** Joe Cupido. **118:** Ted Carlson/Fotodynamics. **119:** Flightline/Rick Llinares. **120:** Flightline/Rick Llinares, Joe Cupido. **121:** Flightline/Chuck Lloyd, Ted Carlson/Fotodynamics. **122:** Grumman (two). **123:** Ted Carlson/Fotodynamics, Dave Parsons via Robert L. Lawson. **124:** Tom Kaminski, Robert L. Lawson (two), Grumman (three). **125:** US Navy, Robert L. Lawson. **126:** Grumman (two), Robert L. Lawson. **127:** Ted Carlson/Fotodynamics. **128:** Grumman, Jan C. Jacobs via Robert L. Lawson, Bruce Trombecky via Robert L. Lawson, Ted Carlson/Fotodynamics, Geoffrey Pearce/Aviagraphics. **129:** Robert L. Lawson (four). **130:** Paul Hart via Robert F. Dorr (two), Ted Carlson/Fotodynamics, Marty J. Isham via Robert L. Lawson, Robert L. Lawson. **131:** Grumman, Robert L. Lawson, Tom Kaminski. **132:** Robert L. Lawson (two). **133:** Ted Carlson/Fotodynamics, Mike Grove via Robert L. Lawson, Douglas Olson via Robert L. Lawson. **134:** Joe Cupido, Ted Carlson/Fotodynamics. **136:** Joe Cupido, Robert L. Lawson, Ted Carlson/Fotodynamics (two). **137:** Lt Tom Twomey via Robert L. Lawson (three). **138:** LCdr Rick Morgan via Robert L. Lawson. **139:** Ted Carlson/Fotodynamics (three). **140:** Ted Carlson/Fotodynamics, LCdr Rick Morgan via Robert L. Lawson, Robert L. Lawson (two). **141:** Tom Kaminski, Vance Vasquez via Robert L. Lawson, Robert L. Lawson. **142-145:** Greg L. Davis and Chris A.Neill/Focal Plane Imagery. **147:** René van Woezik (twelve). **149:** Yves Debay (five), René van Woezik (five), Robbie Shaw, Robert E. Kling. **151:** René van Woezik (nine), Robbie Shaw, Yves Debay. **153:** René van Woezik (all). **155:** René van Woezik (all). **157:** René van Woezik (all).